Computer programs for the building industry

Geoffrey Hutton Dip Arch, ARIBA

Michael Rostron MA, B Arch, ARIBA

Architectural Press, London

First published 1974 Second edition 1979

ISBN 0 85139 312 8

The information in this directory has been obtained from the owners of the programs and every effort has been made to ensure its accuracy. The editors, however, cannot accept responsibility for the content or availability of the programs, or any inaccuracy

The directory has been produced on eight-channel punched paper tape and edited and typeset using a computer. The Index to terms was produced by computer from key words selected from the abstracts. The information is stored on magnetic tape for ease of revision

Printed in Great Britain by Eyre & Spottiswoode (Portsmouth) Ltd

Contents

Introduction

This directory is the second edition of Computer Programs for the Building Industry. The contents have been completely revised as a result of writing to the owner of every program, and many new programs have been added. The revision process is a continuous one and the editors welcome information on the programs in the directory and on sources of new programs

Despite a continuing interest in computers within the building and construction industry, comparatively few architects, engineers or planners make use of them in their everyday work. Such use would be of particular value in developing countries, where construction is urgently required but technical and professional skills are scarce. The directory demonstrates the ready availability of programs throughout the world for a wide range of applications and equipment, and should be the preferred starting point for potential and existing computer users before they buy or write their own software

The second edition of the directory commences with a number of case studies, describing the experience of a selection of professional offices in using computers. This is followed by program abstracts prepared in sufficient detail to enable a preliminary choice of programs to be made. The abstracts are broadly classified but the principal method of searching for an appropriate program is by means of one of the comprehensive indexes given in the end of the book. Extended information is given in the form of program descriptions for several entries. These are grouped together at the end of the abstracts. No attempt has been made to evaluate the programs, which must be judged in relation to the user's own criteria in discussion with the owner, and in subsequent test runs. Comparative evaluation of computer programs requires considerable care and the Design Office Consortium is currently involved in research of this kind in the UK

No charge is made to the owners of programs for an entry in this directory, so that it is as comprehensive and independent as possible. Every effort is made to ensure the accuracy of the information but the editors cannot accept responsibility for the content, performance or availability of the programs. They would welcome notification of any inaccuracy. Among the many bodies who have assisted in gathering information on programs, the editors would particularly like to thank the Design Office Consortium, the Local Authorities' Management Services Advisory Committee (UK), the Association for Computer Aided Design (Australia) and the Danish Building Institute

The editors, who are enthusiastic computer users themselves, are always happy to help readers in their search for suitable programs and may be able to advise on appropriate sources and organisations to approach. They can be contacted at Hutton + Rostron, Netley House, Gomshall, Nr Guildford, Surrey, GU5 9QA, telephone 048 641 3221 or telex 859167

DESIGN OFFICE CONSORTIUM

The organisation

Design Office Consortium is an association which was formed in 1973 to promote the use of computers and related techniques in the building industry. It aims to bring together all the skill and experience required to evaluate, support and develop suitable computer programs. All organisations connected with the industry are encouraged to join, use the services provided and participate in program evaluation and meetings. The following case studies of the application of computers in the industry were provided by firms who are all members of DOC

The management board includes representatives of the Department of Industry Computer Aided Design Centre and the Department of the Environment Property Services Agency, as well as the elected representatives of membership. David Campion of Cusdin, Burden and Howitt and Geoffrey Hutton of Hutton + Rostron are the members' current representatives

The staff of technical consultants, under the managing director Rob Howard, has its offices at Guildhall Place, Cambridge CB2 3QQ, telephone: (0223) 311246/7

DOC was launched with Government aid but is now being established as a non-profit-making company, with staff capable of supporting the use of programs in members' offices and publishing the results for the guidance of others. A Project Manager is responsible for user evaluation of programs and is a member of the steering committee which controls this

Membership

Membership is open to all organisations connected with building and includes those from central and local government, as well as private practice. They represent architects, services and structural engineers, quantity surveyors, contractors, manufacturers and research bodies. Special categories which may also join include educational establishments, computer bureaux and groups abroad

Initially, membership numbered 22 (at the end of the first year) but by December 1978 had risen to 73. A current list of members follows this text

Full members are entitled to all the services, including use of programs, and are eligible for election to the management board and user-evaluation steering committee. Associate members, who are probably less familiar with computer techniques, may use the advisory and information services only but receive publications and may take part in group activities

Subscriptions are based on the number of non-administrative staff in the member's office

The need for computers

Building design was, at one time, largely dependent on local resources and practice but now the designer's approach is circumscribed to a great extent by regulations, standards, the availability of products and energy, and the results of research. Every member of a design team needs up-to-date information on all these subjects, as well as on the current state of his particular project. It is impossible for him to have immediate access to this information without the assistance of data-processing and computer equipment. Vast resources are absorbed in the collection and publication of information, including data on standard products, methods of calculation and building systems. The computer is invaluable for data storage, large-scale calculations and graphic output. Applications in the building field include environmental and structural analyses, management and accounting, bills of quantities, building layout and services design, two- and three-dimensional graphic presentations and information retrieval of all kinds

The need now is for pooled experience among computer-users in the industry and evaluation of programs to provide reliable guidance on suitability and practice. This is particularly important in view of the number of services now being offered, and the development of micro-computers and calculators for specific use in the construction industry

User evaluation

DOC has been commissioned by the Property Services Agency of the Department of the Environment to carry out user evaluation. The process is controlled by a steering committee representing Government departments and other members. Support and subsidy can be provided to enable programs to be tested in design offices. Feedback is then published as a guide to selection for other users

Subjects dealt with, or in hand, include continuous beam design, graphics for building perspectives, daylighting and programs for building contractors

Services available to members

DOC maintains a library of information on computers and programs, through contact with producers of software, and research and development organisations. A quarterly bulletin is issued, containing loose-leaf sheets for filing in binders supplied to members

Free services available to members, in addition to the bulletin, include answers to enquiries, and the opportunity to attend working and discussion groups, general meetings and demonstrations. DOC will visit members' offices for talks and consultancy studies. Some publications, including copies of this book, are issued free and others sold at cost to members

Other services can be provided by DOC at a discount, or a negotiated fee where other organisations are involved. Publications are sold to non-members at a profit. The use of programs, attendance at courses and specific consultancy work can be provided at discounts but computer services are at normal rates

Program development

The programs at present operated or promoted by DOC

include lighting, and thermal analyses; housing-layout and building planning aids; two– and three-dimensional graphics; earth movement on sites; cost analyses; and scheduling

Access to programs can be provided via terminals or a bureau service operated by DOC. Programs can be converted for different computers

Should a member of DOC wish to develop a program or improve a system which may be of general application, special funds can be made available and assistance given in documentation and marketing

List of members at December 1978

Government agencies

Department of Industry Computer Aided Design Centre
Department of the Environment Property Services Agency
Building Research Establishment
Institute for Industrial Research and Standards, Ireland
National Research Development Corporation
Department of Health and Social Security
Scottish Development Department
Department of Education and Science

Local authorities

Cheshire County Council
Lancashire County Council
Clwyd County Council
Greater London Council
Hampshire County Council
CLASP Development Group
Strathclyde Regional Council

Multi-professional

John Laing Design Associates
Ove Arup and Partners
W S Atkins Group
Building Design Partnership
Bechtel Incorporated, USA
Ohbayashi-Gumi, Japan
Honegger Freres Schmitt, Switzerland
Lloyds Bank Premises Department
London Transport
Metropolitan Police Office
Eastern Electricity
Libyan Arab Construction Association
National Building Agency
Sir William Halcrow and Partners

Consulting engineers

Bingham Blades and Partners
Alcock Shearing and Partners
Scott Wilson Kirkpatrick and Partners
Stewart Lyons Partnership
Bradshaw, Buckton and Tonge
Gordon Melvin and Partners, Kenya
Jenkins and Potter
White Young and Partners

Building services

H L Dawson and Partners
Haden Young
Mather and Platt
J Roger Preston and Partners
Ronald Ward and Associates
Ferguson and Partners

Software houses

Applied Research of Cambridge
Genesys
Autoprod
Faber Computer Operations

Research

Plymouth Polytechnic
Royal College of Art
University of Sydney, Australia
Leeds Polytechnic
University of Strathclyde
Ulster Polytechnic
University College Dublin
Bristol University
Scott Sutherland School of Architecture

Architects

Cusdin, Burden and Howitt
Twigg Brown and Partners
Boisot Waters Cohen Partnership
Adams Holden and Pearson
John Brunton and Partners
Fairhursts
Fitzroy Robinson and Partners
Hutton + Rostron
AMCO Corporation, Switzerland
Lion Brewery, New Zealand

Quantity surveyors

Cyril Sweett & Partners

Contractors

Atcost Limited
Melville Dundas and Whitson Limited
Derek Crouch Group

Trade associations

British Constructional Steelwork Association
Association for Computer Aided Design, Australia

Computer manufacturers

British Olivetti

Publications

General

The Design Office Consortium, an introductory booklet	Oct 74 (revised Sep 78)
Notes on the Memorandum and Articles of DOC Ltd	Dec 78
List of members	continuously updated
Energy and environment in some common building types	Mar 75
Computer programs for structural engineering	Aug 76
Computer programs for the building industry 1979 by Hutton + Rostron	Apr 79

Evaluation

Detailed reports:

Computer programs for building perspectives	Jan 77
Computer programs for continuous beams, BS CP110	Jan 78
Computer programs for daylighting in buildings	Sep 78

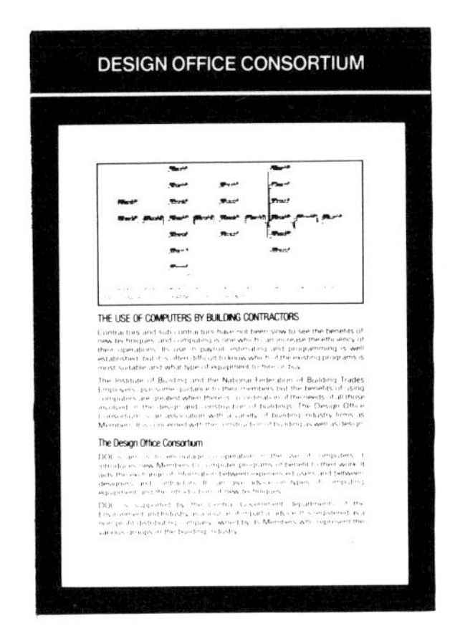

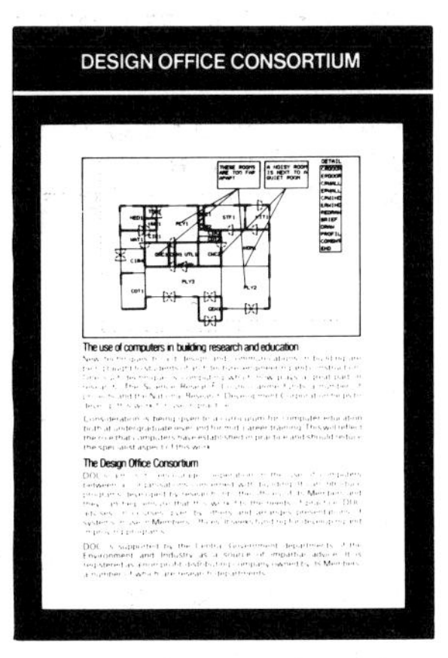

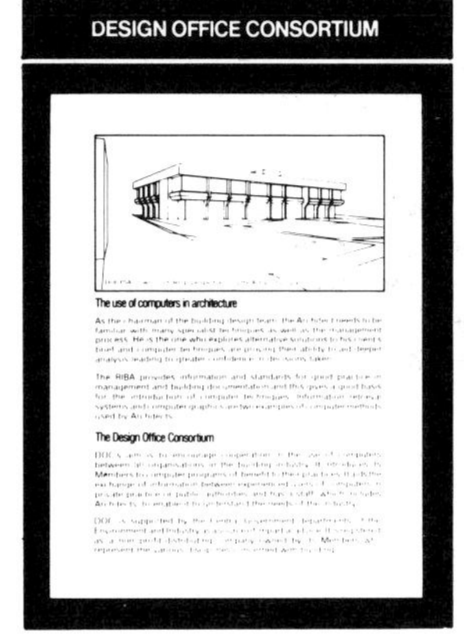

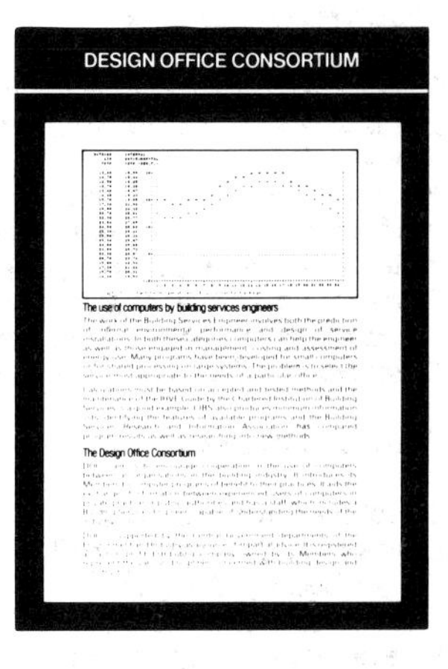

Survey reports:

Computer programs for construction management	Mar 79
Computer programs for energy prediction in buildings	Apr 79

Computer programs

Integrated building and equipment scheduling	Dec 74
GLIM lighting analysis	Jul 73
GLIM Pre-processor	Dec 74
SPACES, school design	Mar 74
General schedule program	Feb 73
LISI, lift simulation	Dec 73
FUME, smoke control	Mar 74
Pilkington air conditioning program	Apr 74
Faber integrated building system	Apr 74
COMPASS on-line accounting	Dec 74
CONDNS prediction of condensation	Mar 75
OAP/DOC Daylight	Jun 78
Site excavation	Oct 75
Edinburgh housing site layout	Oct 75
CAD Centre visualisation	Oct 75
CALI, lift design calculator	Jun 75
LSD2, lift simulation	Jun 75
GLADYS, structural calculations	Mar 76
STIN, frame analysis	Mar 76
REVOP, formula price adjustment	Jun 76
ATKOOL, cooling/heating loads	Sep 76
DRAWNET, critical path diagrams	Dec 76
NETPLOT, network plotting for PCS	Dec 76
Lancs Interactive graphic networking system	Dec 76
Haden Young services design programs	Mar 77
LUSAS, finite element analysis system	Dec 77
JOCO, joint cost estimation	Winter 78

Manuals

FORPA, formula price adjustment of building contracts User's manual Programmer's manual FORPA in Fortran magnetic tape	Mar 78

Restricted to potential users of the systems:

Site excavation programs	Jan 76
OAP/DOC Daylight Introduction, User manual and data forms	May 78
REVOP 2, formula price adjustment User's manual	Jan 78

Case studies

Riyad Faculty of Medicine, Things/Hidden lines	Sep 77
Liphook Secondary School, site excavation	Sep 77
Fulwood Primary School, polyhedral program	Sep 77
BSC Peterborough restaurant, environmental package	Sep 77
Cheshire County Council Dept of Architecture	Summer 78
Bradshaw Buckton and Tonge	Autumn 78
Design Innovations Research/ W J Cairns and Partners	Winter 78

Appearing in CAD Journal during 1979:

Visualisation of the Leyland Vehicles Technical Centre, Fairhursts

The Finite Element method and reinforced concrete slabs, Bingham Blades & Partners

Site excavation at Alton Sixth Form College, Hampshire County Council

Reviews

CAD 74 International conference and exhibitions	Sep 74
Computer programs in environmental design	Sep 75
Interactive design systems conference	Jun 77
Illustrating BASIC	Sep 77
Computer applications in architecture	Summer 78
Computer aided architectural design	Autumn 78

CHESHIRE COUNTY COUNCIL

The organisation

The Research and Development Unit of the Department of Architecture has recently been enabled to allocate resources to an assessment of departmental requirements in the effective use of computers. A co-ordinated strategy is now to be developed, by means of an analysis of possible computer applications in each professional discipline

Initial use

The Architect's Department has used the County Council's computer for some time, for analysis of time sheets and the production of bills of quantity, but has recently broadened this use considerably. As well as using the ABACUS software (especially their ECOLE 1 program) on the NEL computer, it is investigating the use of APL (A Programming Language) for work scheduling, costing and graph plotting, and also running successfully its own program dealing with energy usage (Fuel Monitoring System) which is continuously under development

Initial planning for this system began late in 1974. The fuel crisis indicated that several administrative checks were needed to establish economies in the use of fuel. The most basic of these was to control and predict the topping-up of fuel tanks in buildings so that the cheapest system of distribution could be operated. More generally, it was necessary to monitor the cost of actual fuel usage in buildings and to make comparisons between buildings of the same type, if economies were to be made. Finally, if large amounts of building data could be held, easy and direct comparisons both of theoretical against actual use of fuel, and of maintenance information between buildings, would be possible for detailed cost analyses

Having identified these objectives, the Management Advisory Unit of the Council was consulted. It was asked how these aims could be realised and what manpower would be needed. Its report indicated that, to perform all the tasks effectively, six engineers and sixty clerks would be required. It was then that the Department decided to investigate the use of a computer

An exhaustive search began, to find any software which might be available 'off-the-shelf', either from a bureau or to run on the council's own machine (an IBM 370). No program was available which would meet the requirements originally laid down, although the GLC were considering the development of a similar system. However, it was considered that the time taken for this system to become operative would effectively be wasted. This time could be used to greater effect developing its own program, which would necessarily meet its requirements in all respects, or as many as possible, and at the same time fit into the established methods and processes of working that already existed within the Department. The proposal by the GLC, for example, would have meant the use of external consultants to calculate the norms for buildings. One of the aims of an energy usage program, as envisaged by Cheshire CC, was that theoretical values should be examined critically in the light of data concerning the actual utilisation of the buildings in question

1 Data Dynamics 390 control console

This detailed appraisal took six months, and included evaluation of separate parts of programs as well as whole packages. During this time the FMS program was beginning to be developed. The Computer Services Department of the Council were approached to write the program, with Geoff Brace supervising development from the Architect's Department

A detailed brief was submitted covering all the stated requirements, after which the two departments acted in close liaison during development. Nevertheless, it took some time for the program to become operational. The largest problem to be encountered, apart from the simple one of making time for consultation between the two departments, was that a bridge had to be constructed between the two specialist areas of computer programming and service engineering. In order for the development to continue, the requirements originally stated had to be broken down into simple steps which would form a logical progression. This meant the programmer had to acquire some knowledge of engineering to understand the problems faced, and that the engineers had to begin again from basics: methods and systems of calculation had to be examined in detail in order to rationalise them. Geoff Brace felt that this had been a thoroughly useful process. 'Taking the trouble to make a detailed reappraisal of assumptions that you have made, factors that you have taken for granted, gives you a deeper understanding of the work you are doing and the way in which you carry it out.' This exercise would not have been carried out had it not become necessary

The problem of creating time for the project was overcome only by both departments setting rigid deadlines for each stage of the work. Nevertheless, towards the end of the project, five programmers were working to complete it, although throughout most of the development only one programmer had been employed on FMS

The problems encountered during development were mainly simple ones. For example, it was assumed that all meters had six digits, but it was later found that some gas meters had only four, which effectively confused the results. Mainly, the expertise which was already present in the Council's Computer Services Department helped to prevent problems before they arose, although there has since been some confusion simply because those operating the program have not been engineers. In response to every problem that has arisen however, the validation run has been modified to prevent repetitions

Eventually a pilot scheme, covering eighty buildings, began. (It is planned that the system will be expanded to cover 1250 buildings). During the development period, Geoff Brace attempted to perform the same tasks manually with six buildings. He estimated that it took approximately thirty per cent of his time to do this. Now, after the long and laborious task of creating the data base, a more complex system covering many more buildings was operating automatically

The system immediately showed savings of approximately £6000 a year. Various flaws in energy usage were immediately identified, from data which had not previously been checked and comparisons made, simply because the manpower to do this had not been available. One building, for example, was found to be 830 per cent inefficient against an ideal value. (Average inefficiencies were found to be about 100 per cent). This led to an all-out search for an error in the program. Nothing was found, but a visit to the building showed that thermostats had been labelled wrongly. Consequently, the night thermostat had been set for day and the day thermostat for night. The janitor, who felt the building to be cold during the day, turned up the thermostat. As a result the building was running at full temperature throughout the week

The system uses a simple method of operation. The building user submits data on a form each month, to be checked against the data base that has been established. The forms are input and processed by the Computer Services Department, giving virtually a bureau service to the Architect's Department. Output is on line-print, with an end-of-year print-out stored on microfilm, which is intended to facilitate searches for individual data. Because of the volume of work to pass through the Computer Services Department however, there are often delays in producing the monthly results, and the modelling capabilities incorporated in the program are not used to their full extent. (It usually takes three days for modelled results to be received by the Department). The Department hopes to have its own terminal installed so that use of the program could become fully interactive, and that all the staff in the office could become acquainted with using it. There was certainly a demand for this: up to 100 requests were received each week for data resulting from the program

2 Tektronix graphics display unit

3 GPO Modem unit

Further use

Currently, further ways of developing the usefulness of the program are being investigated. The data base which has been established is obviously important. The checking of operating profiles might be performed more effectively: guide figures from published data are being checked against actual usage (these have been found to be very liberal in their assessments), and dates when components have been replaced have already been tied into the system to enable maintenance costs and future budgets to be estimated in terms of the actual, rather than theoretical, component life. The assessment of usefulness of data generated by the program is a continuous process: 'The big problem is that the computer is throwing out more problems than we have answers for'

Installation

As stated under Initial use, the Council's own computer is an IBM 370

Conclusions

Both Geoff Brace and Phil Wilson, the Research and Development Architect, felt that it was very necessary to take the time to evaluate software, in terms of the problems faced. FMS was developed as an answer to clearly identified requirements, and consequently evolved in a useful way

This approach is also adopted by the Research and Development Unit towards all software. The problem of validation of output from a program is a very real one and blind faith in a program to solve a problem is no answer. How the program works and the assumptions made throughout will affect its usefulness in terms of solving a particular problem. Also, the cost effectiveness using a computer should be carefully evaluated

Apart from these notes of caution however, the Department remains optimistic about the use of computers. Currently, it is evaluating another ABACUS program, SPACES/3, for general use, and hoping to link its own programs written in APL, for graph plotting, with FMS. Another Research and Development project is aimed at incorporating perspective drawings produced on the NEL computer with a photo-montage technique to enable clear and vivid presentations to be obtained

The Architect's Department is co-operating with the County's Computer Services Department to establish a long-term strategy for the use of computers. It will involve identifying problems within the Department, and locating and studying in detail possible solutions computers might offer. Also, by encouraging some familiarity with computer techniques, it is hoped to dispel the mystique thrown up by barriers of jargon and the entrenched scepticism which surrounds a process with the appearance of magic

CUSDIN, BURDEN AND HOWITT

The organisation

The architectural practice of Cusdin, Burden and Howitt has a staff of 35 which includes fourteen qualified architects

Initial approach

The practice first started to investigate the potentialities of computer techniques in 1964, following the attendance of David Campion at the Architectural Association Computer Course No 2 at Oxford that year. At this time, the state of computer development generally was embryonic, while for the architect it was hard to even think of his problems in terms of computer applications, let alone consider any machinery and expertise which might be at his disposal

It was difficult for the average architectural firm to contemplate the expenditure of much time and money in the field of computer techniques without some indication of a potential pay-off. IBM data-processing batch bureaux were common during this period but IBM appeared more interested in selling time than carrying out research in this area. Just as architects had little or no knowledge of computers, so computer experts were ignorant of the problems of the architect. Nevertheless, the few strides forward made with computers in other fields provided the clue to the areas of the architects' work which could reasonably be harnessed to computer techniques. These were areas where the nature of the work was repetitious, as in information scheduling

The next step

It appeared that the best method of approach would be, first, to learn the techniques involved in programming a computer and, second, to apply this knowledge more specifically to architectural problems. To this end, David Campion attended courses on IBM FORTRAN, IBM simulation, Elliott Autocode and Elliott ALGOL. Induction in programming was followed by a period for gaining expertise in program writing, utilising an 803 computer at the NCR Elliott Computer Workshop at Borehamwood. A range of relatively simple architectural programs was written and tested, covering the techniques of area analysis, information scheduling and simulation. As a result, it became clear that in certain specialised cases, programs could aid the architect on time-consuming, repetitious tasks, thereby allowing him to spend more time on problems of design

The problems inherent in batch-processing mainly centred on the delays in turn-round and the inaccessibility of the computer for ironing out the bugs in a program. However, the cost of an in-house installation at this time was prohibitive and, as David Campion explained, the amount of investment in computers is always determined by the size of organisation and the job involved. Although he believes the computer now to be a necessary aid to the work of the practice, he is not slow to point out the problems encountered at the outset. First, it was soon realised that the amount of effort required to develop programs was sometimes quite disproportionate to the return. It was necessary to spend a large proportion of the time bending the problem to suit the computer, rather than concentrating on the problem itself. The limited amount of core storage also meant that sacrifices had to be made in the way certain data-processing facilities were implemented. Apart from the delays associated with batch-processing in those formative years, there was also an element of distrust of the computer within the office, occasioned in part by there being no sight of 'the machine'

Commercial bureau service development

During 1967, the first commercial time-sharing computer services became available in this country, and they were investigated by the practice as

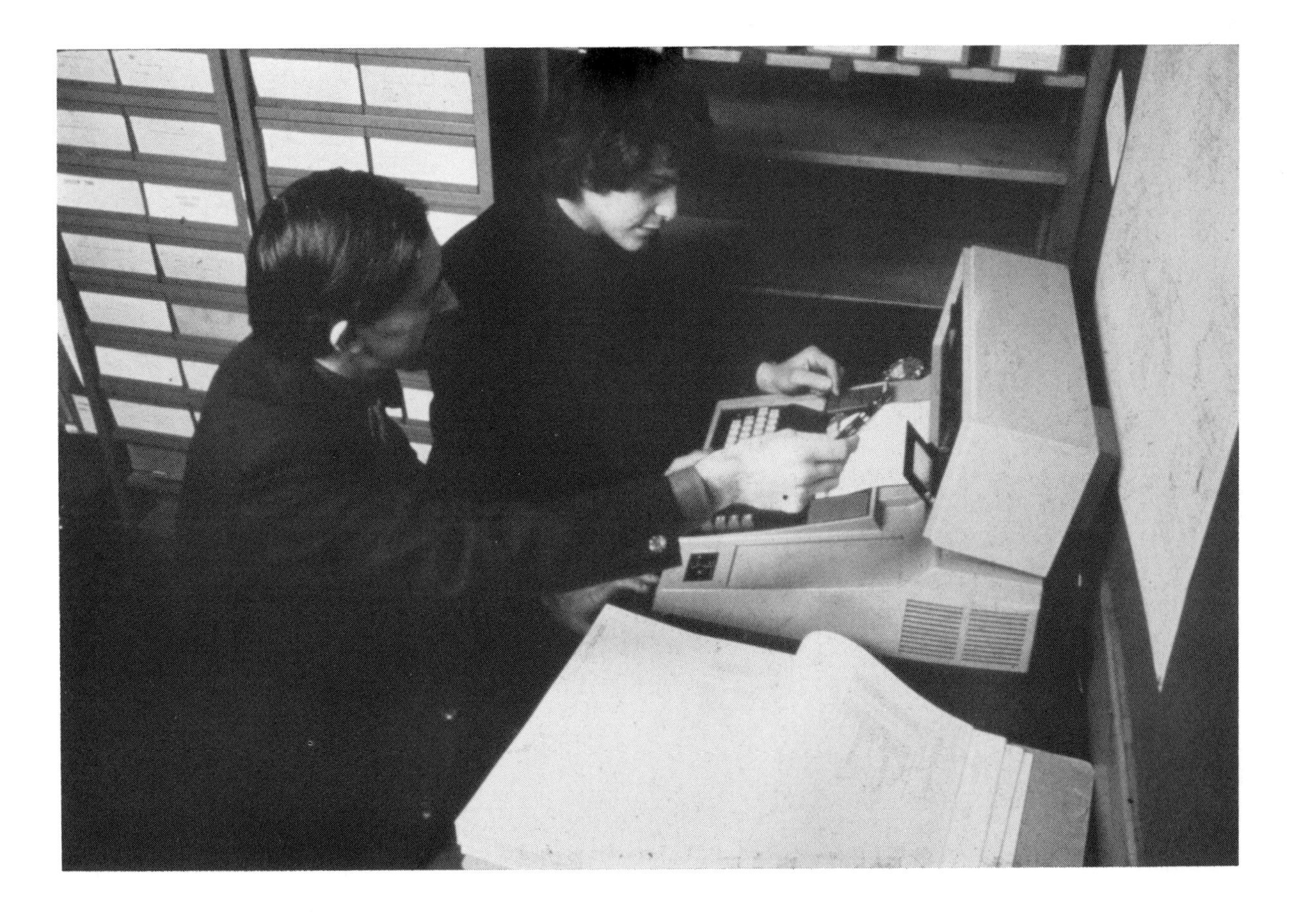

1 Tektronix 4081 graphics system

alternatives to the NCR Elliott Computer Workshop because of their ability to provide better accessibility and faster turn-round. At this time, the 803 computer was being replaced by a 4100 and this meant reprogramming all the applications, in any case

The first commercial test applications were with job-planning and information scheduling programs. As far as job-planning applications were concerned, the bureau could provide a suite of analysis programs, written in FORTRAN, which was capable of handling a network of up to 1000 activities. It was rare however, for the practice to require network diagrams which ran into more than 100 activities. This, coupled with the fact that the programs had limited forms of output, persuaded the practice to try and write an alternative program which could produce results in bar-chart form with activity descriptions in English

The modified programs were written in BASIC. The first versions produced a bar chart without activity descriptions. This disadvantage was soon apparent when attempting to cross-refer the bar chart to the descriptions on the network diagram. The second stage of development incorporated the facility for providing up to fifteen alpha-numeric characters for each activity description. The development cost of this program has been put by David Campion at twenty man days and £90 in computer time

As far as other applications were concerned, the one obvious advantage that computer scheduling has over its manual counterpart is to provide the user with the choice of extracting separate columns of information from the complete schedule, if he wishes. It was considered by the practice that the task of producing schedules was invariably tedious, time-consuming and prone to errors, and they felt that if scheduling techniques could be rationalised and common procedures adopted, then savings of staff time, and therefore cost, could be effected. Another advantage would be that of recording all the information on punched cards or paper tapes, so that unauthorised alterations could be more easily avoided. One of the problems inherent in manually written schedules was the subsequent alterations which were made without notification to those who held the original information

Two programs were developed, one employing numeric codes for representing descriptions, the other, alpha-numeric codes. Numeric codes are more efficient in computer terms since they involve less storage, faster processing and, therefore, reduced cost. On the other hand, alpha-numeric codes are more memorable from the point of view of the user. The program employing numeric codes was intended for fairly simple schedules, such as those for finishes, doors, windows and ironmongery. The program using alpha-numeric codes was used for schedules involving a large number of possible characteristics, as in a furniture and fittings schedule. Development and production were merged into one for the two programs which were written. Because of the prevalence of schedules in the work of the practice and the adaptability of the scheduling programs, frequent use of the programs meant that development costs were recouped more quickly. Today with faster and cheaper computer time all coding is alpha-numeric for the benefit of the user

Middle period

In 1968, Tony Reynolds joined the practice and took over the major computer-programming role. Scheduling was one of the prime areas for which the practice then developed the use of the computer. The benefits derived from computer-aided scheduling affect not only the schedule, but also the design. The fact that a schedule could be manually prepared and then processed to variable requirements by the computer in half a day meant that the design side of a project could be worked on till the last moment and changes could be more easily accommodated. In terms of the work which the practice undertook, a more expanded service could be offered, in some cases; because of the improvements in schedules, furniture and furnishings were often included in a schedule, where required by the client, since the additional effort involved was minimal with the aid of a computer

Some of the programs which the practice used were of 'limited purpose': they covered simulation (eg queueing in dining rooms), lighting calculations, and acoustics. Of the thirty-five staff in the office, two were programmers. Although care was taken to ensure that the monthly bills were within reason, the practice was satisfied that savings were being made on jobs which would otherwise have been carried out manually

The inclusion of a 'HELP' command in programs run via the remote terminal means that a relative novice can 'run' a program. If the operator encounters difficulties, he can type 'HELP' to find out where he stands and which options are available to him. This kind of practical advance should nevertheless be weighed against the problems which still exist for the user of average means. The restrictions on data-handling capacity imposed by the amount of core storage still exist, as do the unnecessarily complicated methods of solution to relatively simple problems which persist in a number of commercial packages. This latter problem has been in evidence in the simulation 'runs' on queueing conditions which Cusdin, Burden and Howitt has conducted. 'The very fact that a problem has to be analysed in great detail before a computer can be used to help in its solution often results in the problem being rationalised to such an extent that the computer is not in the end required'

Installation

In May 1968, the practice installed a teletype terminal in the office on an experimental monthly basis. It was connected to a GE 265 computer at the offices of GEIS Ltd via the GPO telephone network. Although remote access terminals were in their infancy, it was felt to be a risk worth taking in view of the greatly increased accessibility of the computer. If the development of programs was to be the prime objective then the rapid turn-round allowed by a terminal would reduce costs, as well as being far more practicable, with the 'de-bugging' of programs in mind. There had been a choice between GEIS Ltd and Time-Sharing Ltd and the former was chosen because of the greater backing store facilities of its computer at that time

In 1969, the practice started using the large SIA CDC6600 computer at Victoria. With its very high speed and large capacity of both internal memory and disc backing store it was possible to process very large schedules more quickly and cheaply than heretofore. Subsequently SIA introduced a composite Batch/Remote Batch/Interactive Service and the practice switched all its work to this service

From 1974 to 1977, the practice rented a Texas Instruments SILENT 733 ASR terminal, with twin cassettes for recording and storing data. This has now been purchased. The terminal, being very quiet, is situated in a normal office space, where it is close to the users. This was not possible previously with the relatively noisy teletype impact printer

Current situation

During 1977, the practice carried out a study of Computer-Aided Design Centre's MEDALS draughting package for the Design Office Consortium

Following this, Tony Reynolds carried out a comparative investigation of a number of draughting systems: OXSYS (now BDS) developed by ARC Ltd, CARBS developed by Clwyd County Council, MEDALS developed by CADC Cambridge, and the newly-introduced Tektronix 4081 Graphics System. A paper on this work was presented at the CAD 78 Conference

During December and January 1977, the investigation of draughting systems was widened to include RUCAPS developed by GMW Computers Ltd

In January 1978 the practice decided to acquire a Tektronix 4081 computer system with a Benson 1322 plotter, and to develop its own computer-aided draughting system, having been convinced that this represented a satisfactory computer hardware/software package that would be economically viable and provide major benefits for the office. Not only would this system provide computer-aided draughting but also a powerful mini-computer system in its own right for handling all other computer applications

The partners' view was that the practice should make use of its own considerable computer experience and develop applications tailored to its needs rather than adapt the practice to the other systems available

The computer was in production use for draughting purposes by mid-March 1978, and between then and the end of 1978 a number of projects were being handled including: (1) £50 million Phase 4 of the King Khaled Hospital and Faculty of Medicine at Riyadh, (2) £3 million Geriatric Block at Addenbrookes Hospital, Cambridge, (3) £20 million extension to the Mater Misericordia Hospital, Dublin, and (4) a terrace of seven interlocking family houses in London

The draughting system is capable of being linked to the practice's scheduling programs, thereby enabling the scheduling process to be automated; this considerably reduces the manual effort in producing schedules and enables them to be produced very much more quickly and accurately

In order to handle an increasing work load, and to enable the pace of development work to be increased, a second 4081 front-end is being installed early in 1979

Although justified basically as a draughting aid the computer is naturally being used for other purposes including schedules, information retrieval, time-sheet/work in progress costing etc

Conclusions

David Campion, who has written widely on the subject of computer-aided architectural design, offers this advice to the prospective user. To understand the viability of using a computer, it is first necessary to be cognisant of the equivalent manual cost: this may require a more detailed job-costing system than is normally provided. He also expresses the opinion that the computer is still very much a source of advice in making a decision and is not itself a decision-maker. The architect remains the arbiter. It is not surprising then that most computer applications have been relative to the production of detailed information and not to the early design stages, where there are fewer hard facts. This characteristic is evinced by the fact that the architect's work still heavily involves the production of drawings, which are the staple diet and the labour-intensive activity common to all offices. The use of the computer for other aspects of an architect's work can be more contentious

However, David Campion draws attention to the current batch of building perspective programs which now enable the user to 'turn' a structure and view it from any angle. He looks forward to the time when the average practice has access to this kind of facility, as one of the major criticisms of modern architecture has been the failure to consider a design from every vantage point, particularly in terms of planning and civic design. The speed with which computer-stored representations can be altered, or output as hard-copy drawings to any scale, are other advantages to be considered. There is an evaluation of building perspective programs contained in the November 1976 bulletin issued by the Design Office Consortium

Looking to the future, David Campion believes that the computer will continue to play a role in the practice as an aid to the architect, but recognises that the size of this role can only be determined by the management and by its general acceptance by the staff. Despite the steady development of hardware and software over the past twelve years, he feels that architects 'look forward to the next generation of hardware and ignore it when it arrives, anticipating the arrival of the generation after that'. He also believes that 'the state of the art' of computer-aided architectural design would not have reached its present position without the financial support that it has received from central and local government bodies and research grants, and this support 'has without doubt occurred as a result of the use of co-ordinated system building programs'

```
UNIVERSITY OF DURHAM - COURTYARD PROJECT
ROOM CODE SCHEDULE  (RCS   )  PAGE   4
7 JULY 71

 CODE     QUANTITY DESCRIPTION

(CUT 8 )        1    CUT-OUT FOR COMPRESSED AIR OUTLET
(SHL 1I)        4    SHELF COMPONENT 1200 MM (W) 200 MM (D) - IROKO VENEERED
(SIN 6 )        1    SINK TOP COMPONENT 2500 MM (W) 750 MM (D) CONCRETE/TILED + VIT.CHINA INSET BOWL
(SOC 1 )        5    ELECTRICAL SOCKET OUTLET - 13 AMP.TWIN, SWITCHED
(UPR 2 )        3    UPRIGHT WALL SUPPORT FOR SHELF BRACKETS - SPUR 1219 MM (48 IN)
(WAT 1 )        4    WATER OUTLET - COLD TAP
(WAT 3 )        1    WATER OUTLET - HOT TAP
(WOR 8I)        2    WORK TOP COMPONENT 2480 MM (W) 600 MM (D) - IROKO VENEERED


ROOM    05           TANK ROOM

(AIR 1 )        1    COMPRESSED AIR OUTLET
(BRA 1 )       12    BRACKET FOR 200 MM SHELF - SPUR 7 IN
(CUT 4 )        2    CUT-OUT FOR ELECTRICAL CONDUIT
(CUT 8 )        1    CUT-OUT FOR COMPRESSED AIR OUTLET
(SHL 1I)        4    SHELF COMPONENT 1200 MM (W) 200 MM (D) - IROKO VENEERED
(SIN 6 )        1    SINK TOP COMPONENT 2500 MM (W) 750 MM (D) CONCRETE/TILED + VIT.CHINA INSET BOWL
(SOC 1 )        5    ELECTRICAL SOCKET OUTLET - 13 AMP.TWIN, SWITCHED
(UPR 2 )        3    UPRIGHT WALL SUPPORT FOR SHELF BRACKETS - SPUR 1219 MM (48 IN)
(WAT 1 )        4    WATER OUTLET - COLD TAP
(WAT 3 )        1    WATER OUTLET - HOT TAP
(WOR 8I)        2    WORK TOP COMPONENT 2480 MM (W) 600 MM (D) - IROKO VENEERED


ROOM    06           LOBBY

(FIR 1 )        1    FIRE FIGHTING EQUIPMENT - NORSEN TYPE B 60 FT HOSE REEL + FIRE BELL
(HOK 3 )        2    HOOK RAIL WITH 12 COAT HOOKS
(MAT 1 )        1    MAT
(MAT 2 )        1    MAT WELL 1500 MM (W) 900 MM (D)


ROOM    07           STORE

(CON 3 )        1    CONVECTOR HEATER
(DEX 1 )        3    DEXION SHELVING ASSEMBLY 3734 MM (W) 456 MM (D) 2134 MM (H) - 6 SHELVES
(DEX 2 )        1    DEXION SHELVING ASSEMBLY 4648 MM (W) 456 MM (D) 2134 MM (H) - 6 SHELVES
(RFL 1 )        1    ROOF LIGHT 900 MM X 1200 MM


ROOM    08           ENGININEERING GEOLOGY

(BLI 5 )        2    BLIND - BLACK AUDIO-VISUAL,2950MM (W) 1440MM (H)
(BRA 3 )        7    BRACKET FOR 200 MM (D) SERVICE LEDGE
(BRD 4 )        1    BOARD (WALL MOUNTED) 4800 MM (W) 1200 MM (H) VITREOUS ENAMEL
(CON 1 )        1    CONVECTOR HEATER ,TYPE 1
(CUT 4 )        2    CUT-OUT FOR ELECTRICAL CONDUIT
(DES 1 )       16    DESK 1200 MM (W) 750 MM (D)
(FSC10I)        1    FREE STORAGE CUPBOARD 900 MM (W) 300 MM (D) 2000 MM (H) WITH 5 SHELVES - IROKO VENEERED

SCHEDULE OF FITTINGS
CUSDIN BURDEN AND HOWITT  CHARTERED ARCHITECTS
```

PRINCESS ALEXANDRA HOSPITAL HARLOW - RESIDENTIAL BLOCK
ITEM SCHEDULE PAGE 1
3 DECEMBER 71

ROOM	ROOM	FLOOR FINISH	SKIRTING	WALL	WALL FINISH	CEILING	CEIL/FINISH
1501	ENTRANCE HALL	QUARRY TILES 150MM SQ	QUARRY TILES 76MM	FACING BRICK	-	F.F.CONCRETE	PAINT
1502	METER CUPBOARD	SCREED (38MM)	-	F. .BRICK/BLOCK	PAINT	F.F.CONCRETE	PAINT
1503	MAIN STAIR	GRANO TILES	GRANO 76MM	FACING BRICK	-	F.F.CONCRETE	PAINT
1504	CORRIDOR	PVC TILES	PV676	PLASTER	PAINT	PLASTER	PAINT
1505	BEDROOM 2	PVC TILES	PV676	PLASTER	PAINT	PLASTER	PAINT
1506	BEDROOM 1	PVC TILES	PV676	PLASTER	PAINT	PLASTER	PAINT
1507	LIVING ROOM	PVC TILES	PV676	PLASTER	PAINT	PLASTER	PAINT
1508	KITCHEN	VINYL ASBESTOS TILES	VINYL ASBESTOS 76MM	PLASTER	PAINT	PLASTER	PAINT
1509	BATHROOM	PVC TILES	PVC 76MM	PLASTER/GL.TILES	PAINT	PLASTER	PAINT
1510	LINEN CUPBOARD	PVC TILES	PVC 76MM	PLASTER	PAINT	PLASTER	PAINT
1511	STORE	QUARRY TILES 150MM SQ	QUARRY TILES 76MM	PLASTER	PAINT	F.F.CONCRETE	PAINT
1513	CORRIDOR	PVC TILES	PV676	PLASTER	PAINT	PLASTER	PAINT
1514	LINEN CUPBOARD	PVC TILES	PVC 76MM	PLASTER	PAINT	PLASTER	PAINT
1515	BATHROOM	PVC TILES	PVC 76MM	PLASTER/GL.TILES	PAINT	PLASTER	PAINT
1516	KITCHEN	VINYL ASBESTOS TILES	VINYL ASBESTOS 76MM	PLASTER	PAINT	PLASTER	PAINT
1517	LIVING ROOM	PVC TILES	PV676	PLASTER	PAINT	PLASTER	PAINT
1518	BEDROOM 1	PVC TILES	PV676	PLASTER	PAINT	PLASTER	PAINT
1519	BEDROOM 2	PVC TILES	PV676	PLASTER	PAINT	PLASTER	PAINT
2501	HALL	GRANO INSITU	GRANO 76MM	FACING BRICK	-	F.F.CONCRETE	PAINT
2503	MAIN STAIR	GRANO TILES	GRANO 76MM	FACING BRICK	-	F.F.CONCRETE	PAINT
2504	CORRIDOR	PVC TILES	PV676	PLASTER	PAINT	PLASTER	PAINT
2505	BEDROOM 2	PVC TILES	PV676	PLASTER	PAINT	PLASTER	PAINT
2506	BEDROOM 1	PVC TILES	PV676	PLASTER	PAINT	PLASTER	PAINT
2507	LIVING ROOM	PVC TILES	PV676	PLASTER	PAINT	PLASTER	PAINT
2508	KITCHEN	VINYL ASBESTOS TILES	VINYL ASBESTOS 76MM	PLASTER	PAINT	PLASTER	PAINT
2509	BATHROOM	PVC TILES	PVC 76MM	PLASTER/GL.TILES	PAINT	PLASTER	PAINT
2510	LINEN CUPBOARD	PVC TILES	PVC 76MM	PLASTER	PAINT	PLASTER	PAINT
2511	STORE	QUARRY TILES 150MM SQ	QUARRY TILES 76MM	PLASTER	PAINT	F.F.CONCRETE	PAINT
2513	CORRIDOR	PVC TILES	PV676	PLASTER	PAINT	PLASTER	PAINT
2514	LINEN CUPBOARD	PVC TILES	PVC 76MM	PLASTER	PAINT	PLASTER	PAINT
2515	BATHROOM	PVC TILES	PVC 76MM	PLASTER/GL.TILES	PAINT	PLASTER	PAINT
2516	KITCHEN	VINYL ASBESTOS TILES	VINYL ASBESTOS 76MM	PLASTER	PAINT	PLASTER	PAINT
2517	LIVING ROOM	PVC TILES	PV676	PLASTER	PAINT	PLASTER	PAINT
2518	BEDROOM 1	PVC TILES	PV676	PLASTER	PAINT	PLASTER	PAINT
2519	BEDROOM 2	PVC TILES	PV676	PLASTER	PAINT	PLASTER	PAINT
3501	HALL	GRANO INSITU	GRANO 76MM	FACING BRICK	-	F.F.CONCRETE	PAINT
3503	MAIN STAIR	GRANO TILES	GRANO 76MM	FACING BRICK	-	F.F.CONCRETE	PAINT
3504	CORRIDOR	PVC TILES	PV676	PLASTER	PAINT	PLASTER	PAINT
3505	BEDROOM 2	PVC TILES	PV676	PLASTER	PAINT	PLASTER	PAINT
3506	BEDROOM 1	PVC TILES	PV676	PLASTER	PAINT	PLASTER	PAINT
3507	LIVING ROOM	PVC TILES	PV676	PLASTER	PAINT	PLASTER	PAINT
3508	KITCHEN	VINYL ASBESTOS TILES	VINYL ASBESTOS 76MM	PLASTER	PAINT	PLASTER	PAINT
3509	BATHROOM	PVC TILES	PVC 76MM	PLASTER/GL.TILES	PAINT	PLASTER	PAINT
3510	LINEN CUPBOARD	PVC TILES	PVC 76MM	PLASTER	PAINT	PLASTER	PAINT
3513	CORRIDOR	PVC TILES	PV676	PLASTER	PAINT	PLASTER	PAINT
3514	LINEN CUPBOARD	PVC TILES	PVC 76MM	PLASTER	PAINT	PLASTER	PAINT
3515	BATHROOM	PVC TILES	PVC 76MM	PLASTER/GL.TILES	PAINT	PLASTER	PAINT
3516	KITCHEN	VINYL ASBESTOS TILES	VINYL ASBESTOS 76MM	PLASTER	PAINT	PLASTER	PAINT

FINISHES SCHEDULE
CUSDIN BURDEN AND HOWITT CHARTERED ARCHITECTS

H L DAWSON AND ASSOCIATES

The organisation

H L Dawson and Associates are consultant mechanical and electrical services engineers. Approximately forty people are employed designing and supervising projects incorporating air-conditioning, heating and ventilation, electrical and water distribution and fire and public health engineering

Initial use

H L Dawson, who founded the firm, has been involved with the use of computers to solve engineering problems since programs first became commercially viable. The practice had been formed mainly to capitalise on the expertise gained with the first Swedish and American programs, but generally to make use of all modern techniques available

Initially the practice wrote its own programs for bureau machines and, at one point, installed a terminal

This attempt to link with a large computer did not prove to be economic, mainly because the expenses involved were not justified by returns on the investment. Rental of the terminal was felt to be high, as also were the charges for the telecommunication lines. The lines connected to the Modem were occasionally faulty, which was proved only after a long and tedious fault-tracing exercise, within the electro-mechanical systems in use at the time. These recurring faults at one point meant that a figure input at the terminal as 0·3 was given a value during processing of 3·0, despite a tolerance check. The run was immediately aborted as soon as ridiculous values began appearing in the calculations but, nevertheless, the time taken had to be paid for, and the run repeated. These problems with the lines and the system could have been resolved, but only at a considerable cost in time and effort. Though this illustrates only one of the problems involved in accepting software 'off-the-shelf', it well represents the need to understand how a program works before accepting its results, a lesson often learned only by bitter experience

Further use

The type of problem outlined above, and the fact that possession of a terminal does not guarantee immediate access to, or results from, a computer, led the practice to adopt a different strategy. This involved the abandonment of the terminal, and the purchase of a Hewlett-Packard 9830. Bureau services would in future be used, as sparingly as possible, for more complex problems. Although using bureaux is a more expensive method of employing a computer, it proved, in fact, to be far cheaper than the terminal when complemented by the Hewlett-Packard. This system has now become accepted as the most efficient way of dealing with the problems encountered in the office. The desk-top machine and peripheral equipment allow much easier access to data-processing

The company policy was to employ specialists in two fields, engineering and computers, and could draw upon the resources of five programmers. There was, therefore, no need to accept programs 'off-the-shelf': they could be developed to answer particular problems which arose or to satisfy the requirements of a particular client in the evaluation of specific factors. A large program run on a bureau machine might give too much information in this particular case. It would be like using a sledgehammer to crack a nut, and in this situation the costs involved in using the large program could not be justified. The familiarity of the programmers with the machine in the office meant that small sub-routines to deal with this kind of problem could be quickly developed. Even if this were not possible, the Hewlett-Packard could be used as a front-end processor and help save time and effort on the bureau machine

1 Hewlett-Packard series 9800 model 30 calculator

Installation

The practice, which uses bureau services all over the country, ('We use the bureau with the program to solve our particular problem') also possesses its own Hewlett-Packard 9830 programmable calculator (mentioned above) and various similar machines

These desk-top calculators have generally been found to be most useful pieces of office equipment. Their potential was realised very quickly, not only for solving simple problems, but also for adapting to the more subtle needs of a particular job, the sort of flexibility which could not be obtained from a bureau using standard software, or only obtained at too high a price

Conclusions

Up-to-date methods do not add up to instant engineering, or even instant problem-solving. Robin Dawson, who has shared the interest in computers developed by his father, felt that 'the computer is simply a necessary tool, and using it does not mean that expertise is no longer necessary. It is essential for correct interpretation of both input program and results.' Although use of computers, computer services and programming techniques had developed as a natural progression for the practice, the need for a deep knowledge of engineering practice was an essential parallel requirement. Results printed-out from a computer may look more authoritative, but, unless

2 With the Hewlett-Packard model 11285A Datacommunications Interface, the model 9830A calculator is used as an interactive or batch terminal, communicating through a Modem (in the background) and telephone lines with large computers, time-sharing systems and other terminals

the parameters built into the program are understood, they may be useless. Nevertheless, the era of manual calculation seems to be at an end. 'There is simply no point in using traditional manual techniques, when a computer can perform much of the tedious, repetitive and time-consuming work. A small team performing manual calculations no longer stands a chance in this field in terms of cost or accuracy'

Although 'one cannot expect miracles from small programs', the fact that a particular problem can be isolated means that a large program, operating on a large machine, is often unnecessary. Also, the in-house program allows total control. Either validation processes are inbuilt to obtain the sophistication required, or the limitations of the program are recognised. Parameters set may be closely or loosely defined, depending on the accuracy required from the results. This emphasis on personal programming to solve individual problems is an attitude which is becoming much more generally held. The advances being made with mini-computers, in the lowering of prices and the possibilities of running longer processes, would seem to be encouraging this view

In part, the emphasis on programming for one's own needs appears to be a direct consequence of the reluctance of those offering programs to explain how these programs work. The bland statement that a program is, for example, based on the IHVE guide, is really no guarantee of the program itself. A program within which simple parameters have been set will give no more than simple answers. The assumption of one value, which often can provide a simple answer to programming problems, can give a disproportionate bias to the result obtained. To produce an accurate result to a large design problem, a large data base has to be used, employing as much published data as possible. An examination of the kind of data base used by a program will indicate its limitations, but it may not indicate inaccuracies in results caused by expressing a value vital to calculations in too simple a way. Verification of results rests largely on the skill as engineers of those people who are confronted with output from the program. Skilled staff must be employed to evaluate results. 'Because a computer is used, many people think that expertise is unnecessary: in many ways, it is much more important'

Many users new to computers tend to trust values produced by a computer, often going against their instinct and experience as engineers or architects. This trust is entirely misplaced. For example, Dawson and Associates had never installed a boiler of the capacity recommended by a computer program. Results had necessarily to be checked critically and thoroughly. Eventually, experience with using particular programs enabled anomalies in results to be predicted to some extent, but the engineer is always necessary to evaluate them in the light of his experience and bearing in mind the requirements of his client

Robin Dawson felt that a critical study of all available programs in certain areas was long overdue. 'An unbiased expert appraisal, even if this expresses opinions, is desperately needed.' The 'sea of computer programs' which confronts a prospective user is both vast and confusing. Consultation is necessary with people who have used a particular program, with bodies who have some experience of computers, such as Design Office Consortium, DoE Property Services Agency and the Building Services Research and Information Association, in order to build an effective picture of advantages and limitations. No programmer would think of giving tolerances on the results from his program which, obviously, can lead people to expect accuracy, when all they really obtain is an approximation. Three questions should be clearly answered before attempting to use a program. First, has the problem been clearly identified? Detailed results will not be required to answer a simple problem, but a complex program will be required to perform a complex calculation. Second, can the problem be solved? A program which operates in a particular area may not necessarily provide the required results: it may provide a wealth of detail, but not the answer required. Third, how accurate should the results be? Many simple programs can be used to give notional results. On the other hand, many large programs, although giving complex all-encompassing results, may be no better in terms of accuracy. 'If there has been no consultation with someone who has used the program, check the results by the method you know'

Robin Dawson added a further note of caution on the matter of costing. 'An expensive man is necessary to put data together and to interpret results.' He pointed out also that claims made by programmers with regard to cost savings were often over-simplified. 'It takes time to check input and output, to learn a new technique, to write a program and to eliminate the errors from it.' Nevertheless, when used intelligently, the computer becomes a valuable tool. Shading patterns, for example, were produced automatically at an eighty per cent saving in terms of costs, and gave a much greater time saving. Certainly, the development of a system which fitted into the routine of the office, and which was both economical and flexible to use, had taken some time and some bitter experience. Nevertheless, Robin Dawson remained confident: 'We shall continue to use the most modern techniques as they become available to us, and those which we develop ourselves'

JOHN LAING DESIGN ASSOCIATES LIMITED

The organisation

John Laing Design Associates Limited is the company within the Laing Group responsible for design to the Group and its customers, both in the UK and abroad. It consists of five specialist sections: architecture, civil and structural engineering, building services engineering, temporary works engineering (which includes formwork) and land survey. The main office is at the Group headquarters in Mill Hill, London, there are branches in Bristol, Manchester, Glasgow and Surbiton and a survey company is working in the Persian Gulf states. It has a staff of 350 and in 1976 earned approximately £3 000 000 in fees for the Group

Initial use

Structural engineering

The engineers were the first to realise the potential of using computers and, as long ago as 1957, began batch-processing on the Ferranti Pegasus. In June 1966, the Laing Group acquired an IBM 360–30 and later, in 1968, added a model 360–50. These were used mainly for commercial and administrative applications

Architecture

The architects first became interested in computers in 1968 when they were invited by West Sussex County Council to participate in parallel work. At this time, the Architect's Department of West Sussex County Council had a computer-aided design method in an advanced state of development. The architects' first excursion into programming took place shortly afterwards with an appraisal program called Laingwall. This was a design aid intended for use at the sketch stage of development of office blocks using the Laingwall building system. It took outline information, such as the required floor area, optional widths and number of storeys, and worked out alternative volumes to meet these criteria. Given the module, the actual volume and the population, it assessed the notional non-office area, ie the area taken up by stairs, lifts and sanitary arrangements. It also computed the number of Laingwall units required, the column spacing and the beam size. It calculated plant-room sizes and the heat load and, from the crane size and construction period, it worked out the quantities for in-situ and precast concrete. It then costed the building, based on up to 370 cost centres, and produced schedules and bills of quantity

1 Computer graphics installation

Graphics

In 1971, John Laing Design Associates sponsored a graduate in the Mechanical Engineering Department of Imperial College to undertake a PhD, in a joint development of an information system based on graphics. Their aim was, and still is, to produce an integrated system for handling and interpreting graphic information by computer and linking it to specifications. This should then generate costing and construction information, regardless of building type or construction method. At this time, the only comparable programs were OXSYS, which was at the detail stage, but was restricted to hospital design, and CEDAR, which was only at the sketch stage

Further use

This company has used computers since 1957 for solving structural engineering problems and, since 1971, has been interested in computer-aided design of buildings as a whole, as distinct from structural analysis and calculations only. It is developing a system for handling and interpreting graphic information and linking it to specifications

Structural engineering

The engineers continued to make use of bureaux and, in 1968, the Engineering Computer Group was set up and an ITT interactive terminal was installed. ITT also had an IBM 360 and so software development was made considerably easier. Programs from the ITT Library of Civil Engineering were used and, as and when necessary, the engineers wrote their own, many of which were later incorporated into the ITT Library

These programs were used to solve problems in structural analysis, co-ordinate geometry for survey work, excavation volumes and, for the services section, lift analyses and heat losses. Computers were considered for this kind of work because of the complexity of analysis involved and their ability to handle large numbers of repetitive calculations. It is estimated that ninety-five per cent of programs save time and eighty per cent save money

Other batch programs which have been tried by the engineers include those of GENESYS, on which they conducted field trials but which they decided not to use, the BCS suite for reinforced concrete design, which they continue to use in-house, and IBM programs, including STRESS. They have also rewritten existing programs so that they can be used on the Group's IBM computer. The Group has recently installed an IBM 370–145

Throughout this period, they have continued to write and develop their own programs. The civil engineers have written their own programs, as this has proved the most effective way of incorporating engineering logic and experience. The engineers are mostly self-taught as programmers, but, as computer use has been included in the curricula of most university engineering courses for the past seven or eight years, people are now coming into the department with more formal training

Architecture

The major drawback of the Laingwall program was that, as it was a totally alpha-numerical program, it could only be used for office buildings of a simple rectangular shape. It became increasingly obvious that, in order to handle complex shapes, alpha-numeric programs would require large amounts of manual design generation. With a graphics capability, however, the entire process could be simplified considerably. Any shape could be input directly via a digitiser and, more important, could be linked, in the computer, to the specifications

The engineers were also quick to see the advantages of a graphics system, especially in reinforced concrete beam detailing, for, as architects are beginning to demand longer spans, so engineers are being urged to compare costs of structural alternatives to find the most economical. The engineers can also detail by computer non-orthogonal, irregular reinforced concrete members, which it is impracticable to process manually

Graphics

Following the success of the joint research with Imperial College, in the autumn of 1975, John Laing Design Associates acquired the core of their present graphics equipment

The hardware comprises a Nova 1200 computer with 14M word disc-drive, a 19in Tektronix display terminal with hard-copy unit, a 12in Infoton alpha-numeric screen, two tablet digitisers, small and large, a mechanical digitiser/plotter and a ten-character Westrex teletype. Their most recent acquisition is a CalComp 950 plotter. The relatively small screen of the Tektronix means, however, that when parts of the plan have to be enlarged to fill the screen, it is difficult to maintain an overall impression of the design. Ideally, they would like a screen as big as the large tablet digitiser, but the only equipment available at present is a laser device which is beyond their resources

The graphics software is centred around a 'menu', which is positioned on the tablet digitiser. The menu contains common architectural symbols, such as those for doors, windows and wc pans. It also includes command symbols and an array of numbers, so that a line of, say, 3·2m can be 'drawn' on the screen. To draft a design, a rough pencil sketch is first drawn on graph paper. The drawing is then constructed from symbols and lines. The architect, using the 'light pen', touches the menu for a wall, for example, and then touches the tablet surface at the position for a corner of the plan. The program digitises the co-ordinates of this point and a spot of light appears on the screen. By touching with the light-pen appropriate portions of the menu which indicate length and direction, a wall of a given length can be drawn from this point in, for example, the x direction and displayed on the screen. If the architect wishes to place a door in the wall, all he has to do is touch the appropriate section of the menu with the light pen, indicate the position of the door in the wall by moving the light-pen over the tablet until the 'gunsight' on the screen is at the right place, and a sub-routine will be initiated which will 'draw' the symbol on the screen. These sub-routines are written in a FORTRAN-based interpretive language, developed in-house, called PEST. All the doors are covered by one routine, windows by another and all symbols including curves, such as for wc pans, by yet another. The drawing can be output at any time as a photocopy from the hard-copy unit and, when the drawing has been completed, it can be plotted

To use the graphics facility merely as a drafting aid, however, is seriously to underestimate its potential. Also included in the menu are 'design' aids. One such program is used to design staircases. Given the floor-to-floor height, it will produce alternative solutions and give such information as the number of risers, the going and the headroom. Any of these parameters can be specified to give the final design. It is also possible to give three-dimensional representations of designs. Considerable effort is now being expended on the development of an integrated system which, from an original rough sketch, will produce the working drawings, details, schedules and bills of quantity for entire buildings, regardless of their type or construction method

Design management and control

A program called 360 Design Management System has been developed to run on the Group's IBM 360 to assist in the management of design offices. This provides information on fees, cost budgets and forecasts, progress, expenditure, valuations, non-productive time and other items for all projects for John Laing Design Associates. A variety of reports is produced which cover management planning for the office as a whole, as well as control of individual projects

Installation and bureaux

The engineers continue to use bureaux, in spite of transmission problems, because the turn-round time on the Group's own computer, which is governed by the process of punching the necessary tapes or cards, is comparatively slow. However, they have installed a thirty-character Texas Instruments ASR 700 for bureau and in-house calculations and eventually hope to use it as a front-end processor to the Group's IBM 370. As well as achieving considerable savings in storage costs, this should result in a more convenient arrangement. The bureaux they are using at present are CDC Data Services' SCOPE remote-job-entry network in The Hague, where they use a CDC 6600; CRC Cybernet; Atkins Computer Service; and SIA

The company has installed the following hardware

Engineering
Texas Instruments ASR 700 at the Mill Hill, London, and Manchester offices

Architecture and graphics
Nova 1200
14M word disc drive
19in Tektronix
12in Infoton
Small tablet digitiser
Large tablet digitiser
Mechanical digitiser/plotter
CalComp 950 plotter
Tektronix hard-copy unit
Westrex teletype

The following bureaux are used:
Laing Computing Services, IBM 370–145
CDC Data Services, CDC 6600
CRC Cybernet
Atkins Computer Service
SIA

Conclusions

John Laing Design Associates entered the field of computers relatively early, albeit cautiously, and are now happily committed to a policy of encouragement, confident that the use of computers makes the company more effective as designers and keeps them one step ahead of their competitors. The Group is continuing to invest in hardware, which can only be seen as a good sign in the present recession

On the calculation side of design, they find computers helpful and efficient. In producing reinforced concrete detailing, they are not showing great savings yet, but are likely to do so in the near future. In construction, they use computers for estimating, planning, cost control, surveying, plant allocation, management accounting, stock control and payroll. The processing of a survey, which used to take two weeks, can now be made in three days, and this includes plotting. Computer interpretation of graphics, however, is seen to be the key to a large proportion of future progress and it is here that most energy is being concentrated

LONDON TRANSPORT CHIEF ARCHITECT'S DEPARTMENT

The organisation

The Chief Architect's Department has four sections, architects, quantity surveyors, structural engineers and administrators. Approximately 270 staff are employed on a programme of 200 major and 500 minor projects

Initial use

Starting several years ago with programs for project planning, the Architect's Department has made increasing use of computers. At present, they are used for a range of tasks from bills of quantities to computer-aided architectural design (CAAD), including automated administrative procedures and interactive engineering calculations. This work has been carried out in conjunction with the Data Processing Department, mainly on London Transport's own computers

Originally, the Architects' Department used the ICL PERT package (a network analysis tool for planning and control of projects) which, early in 1975, was developed by the Data Processing Department to provide an on-line, interactive service via a local terminal and programs were developed to allow interaction with PERT data. As experience with the computing system grew, several small programs were written in the BASIC language by the department. The experience gained indicated the wide scope available for applying computers to all disciplines within the department, and in November 1975, a working party was formed by the two departments to extend the use of computer techniques

An early result of this co-operation was the investigation and trial of several commercially available packages for such uses as computer-generated perspectives, preparation of bills of quantities and structural engineering calculations. This approach provided the department with a more realistic idea of the possibilities of computer systems, without large capital outlay. Several of these investigations led to the development or purchase of the systems which are discussed later in this case study

Computer-aided architectural design

A trial was held for six months, in 1976, of computer graphics for architectural design. The CADC THINGS/HIDDEN LINES packages were used via a display terminal in the Architect's Department connected to the North West CAD Centre. Two projects were shown, Thamesmead Bus Garage and the ticket hall at Shepherd's Bush Underground Station, and many views of each were produced. The exercise yielded two main benefits, a greater understanding by the architects of the value of the computer as a design aid and, in particular, the production of many views of the two projects which would not otherwise have been drawn, giving a deeper insight into various aspects of design

1 Tektronix digital plotter

In parallel with this trial, the Architect's Department prepared a cost/benefit analysis of a long-term commitment to CAAD, while the Data Processing Department undertook a survey of the equipment and software necessary to provide a CAAD service within London Transport. Although it was clear that interactive architectural design was an exciting prospect, it was considered that, initially, a better approach was to automate the storage, graphic amendments and on-line retrieval of standard detail drawings and so eliminate much repetitive work. Two- and three-dimensional projections could also be produced. The chief aim for the computer system was to retain traditional skills while using new techniques to reduce repetitive tasks, and allow the architect to devote more time to analysis of design. The ultimate objective is a data-based, highly interactive graphics system which would hold information on, and provide a means of analysing, any project in the department throughout an architect's design process. The department has now acquired a Tektronix storage tube, and the AUTOPROD package, which produces three-dimensional displays

Quantity surveying

The Quantity Surveying Section was introduced to computer software early in 1976. They were interested in a package supplied through LAMSAC (Local Authorities' Management Services and Computer Committee), which is supported for IBM users by Derbyshire County Council. The package produces bills of quantities from initial measurement carried out in the traditional manner and, with little extra preparatory work, offers several additional or alternative presentations of the data, including a cost analysis based on building elements

After a trial run at Derbyshire County Council's offices, it was decided to purchase the package. The main justification for purchase was that, while there were unlikely to be immediate savings of staff costs, the program produced significant additional information, as well as offering a reduction in the overall time required to produce the initial bill-of-quantities document. In particular, the cost analysis could save several man/weeks' effort and priced bills of quantities could be made available, with better quality presentation than previously achieved. In due course, with the inbuilt short coding techniques, it is expected that measurement time can be reduced

Resource planning and administration

The PERT package was the first software to be used by the department and the Resource Planning Section has been a major user of computers ever since. Once the BASIC programming language had been learnt, the section was able to take advantage of the Data Processing Department's interactive programming service (MAXIMOP) to produce various reports on the progress and running of the department's projects. Programs were written for budget control and PERT data preparation, and for recording details of all current and planned projects

Further use

Computer-aided architectural design

The objective is a gradual move towards more sophisticated aspects of CAAD, so that applications never overreach experience, and benefits can be seen at every stage, rather than only after completion of the entire project

Quantity surveying

During 1976, the department developed its own program (COST) for more effective design/cost control. This enables the architect to vary his specifications for individual elements within a given budget without having to produce a complete re-assessment of the job. The section has also been working on a program which calculates work category valuations for contracts in progress, with a weighted index of thirty or more values. This is being developed further in conjunction with the DOE Property Services Agency's Directorate of Quantity Surveying Development and the DOC. These new methods are still in an early exploratory stage and the Quantity Surveying Section, in common with the Architect's Department, feels that, while the computer techniques have so far shown themselves to be highly effective, it is important to maintain traditional skills

Resource planning and administration

Through this section, the Administration Section was introduced to computing. Its main use of the computer is via a program for recording and reporting timesheet information. The program uses timesheets completed by each professional and technical member of staff each week and produces a tabulation of work completed and notional costs for each project, by profession. As an adjunct, a separate program compares the percentage completion of each stage of each project, using predetermined targets

Installation and current programs

The Data Processing Department provides computing facilities to London Transport using three main frames. These are two ICL 1904S machines (one operating under George 3 for scheduled production work and one providing interactive computing via the MAXIMOP service) and an IBM 370/148. The MAXIMOP service supports over forty terminals

The Structural Engineers have been regular users of the MAXIMOP service. The programs used are mostly for the analysis of structural frames and include ICL's PLANE, GRID and SPACEFRAME. At first, all jobs were run in batch mode but the Data Processing Department later wrote a small interface program which allowed data to be collected and prepared interactively. More recently, a survey of packages has been conducted with the object of increasing the range of analyses to include design of reinforced concrete elements to BS CP110. Two packages have been selected for further investigation

Conclusions

From a simple start, the Architect's Department is now a significant user of computers within London Transport. They have three computer terminals (one graphic) and expect to use more in the future. All sections of the department make use of computers and the work is increasing. It is felt that much of this growth has been due to the general awareness of the advances in computing (eg CAAD) and the general feeling within the department appears to be one of cautious optimism

OVE ARUP AND PARTNERS

The organisation

Ove Arup and Partners works from ten offices in the United Kingdom and more than forty overseas. The Partnership has a staff of over 2000 throughout the world, of which 800 are located in London. The UK organisation consists of a practice covering England and Wales and one separately registered in Scotland. Each comprises a number of groups responsible for building and civil engineering. The former consist of structural engineers or multi-professional design teams with skills covering all aspects of structural and services design. The latter not only include civil engineers but also specialist disciplines responsible for geotechnics, transportation planning, infrastructure engineering, water supply and drainage

The firm works in close collaboration with Arup Associates, a practice within the Ove Arup Partnership which undertakes the total design of buildings

Specialist technical support is provided by the Central Services department, which includes groups responsible for computer services, research and development, structural pathology, project planning and site services, and building economics. Each engineering group uses the computer extensively, as do those parts of the firms concerned with administration, finance and staff. The demand on the computer is intensive and wide-ranging

Initial use

A computer was first used on a project in the late 1950's. The subject was the shell frame of the Sydney Opera House. The numerical complexity of analysing the proposed structure made an alternative to manual methods desirable. The universities were approached, where Ove Arup had already established close ties with research departments. The main computer runs were carried out at a polytechnic and not through a commercial bureau

Further use

The initial experience convinced the organisation that, as design became more complex, the computer would be an essential tool for the designer. It was then necessary to decide whether to use outside expertise (a bureau) or purchase a computer and develop its own programs. The second course was adopted, mainly to develop in-house expertise. The competitive nature of the work favoured self-sufficiency. Changes in hard- or software could be made whenever necessary and the service adapted to suit requirements. The anticipated volume of work also made it the cheapest solution

Structural analysis programs were the first to be developed throughout the engineering field generally and the first to be used by Ove Arup when, in 1964, they installed an Elliot 803. Software was located through technical journals (mainly university publications) and the press except, notably, the architectural papers. Some programs were supplied by manufacturers but most were written inside the firm. The problems during the early years were mainly restricted to operational hitches; accessibility of outside software; lack of familiarity with computers on the part of the user; and producing the right programs for the designer's needs

For the past ten years at least, there has been a settled acceptance of programs for structural-framework analysis. The early mystique has been dissipated and the limitations of these programs are now reasonably well understood. Developments now being made within Ove Arup are towards improving and, if necessary, increasing the number of tools at the designer's disposal. Where this means more computer programs, this is accepted

There has never been a fixed policy of expansion of hard- and software resources but, now that the usefulness of computers is recognised, the introduction and adaptation of programs, and the acquisition of equipment, is willingly paid for. The progression (over twenty years) has been in small, easy

1 DEC System 10 installation

stages. Only in the last two years have any savings been made on the computer services: initially, research into the designer's needs was expensive

The Hytype mechanism (developed in Belgium) in the Diablo terminal made a significant contribution to the user's satisfaction with the computer. This mechanism portrays results graphically, if possible, with tabulated output. Instead of large, upper-case lineprinter output, data can now be presented on A4 pages, in upper- and lower-case, with sub- and superscripts, and Greek characters where necessary. This enables engineers and site-managers to take and use output straight from the terminal

Installation and staff

There are ten operators and system staff at the central computer site (London Office), including management; three commercial programmers; ten technical programmers; and a large number of part-time engineer programmers. The central equipment consists of a DEC System 10 computer, discs, tapes, card reader, paper-tape reader, punch, two drum plotters and line printer. Remote equipment linked to the DEC 10 includes the following terminals, in various numbers, situated at points throughout the London and provincial offices: Diablo, Tektronix, Terminet, visual display units, Decwriter and HP9830

Conclusions

David Taffs, who was interviewed, puts the computer into perspective. Despite the rapid changes and constant improvements in hard- and software, he does not see the advent of the 'instant design' predicted in The Architects' Journal in 1962. This would be remotely possible only in an age of completely standardised buildings, and this is unlikely in a competitive market

He deprecates the notion of the computer as a deity. Programs are simply a guide and can never supplant the skill, judgement and experience of qualified professionals. To emphasise this, he pointed out that not one of Ove Arup's architects uses the computer aids available

Many practical considerations affect the use that can be made of results. For example, a reinforcement schedule may specify different sizes of reinforcement for each column in a structure, based on the theoretical ideal. In practice, the availability of materials and the possibility of site errors make it more sensible to choose an acceptable mean, equal for all columns. The program will have provided the designer with the information from which to make this choice

Sometimes, a program, or the input data for it, is too sophisticated for the work in hand. For example, the designers of a multi-storey hospital in Thailand might like to calculate heat losses and cooling loads by a program which can deal with cloud covers and solar azimuths, but the figures for the area do not exist. This type of reality keeps the wilder enthusiasts in check. David Taffs would like to see the computer treated like any other employee, as this often helps to avoid misunderstandings

He mentioned the soil-analysis programs now available which enable a user to carry out tests which were previously impracticable. He also stressed the benefits in the field of highway engineering where it is now possible to prepare schedules of depths and cross-sectional properties for the next stage while the present stage is already under construction, permitting an earlier start to be made and keeping the project continuously moving

HUTTON + ROSTRON

The Organisation

This practice was begun in 1963 to specialise in building research and information systems, with a view to improving the performance, documentation and organisation of building. No conventional building design is carried out. Activities comprise research into user requirements, and building and manufacturing techniques; the analysis of building products; component and system selection and specification; market research; the production of technical information and consultancy on publishing; and information handling and retrieval. Special fields of interest are tropical building, security and protection of buildings, cladding and curtain walling, sealing, the design of educational buildings, systematic design methods, systems analysis and computer programming. Typical recent projects have been a study of the natural stone industry and its market in the United Kingdom for the Department of the Environment and the Stone Federation; the code of practice on non-loadbearing external walls and the computerisation of the UDC classification for the British Standards Institution; and the Architectural Periodical Index for the Royal Institute of British Architects. The firm is well known for technical publications produced for Cape Universal and British Gypsum, and provided the technical consultancy for many of the new services offered by Barbour Index. This type of consultancy has now expanded outside the construction industry and systems have been set up for the British Defence Equipment Catalogue and Woodfall's Landlord and Tenant

The partners originally met at The Architects' Journal in 1961, where Michael Rostron and Geoffrey Hutton were research fellows on a large publishing project sponsored by the magazine to produce guides to design procedure and technical information for all the major building elements. Before this, Geoffrey Hutton worked on a variety of buildings in this country and abroad, including a 25–storey building to celebrate Nigeria's independence: Michael Rostron had worked in a private practice and for the GLC on special school projects. A mutual interest in the problems of communication and industrialisation in the building industry led to the formation of the present practice, with its special interest in research and information

Early work in 1964 on a project to analyse building systems and the market for building components, on behalf of a major manufacturing group, showed the advantages of using optical coincidence cards for recording and retrieving information. These cards use binary co-ordination to identify the presence or absence of particular attributes in objects. These attributes may be gathered into groups to represent bands of values and, by coding, developed to deal with fairly abstract characteristics, such as colours and function. The essentially binary nature of the co-ordinate index system proved a wonderful discipline and led the partners to reconsider the value of conventional library and classification techniques when dealing with technical characteristics and the selection of products by performance. About the same time, the practice was in the process of preparing the second edition of a substantial technical manual for Cape Building Products and it was realised that, using conventional publishing and printing methods, the revision, proof-reading and typesetting involved were laborious, repetitive and prone to error. As printing machines were commonly driven by punched tape, the logical next step was to produce and revise the copy for publications in machine-readable form and establish a mechanical link between the processes. At the very least, the amount of copy-typing and checking would be reduced. At this stage, the possibility of using automatic typewriters was investigated, as analogous to the Telex machine but using upper– and lower-case characters. The first Dura automatic typewriter was installed in 1966 (the firm now uses four). This was an electro-mechanical machine with an IBM golf-ball, and punch and photo-electric reader for eight-channel paper tape, working at 15 characters per second in a non-standard tape code. The cost of this machine at the time was in the region of £2000 but immediately a number of possibilities became apparent, apart from the speedier and more accurate handling of text. The ability to produce machine-readable data meant that computers could be used directly to process it and take much of the routine clerical work out of the administrative and professional work of the office

1 General view of H + R computer system

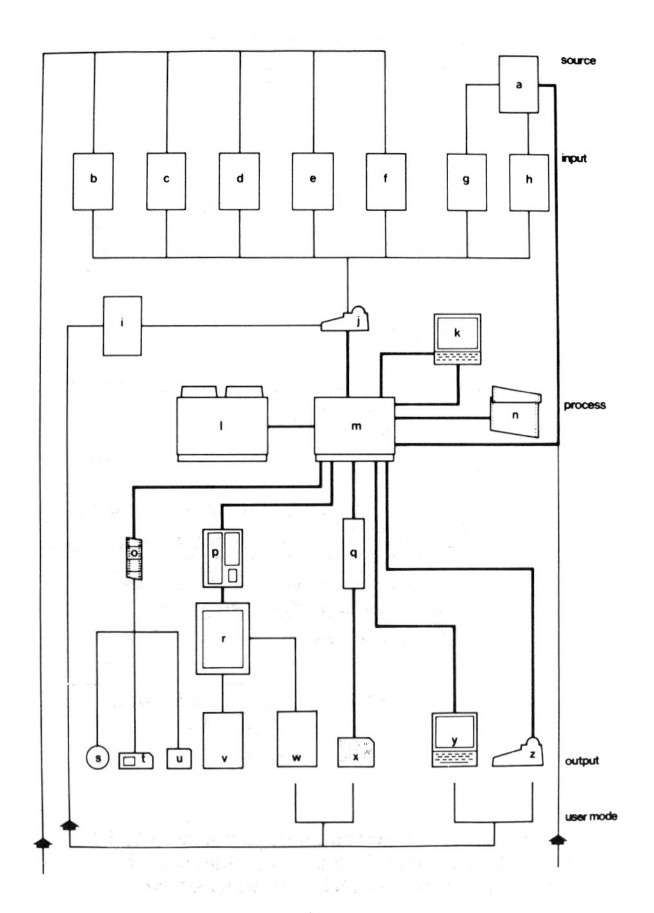

a Data collection (can be machine-readable)
b Standards
c Directories
d Bibliographies
e Technical data
f Building analyses
g Product data: text
h Product data: analytic
i Keycode dictionary and code systems
j Machine-readable input
k Visual display
l Back-up storage H + R computer system
m Processor
n Hard-copy output
o Microfilm generation
p Photocomposition
q Punched-card generation
r Plate-making and printing
s Roll film
t Aperture cards information media
u Microfiche
v Printed technical information
w Printed indexes and directories
x Co-ordinate index cards
y Visual display
z Teletype terminal

2 Diagram of integrated computer-aided data base and publishing system operated by H + R. Heavy lines represent direct computer outputs

Initial use

During the mid-60's, the NCR Elliott computer bureau had what was called a 'Computer workshop'. This enabled members to have 'hands-on' access to an Elliott 4120 computer at attractive off-peak rates, with the assistance of a trained operator, if required. This provided the essential experience in computing for the firm. The partners each took a three-day course in computer programming, in which Michael Rostron has since become highly skilled. The first languages used were ALGOL and NEAT (the assembler language of the 4100 computer). This experience was then used to write programs to handle the firm's time sheets, invoicing and job recording, which, although systematic, was obviously irksome when done manually. This course proved of immediate advantage, giving better cash-flow and more precise records, and freeing the partners from administrative work. As a result of the confidence gained, work began on linking the experience of co-ordinate indexing to a retrieval language for computer use, with the object of setting up a system to handle data-bases for research projects. At the same time, Geoffrey Hutton (taught printing during his National Service) started to investigate computer-controlled text-processing and photo-composition, with the object of totally mechanising book production. Arising from this work, and the enlightened support of the clients concerned, a specification was written for the bulk processing of text and the numerical control of a Photon 713 photo-composition machine. This system proved highly successful and was used in the production of a number of editions of catalogues and text books from 1967 onwards, using the Elliot 4120 bureau service. The suite of programs involved provided for retrieval of text by content and paragraph reference, a range of revision modes, format and numerical control of photo-composition on a variety of machines. For example, in 1968, a job was typeset and made up in Switzerland from paper tapes provided by H+R. The increasing importance of information retrieval, and the unsuitability of conventional classifications for computer use and co-ordinate indexing, led the partners to develop a special retrieval language, Keycodes. This uses some 300 four-letter ciphers to represent concepts which, in combination, can be used to retrieve information on building topics in a number of languages. Associated with this was programming for maintaining the system, using the language to generate indexes and the production of co-ordinate index cards

Further use

With the increase in the use of computers in administration, research and publishing, H+R became heavy users of the bureau, particularly as jobs were now also being processed on behalf of other firms. The travelling involved, and the need to book time, began to make attractive the ownership of a computer or computer terminal. The latter was rejected, as the cost of telephone-line time when transferring very large files was considerable. However, with the aging of the 4120 and the proposed cessation of the computer workshop, the time seemed ripe to develop an in-house system. It was decided that this should be based on a modular mini-computer which could be up-graded as demand and experience increased. The model selected was a Digital PDP8e in the form of an 8K CPU, to which was linked a Hazeltine 2000 visual display unit and a high-speed paper-tape reader (1000 cps) and punch (75 cps), manufactured by Facit. This system was delivered in 1970 and was used to gain programming experience and gradually take over some of the simpler production work. The CPU was then extended in two stages to 12K and 20K, to increase processing power, followed by the addition of two cassette disc drives, a Pertec seven-track magnetic-tape handler and a Tally 2000 line printer. However, it was not until mid-1977 that all work was finally transferred from the Elliott 4120, which was now in new ownership. This gradual transition was a necessary way of ensuring continuity of production and providing a back-up in case of machine failure

Installation

The current system is the original PDP8e, with eight-channel paper tape input and output, teletype, upper/lower-case visual display consol, two interchangeable disc cassettes, switchable code and density seven-track magnetic-tape handler and a high-speed line printer. Plans for the future development of this system envisage a second PDP8 processor to give standby capacity and assist with normal work, further disc drives, the installation of a Modem and the introduction of an in-house time-sharing system using existing visual display units for library and editorial work, and data preparation. The system uses industry-compatible data media throughout, to aid data exchange, and extensive programming is available for code conversion

Conclusions

The practice now has a powerful facility in hardware, software and techniques to tackle communication problems. In the partners' opinion, too little attention is given to the compatibility of media in setting up systems and this is aggravated by the tendency of manufacturers of such equipment as 'word processors' to build in variations which limit the degree to which information can be transferred from machine to machine. In addition, files vary in structure and content, leading to expensive re-programming if they are to be used by others. Thus a prime aim of the practice in choosing hardware, writing programs and creating files of data has been to ensure that systems are as generalised as possible, to maximise the use of the facility concerned and to enable work on individual projects to be done economically. In the case of hardware, total replacement is not practicable and, therefore, the system must be capable of growth

Hutton + Rostron • RIBA British Architectural Library API accession form

O Accession number 11538
X Subject headings
B Building types/applications "Houses: town
C Country GB (x) FE ( ) EG ( ) IY ( ) AU ( ) CA ( ) IR ( ) NZ ( ) SN ( ) ND ( ) US ( ) WG ( ) GY ( ) SI ( ) AA ( ) DE ( ) JN ( ) SA ( ) SD ( )
T Location (town/city) "Bath
K Building name 15 & 16 "Royal + Crescent
S Series title
F Full title King of the Crescent
A Profession AR ( ) LA ( ) ER ( ) ID ( ) TP ( ) DG ( ) SE ( ) archts for hotel renovation William Bertram & Fell
W Authors
L Languages (if not English) EN ( ) GE ( ) IT ( ) JA ( ) AF ( ) SW ( ) HU ( ) FR ( ) SP ( ) DU ( ) RU ( ) DA ( ) SC ( ) CH ( )
G Graphic material PL ( ) ST ( ) SK ( ) DI ( ) GR ( ) PH (x) RF ( ) CS ( ) IL ( ) DL ( ) EL ( ) AX ( ) TA ( ) MO ( ) PO ( ) BI ( ) MA ( ) FI ( )
N Hotel occupies two central town houses of John Wood the Younger's Royal Crescent (1767)
M John 'Wood 'the Younger'
E
J ABGK2 D Date of issue 1979 Feb
I P Pages 40

4 Form used for collecting bibliographical material to create data base. This uses combination of full text and ticks, which is key-punched for input

Hutton + Rostron mark form 1

Please use PENCIL only. Fill in the lozenges like this NOT like this

3 Typical mark-reading form used to generate machine-readable input for large data bases

5 Page of the RIBA Library Architectural Periodical Index generated from data shown on input form 4

Pao–Ros

Paolo Favole [Studio] C0040 S0056
Papademetriou Peter G0020 H0238
Papineau Gerin-Lajoie Leblanc Edwards R0017
Paproth Lutz T0065 T0166
Parat Pierre A0064 A0069
Parish Nathaniel J. L0065 T0158
Parker G Brian E0064 T0284 T0347
Parker Michael T0075
Parkin Archts Planners M0104 M0105
Parkin John C M0104 M0105
Parkinson John A0003 B0062 B0213 C0029 C0244 D0030 F0054 H0021 M0016 P0042 P0045 S0252
Parnell Alan C B0025
Parnell Alan C F0060 F0094 F0095
Parnell Alan C H0282 H0388 S0247 W0042
Paroubek Jaroslav U0012
Pascall & Watson A0011
Passarelli Lucio C0094
Pastier John H0181 H0192
Paterson John C0225
Paterson LJ Barrie & Assocs H0203 H0360 H0738
Patko Sandor H0680
Patrick Rooney & Assocs H0086
Patterson Doug A0072 A0234 B0076 C0214
Paulson Jr Boyd C T0350
Pawley Martin A0385
Payne H Morse S0014 S0062
Peacock John A0106 S0242
Pearce David A0035 A0093 A0099 A0101 A0259 A0286 A0311 A0350 B0005 C0061 C0074 C0075 C0272 E0125 H0311 H0605 P0002 P0075 P0103 P0104 P0105 P0107 P0108 P0110 P0112 P0116 R0013 T0132 T0239 T0242
Pearce Edward C0068 R0034
Pearson F K B0198
Peckham Guyton Assocs O0092
Pediconi Giancarlo C0094 H0337
Pedio Renato H0338
Pei CC F0073 F0075
Pei IM & Ptnrs M0101 M0119
Pei IM B0214
Pei J M A0201
Pena Ganchegui Luis A0183 S0179
Pengarah Jabatan Akitek T0127
Pentagram Design Ptnrship D0014
Penton John H0077 H0566 H0568 H0571 H0751 H0753
Penttila Timo A0062
Penven J H0165
Pepper & Dixon H0361 H0362 H0423
Percy Thomas Ptnrship A0116 A0299 H0194 L0004 L0005 L0010 L0011 V0006 V0007
Perea Caveda Enrique S0160
Perila Bert B0007
Perini Luciano H0088 H0175
Perkins & Will C0135 C0136 C0137
Perkins Brian C0028
Perlia Bert C0196 S0202
Peroff Kathleen S L0025
Perotti Artur U0008
Perrier Antoinette V0015 V0016 V0017 V0018 V0019
Perrot Francoise G0015
Perrotet Jean O0014
Perry Dean Stahl & Rogers Inc H0125
Pesce Gaetano C0098 U0004
Peter Bell & Ptnrs C0269 O0101
Peter Bond Assocs E0066 H0555
Peter Moro & Ptnrs A0447 T0022
Peter Smith Assocs H0609
Peter Wood & Ptnrs C0105 O0022
Peter Y.S. Pun & Assocs B0011
Peters Jens A0481 H0002 S0025
Petersen Ebbe Lehn M0123
Petherbridge Deanne I0004
Peto RJ H0147
Petri Gunther A0437 B0201
Petruccioli Sergio A0097
Petrucz Gyorgy P0060
Petsch Horst B0040 B0047
Petsch Joachim T0155
Pfister Hans F0044
Phaltoon & Assocs B0021
Phillip Cox & Ptnrs Pty Ltd S0191 S0239
Phillip Ives Assocs V0043
Phillip Johnson & John Burgee A0451 C0156
Phillips Jr W Irving H0325 H0437
Phillippides Dimitri H0794 V0014 W0045
Phillips Cutler Phillips Troy H0317 H0646 S0227
Phillips Roger A T0037
Phippen Randall & Parkes H0138 U0016
Phipson Richard Makilwaine A0117 C0066
Piano & Rogers A0441 A0442 A0443 A0444 C0239 F0028
Pica Agnoldomenico A0154 J0001 M0122 O0061 S0169 U0052
Pickering Maurice A0028 H0139 L0023 L0046 U0019
Pieper Jan I0001 I0003 T0351
Pietila Reima A0063 A0466 H0420
Pinion L.C. T0053 T0055
Pinon Pallares Helio A0445 F0090 S0161
Pinto John A F0086
Piper Milburn & Ptnr F0007 F0010 F0051
Piper Robert R T0287
Piraina Giovanna H0710 T0178
Piramide Renato H0087 H0174
Pitkanen Pekka R0030
Pittavino Silvio H0117
Pitz Helge C0150 C0151
Pizarro Jose A A0183 S0179
Plan Marienburg Architekten & Ingenieure T0124
Planen & Bauen Lemgo GmbH B0053 R0027 S0055 S0207
Plater-Zyberk Elizabeth H0329 H0428
Platte Karl B0055 H0028 H0105
Pletz G S0203
Pletz Gunther B0009
Ploeger JH O0068
Pluck & Walther H0230 H0400
Plummer Ivor S0080
Poche Emanuel C0112
Pocock M.D. H0596
Poelzig Hans H0673
Pohan Alois T0167 T0309
Pokorny Z. E0024 E0027
Pol G van der [Architektenburo] M0078 O0067
Policar Frantisek T0170
Pollen & Beer O0037
Pollen Francis O0037
Polston David A0232 C0010 P0096 P0098 T0297
Polydorou Soteres A0072 A0234 B0076 C0214
Polytechnic of Central London. Dept of Archre Surveying & Town H0044 H0556
Pomeroy Lebduska Assocs A0472 C0278
Pomeroy Lee A0472 C0278
Portman John A0200 A0201
Positano Giuseppe M0070 S0091 S0215 V0004
Potomac Group C0302 R0014
Potter & Golder Assocs C0042
Potter David E0100 E0101
Potvin Jean H0478
Poulson John B0037
Poulter Alan C0314
Powell A.G. T0097
Powell Alport & Ptnrs H0642
Powell M.J.V. H0588 H0824
Powell Moya & Ptnrs M0125
Powell Richard A0118
Powell Robert H0683 T0045
Powley John A T0183
Prader Herbert H0470
Prak N Luning A0376 A0423 D0044
Prakash Rajendra H0023 H0052
Pran Peter C A0192 T0340 U0057
Pratt Allan S0197
Presoly Anton C0083 C0233
Presoly Egon C0083 C0233
PREVI H0506
Price Cedric A0072 A0234 A0266 B0076 C0214
Priest Keith A0072 A0234 B0076 C0214
Prinsloo Ivor C0211 L0059
Prizeman John S0104 S0129
Project for Public Spaces Inc O0120
Projectgroep Binnenstad Leiden T0229
Promotour H0161
Prowting Arthur B0088
Pugh Brian B0096 B0099
Purini Franco A0148
Pystynen Veikko H0493

Quantrill Malcolm A0063
Quist [Architectenbureau] M0098 M0114
Quist W G M0097 M0098 M0113 M0114
Quist WG M0099 M0115

Raab Rex S0035
Rabeneck Andrew A0285 E0059 F0051
Rabinel J H0575
Racionero Luis T0165
Rading Adolf H0673
Rahe Jochen H0055 O0011
Rai Mohan P0044
Rainer Roland C0178
Raineri Giorgio H0087 H0174
Rakosnik B E0105
Ralph Erskine Arkitektkontor AB H0838 H0839 T0277
Ralphs & Mansell T0017
Raman Pattabi G A0401
Rambert Charles A0140 B0002
Ranalli George S0133
Randell J.E. H0026 H0048
Rangelov Vladimir H0508
Ranzi Maurizio I0046
Raphael Guastavino & Sons M0008 M0011
Raphael Raffaelle Sanzio P0028
Rasmussen Jorgen H0534 H0756
Ratti Paolo H0334
Rauch John C0118 U0053
Rauh Wolfgang H0308
Rawlinson John B0193 B0194
Ray Tony T0071
Raymond Moriyama Archts & Planners L0067 L0075
Read Pat M0130
Rechter Zarhy Peri H0168
Redfern Roger A T0077 T0327
Redgrove Tom D0022
Redman R W B W0010
Redundant Churches Fund C0062 C0074 C0075 C0272 C0273
Reed & Barnes E0104
Reed Smart & Tappin C0019
Reed William G C0191 S0013 S0068 S0197 S0241
Rees Peter Wynne P0070
Rehter Zarhy Peri M0145
Reiach Hall Blyth Ptnrship F0022 O0018
Reichen & Robert C0283 C0284
Reichlin Bruno T0335
Reid Esmond B0191
Reimers Per H R0019 R0020
Reinhart Fabio T0335
Reiser Roman S0145
Reist F.E. H0844
Reitmeier Wendy A0232 C0010 P0096 P0098 T0297
Rellstab Ursula T0224
Renaud Philipe A0151
Rendle Timothy H0225 H0279
Renfro Robert T C0118 H0329 H0428 U0053
Renton Howard Wood Levin Ptnrship H0624 T0025 T0036
Reschovsky Andrew T0175
Restany Pierre A0453 M0110
Reuschel Christa A0474 H0654 S0096
RHWL Design Intl Ptnrship B0006
Ricaud de Tirregaille Pierre H0430
Rice Dick C0160 M0102
Rice John S0198
Rice Michael M0131
Rice Richard C0118 U0053
Rice Roberts Archts S0198
Richard & Dion Neutra & Assocs H0447
Richard Meier & Assocs H0014 H0015 H0111 H0112 M0085
Richards Ivor M0144
Richards Penny A0072 A0234 B0076 C0214
Richardson Henry Hobson A0202
Richardson Martin A0119 A0385
Richardson Nagy Martin H0885
Ridolfi Mario H0202
Riepl Franz C0143
Rigby A H0498 H0871
Righter James V. H0133 H0173 M0058
Rihal Baldip H0544 H0702 H0721 H0817
Riley Robert B G0027
Rimek Erhard S0085
Rinehart Arley H0406 H0450 H0451
Rippeteau Jane A0231
Riseng Amund C0073
Ritter John P0032 S0251
Robert A M Stern & John S Hagmann H0454
Robert AM Stern & John S Hagmann H0207
Robert A.M. Stern & John S. Hagmann H0455
Robert AM Stern & John S Hagmann H0456
Robert M Douglas B0160
Robert Maguire & Keith Murray C0154 H0142
Robert Maskens. Awards & prizes H0244
Robert Matthew Johnson-Marshall & Ptnrs H0799
Robert Matthew Johnson-Marshall C0322
Robert-Niel Yves H0853
Roberts Denis Michael A0120
Roberts Francis B. H0495
Roberts-Jones Philippe A0460
Roberts Sir Gilbert E0087
Robertson Alexander H0114
Robertson Jaquelin T0208 T0332
Robillard Jette Caron S0193 S0240
Robin Wade Design Assocs C0299
Robins John A0072 A0234 B0076 C0214
Robinson John Martin H0252
Robinson Keefe & Devane O0058
Robinson L.K. H0629
Robinson Peter H0714
Roche Kevin A0203
Rock David A0286 A0311 E0116
Rock Townsend C0149 C0312 G0014 H0220 H0633 I0023 O0032
Roderick Ham & Ptnrs T0020 T0021
Rodl Kieferle O0047
Rodriguez G I0037 M0017
Roemer Ludwig C0033 C0035
Roger Marshall Assocs S0008 S0011 S0027 S0053
Roizenblatt I T0355
Rolfe Judd Group Practice S0156 S0164
Rolfe Judd Group Ractice S0165
Rollenhagen Lindemann Grossmann H0310
Roman Hirschmann [Arbeitsgemeinschaft] O0049
Romanowicz Arseniusz R0012
Romero Andreas R0051
Romero Stephan R0051
Rosa Giancarlo A0149 A0150 T0015
Rose Gordon A0218 B0221 F0031 P0034 S0001
Rose Kim L0081
Rose Peter D. H0133 H0173 M0058

142 *Architectural Periodicals Index, Volume 6, Number 1, January to March 1978*

6 Page of names index generated from data on input form 4

```
INDUSTRIAL ARCHITECTURE: IRELAND (REP)
  Expressive monuments of industry and order:
  early industrial architecture in Ireland.
  Article by Deanne Petherbridge; plans,
  elevns, photos, refs.
  ARCHTL DESIGN, vol 47, no 11/12, 1977
  Nov/Dec, pp742-749

                                         01798
```

7 Library catalogue card generated from data on input form 4

When related to information systems, this attitude is illustrated by the diagram opposite, which shows the general relationship between the inputs and outputs in the computerised information system developed by the practice. (Initially for the Canadian Department of Commerce BEAM program). Each stage is systemised, from the use of computer-produced and machine-readable questionnaires through to the production of particular types of document, of which this book is an example. Standard data structures are used for bibliographies and files of technical information and much of the data is coded to reduce the key-punching or other input effort, simplifying checking (often done by program) and allowing text in different languages and formats to be inserted at output. A typical machine-readable form and the input form used for a bibliography are illustrated with examples of the printed output

The computer at H+R has, over the years, become such an integral part of the firm's activities that there is no task in which it is not involved, to a greater or lesser degree. The benefit cannot be measured against an alternative because, without the use of a computer, either the work could not be done at all, or the time and cost involved would be prohibitive. The machine is regarded as a common facility and it is operated by any suitably-inclined and competent member of staff. Most of the programs involved are operated from the consol, which displays the necessary instructions. For the future, H+R intends to continue generalising its data bases and extending their applications, while providing administrative and research support within the practice and a range of data-processing services for information systems and publishers externally

Management

CPM/PERT
Land use
Mailing lists
Other

001

001

Program name
CLUSTR

Abstract
This program produces a suitable structure for solving design problems. The designer describes the elements of the problem and the relationship between them. The program breaks the problem down into the sub-sets that most closely relate to these elements. It then builds the sub-sets into larger clusters and outputs a tree diagram showing the resulting problem structure

References

Source
ABACUS studies
University of Strathclyde
131 Rottenrow, Glasgow G4 ONG
UK
Telephone 041-552 4400 ext 3021

Availability
Purchase, hire, interactive bureau service

Language
Fortran

Computer
Univac 1108
Tektronix graphics terminal

002

Program name
P1

Abstract
This is a comprehensive interrelated suite of programs for project management, incorporating free-format input and output, time, resource and cost analyses to user specification and special features of time, resource and cost simulation

References

Source
Atkins Computing Services Limited
Woodcote Grove, Ashley Road
Epsom, Surrey
UK
Telephone Epsom 40421

Availability
Bureau service, time-sharing. Available in Netherlands

Language
Fortran

Computer
Honeywell Sigma 9

003

Program name
PERTPAC

Abstract
This suite of programs provides analyses of time, resources and costs and is extremely flexible. Reports can be produced in many forms including bar charts, tables and histograms

References
Developed by ICL

Source
Boeing Computer Centres Limited
31–35 Clarendon Road, Watford
Herts WD1 1JA
UK
Telephone Watford 38321

Availability
Bureau service

Language
Cobol

Computer
ICL 1900

004

Program name
SMART 2

Abstract
This program for planning and control is designed to cover single projects and those which involve several activities. A network-based time-analysis facility is complemented by a resource allocation capability enabling the user to control the scheduling process. The financial processor enables value to be monitored and progress payments to be made in direct relation to work done. The program supports multiple calendars and many dating systems

References

Source
CEGB Engineering Document Unit
Sudbury House, 15 Newgate Street
London EC1
UK
Telephone 01-248 1202

Availability

Language

Computer

Program name
SNAP

Abstract
This program aids the planning and control of construction or manufacturing projects by network analysis, which gives management reports and identifies the critical paths for each level of management. The program also produces a financial statement for customer or contractor budgetary control, to enable payments to be made in relation to job progress

References

Source
CEGB Engineering Document Unit
Sudbury House, 15 Newgate Street
London EC1
UK
Telephone 01–248 1202

Availability

Language

Computer

006

Program name
1900 PERT (Program evaluation and review technique)

Abstract
Critical path analysis for the examination of complex projects. It has been used successfully in the aerospace, shipbuilding and motorway construction industries, although it is also suitable for activities such as moving or installing plant, controlling subcontract work or maintaining schedules. Time, resource and cost analyses may be produced for a single project or several linked activities

References

Source
Centre-File (Northern) Limited
Westinghouse Road, Trafford Park
Manchester M17 1PY
UK
Telephone 061 872 1982

Availability
Bureau service, remote batch

Language
Plan

Computer
ICL 1900

007

Program name
PERT

Abstract
A comprehensive set of interrelated programs for network analysis, resource allocation, multi-project scheduling and cost control

References
Program made available by ICL

Source
Computel Limited
Eastern Road
Bracknell, Berkshire
UK
Telephone Bracknell 23031

Availability

Language

Computer

008

Program name
ONENET

Abstract
This program processes data from a project network diagram to produce time schedules. The size of the network depends upon the size of the computer used. For example, using the small-core memory of the CDC 7600, 3000 activities can be handled, and 7000 with the large-core memory of the same machine

References

Source
CSIRO, Division of Building Research
Graham Road, Highett
Victoria 3190
Australia
Telephone 95 0333

Availability
CSIRONET, La Trobe and Queensland Universities, and Maunsell Partners Pty

Language
Fortran

Computer
CDC 7600
DEC10
HP 3000

009

Program name
Precedence diagram analysis (PDA)

Abstract
This program analyses precedence-diagram (activity-orientated) networks and provides printed bar-charts, lists of important dates or, using DRAWNET program, network diagrams. All semantic and syntactic checks are performed and informative error messages are produced. Network start date, duration units and holidays can be controlled on input. Standard data sets are available for RIBA Plan of Work and the DHSS Capricode

References
DRAWNET interface is possible

Source
Cusdin Burden and Howitt
Greencoat House
5th Floor
Francis Street
London SW1P 1DB, UK
Telephone 01–828 4051/7

Availability
Purchase or hire on a royalty basis

Language
Fortran

Computer
CDC 6000, Cyber

010

Program name
ACSPERT

Abstract
An on-line system of project control, able to evaluate a specified project with constraints on time and resources. The project may be extended in duration or extra resources required to meet the completion date, and cash flows during the project may be calculated if required. The performance of the project may be monitored against the schedule, and the network updated and reviewed as necessary

References
Program based on PERT

Source
Cybernet Time Sharing Limited
83 Clerkenwell Road
London
EC1R 5HP
Telephone 01-242 0747

Availability
Time-sharing, remote batch

Language

Computer

011

Program name
EMPRENT

Abstract
This program is suitable for planning and progressing networks, controlling projects, managing data and producing equipment schedules. It is based on the PERT time, cost and resource system and generates reports in a form defined by the user

References
PERT

Source
Easams Limited
Lyon Way, Frimley Road
Camberley, Surrey
GU16 5EX, UK
Telephone Camberley 63377 Telex 5115

Availability
Lease, bureau service

Language
PL/1
NEAT

Computer
IBM 370
ICL 4130

012

Program name
CPMSYSTEM (Critical path method system)

Abstract
This package creates a program network which estimates the duration and cost of activities. It consists of the following sub-routines: CPMSYST governs the overall system; CPM1 prepares the basic solutions and runs them; CPM2 and CPM2A are one-level and three-level sorting programs; CPM3 is an updating program; CPM4 makes a tabular analysis of progress; CPM5 provides graphic displays of status; and REAL solves networks

References
Mark III software library
User manual 5602·03

Source
Honeywell Information Systems Limited
114 to 118 Southampton Row
London WC1B 5AB
UK
Telephone 01-242 5725

Availability
Bureau service

Language
Basic

Computer
Honeywell 6000 series

013

Program name
ASTRA

Abstract
This resource-allocation package develops schedules for large or complex projects where resources are available in given quantity. A project can be planned so that the cost of the resources is minimised or deadlines can be met within known cost limitations. Working from a project plan, it creates a PERT schedule based on the time taken for each activity. It then modifies this to take account of the resources available. It can handle up to fifty projects

References
Mark III software library
Manuals 5602·40 (DB55), 5602·41 (DB34)

Source
Honeywell Information Systems Limited
114 to 118 Southampton Row
London WC1B 5AB
UK
Telephone 01-242 5725

Availability
Bureau service

Language
Basic

Computer
Honeywell 6000 series

014

Program name
Compact II

Abstract
This program establishes a precedence network for a project by means of stored planning routines, which are amended to suit the individual requirements of a project. The system can handle projects with up to 30 000 activities. Both time and resource analyses can be produced, and resource allocation may be limited either by time or resources

References

Source
Humphreys and Glasgow Limited
22 Carlisle Place
London SW1P 1JA
UK
Telephone 01-828 1234

Availability
Bureau service, purchase

Language
Cobol+Compass

Computer
CDC 6600

015

Program name
NETPLOT

Abstract
This system consists of a suite of programs which allow output data from the PCS network analysis system to be plotted. The plotted networks are generated in precedence or activity-on-node format. Facilities exist for highlighting the critical path by placing critical activities along the top of a network. PCS handles both arrow and precedence networks. Input requirements for NETPLOT are loaded on cards

References

Source
Institute for Industrial Research and Standards, Building Industry Division
Industrial Research Centre, Ballymun Road
Dublin 9, Eire
Telephone Dublin 370101

Availability

Language

Computer
PCS operates on IBM 1130. Calcomp 663 plotter is used for NETPLOT

016

Program name
I/J System

Abstract
A critical path/resource levelling system for the analysis of arrow networks. Input and output formats are at the discretion of the user and activities can be sorted to any required sequence. Bar charts can be plotted, and a plotting and design facility for networks is available. Library network facilities and cost and historical data routines are also included

References

Source
K & H Business Consultants Ltd
9 Villiers Road
Kingston-upon-Thames
Surrey UK
Telephone 01–549 5777

Availability
Bureau service, purchase, hire

Language
Fortran

Computer
Univac 1108

017

Program name
I/J System

Abstract
A critical path/resource levelling system for the analysis of arrow networks. Outputs are variable and can be sorted into any required sequence. Bar charts can be plotted and a plotting and design facility for networks is available. Library network facilities are also included

References

Source
K & H Business Consultants Ltd
9 Villiers Road
Kingston-upon-Thames
Surrey UK
Telephone 01–549 5777

Availability
Bureau service, purchase, hire

Language
Basic

Computer
IBM 360, 370

018

Program name
PREMIS

Abstract
A program for time and resource analyses of critical path networks. Input and output formats are variable, as are master-file contents. Bar charts and histograms may be plotted via the report-generator section of the system. General data-processing facilities are also included

References

Source
K & H Business Consultants Ltd
9 Villiers Road
Kingston-upon-Thames
Surrey UK
Telephone 01–549 5777

Availability
Bureau service, purchase, hire

Language
Basic

Computer
IBM 360, 370

019

Program name
Precedence System

Abstract
A suite of programs for time analysis and the scheduling of resources of precedence networks. The program can determine the latest time for ordering materials or equipment, to ensure the most convenient time for delivery. Projects consisting of many sub-projects can be dealt with. Outputs can be in bar-chart, list and tabular form. A network package is also available

References

Source
K & H Business Consultants Ltd
9 Villiers Road
Kingston-upon-Thames
Surrey UK
Telephone 01–549 5777

Availability
Bureau service, purchase, hire

Language
Basic

Computer
IBM 360, 370

020

Program name
Precedence System

Abstract
Precedence network system with resource levelling, library facilities, variable output formats and automatically plotted network. Multiple calendars can be specified to overcome the problems of different office and site working times, and curing time for concrete

References

Source
K & H Business Consultants Ltd
9 Villiers Road
Kingston-upon-Thames
Surrey UK
Telephone 01–549 5777

Availability
Bureau service, purchase, hire

Language
Compass
Plan
Cobol

Computer
ICL 1900
CDC 6600

021

Program name
Cascade

Abstract
This program processes critical path networks and will accept data from either arrow or precedence diagrams. Intended for the planning of construction projects, the program presents the stages of construction as a bar chart which features a series of vertical lines linking the bars, to show the logic of the network. Plans may be updated and up to fifteen reports can be produced for one network, including resource allocation and cost reports

References

Source
Laing Computing Services
Elstree Way
Borehamwood
Hertfordshire
WD6 1NF UK

Availability
Sale, bureau service

Language
Fortran

Computer
IBM 370–50

022

Program name
Lancashire interactive graphic networking system

Abstract
This suite consists of five programs: control program, balanced activity length analysis, minimum crossing analysis, interactive program and plotting program. Details of activities are provided on cards. Activities are located and the network balanced. The interactive program allows input from a menu with options to move or delete an activity, to indicate a finished activity, to change duration, to add a new activity, to redraw the network and to plot

References
Uses GINO-F graphics software

Source
Lancashire County Council
PO Box 78, County Hall
Preston PR1 8XJ
UK
Telephone Preston 54868

Availability

Language

Computer
ICL 1904

023

Program name
PNA-Time, PNA-Resources (Aggregation)

Abstract
This suite of programs provides an analysis of time and resources associated with a complex construction project, for which a network has been designed. PNA-Time output is in the form of source data, time master-file, control master-file and free-format reports; PNA-Resources output is in the form of a histogram report, a tabular report and free-format reports. Standard NCR validation techniques are used, including check to master-file

References

Source
NCR Limited
206 Marylebone Road
London NW1 6LY
UK
Telephone 01–723 7070

Availability
Purchase, hire

Language
NCR Neat/3

Computer
Century 16k
Memory
(PNA-Time), 32k
Memory
(PNA-Resources)

024

Program name
HOCUS III

Abstract
This program builds flow-diagrams which can be tested by hand simulation. Once validated, the flow can be run on a computer using the standard HOCUS program. The program can be loaded on any computer with a Fortran compiler and sufficient core, and applications include brewery, hospital and warehouse design, machine-shop layout and production planning. No programming experience is necessary to carry out simulation studies

References

Source
P-E Consulting Group
Park House, Egham
Surrey TW20 OHW
UK
Telephone Egham 4411

Availability
P-E Consulting Group, D-A Computer Services, SCICON, SIA, Time-Sharing

Language
Fortran

Computer
Various

025

Program name
PMS

Abstract
A suite of programs covering many aspects of project management. Critical path networks may be processed and reports produced in accordance with the user's requirements. The system may also be used for cost accounting and for resource levelling

References
NBRI (South Africa) abstract
X/BOU-COMP 2

Source
Sigma Project Services
PO Box 31714
Braamfontein, Transvaal
South Africa
Telephone Johannesburg 21–5775

Availability
Bureau service

Language

Computer
Univac 1108

026

Program name
PERT7

Abstract
This system is suitable for planning and controlling projects. It checks data, analyses time, resources and cost, updates and reports on progress. It is capable of handling networks of up to 100 000 activities, multiple projects and multiple start-and-finish events. Features include elapsed-time or calendar modes; multiple work patterns, with the working day or week and holidays specified by the user, and output in time units or on the basis of a calendar

References

Source
Time Sharing Limited
179 to 193 Great Portland Street
London
W1N 5TB UK
Telephone 01–637 1355,Telex 28638

Availability
Time-sharing

Language
Fortran-based

Computer

027

Program name
FASNET

Abstract
This is a program for the analysis of critical-path networks, with multi-network reporting ability. It will perform straight critical-path runs, dynamic crashing runs, master schedule set-up runs or monitor runs. The program will handle a project from implementation to completion

References

Source
UCC, University Computing Company
344–350 Euston Road
London NW1
UK
Telephone 01–387 9661

Availability
Bureau service

Language

Computer

028

Program name
K & H

Abstract
This is a critical-path/resource allocation system for the calculation of arrow networks. Printed and plotted output includes histograms, bar-charts and cost reports

References
Developed by K & H Business Consultants Ltd

Source
UCC, University Computing Company
344–350 Euston Road
London NW1
UK
Telephone 01–387 9661

Availability
Bureau service

Language
Fortran

Computer

029

Program name
CPM

Abstract
This program analyses complex tasks by the CPM method, enabling a logical sequence of events to be established within the task

References

Source
University of Arizona, College of Architecture
Tempe
Arizona
USA

Availability
Remote batch

Language

Computer
CDC 6400

030

Program name
FOCAS (Forecasted cost and schedule)

Abstract
This system for project management prepares PERT/CPM schedules, and cost-control and resource-allocation reports. These reports reveal the current status of a project, as well as forecasting the schedule and cost of completion. Up to 32 000 activities can be handled

References

Source
Westinghouse Electric Corporation
2040 Ardmore Boulevard, Pittsburgh
Pennsylvania 15221
USA

Availability
Bureau service, remote batch

Language
Cobol
Fortran

Computer
IBM 370

031

Program name
HIM

Abstract
This system is for the analysis of housing investment decisions within a local authority. Figures related to small areas are used as a basis for generating costs and benefits of different investment alternatives, such as improvement or rebuilding

References

Source
ARC Limited
4 Jesus Lane
Cambridge CB5 8BA
UK
Telephone 0223 65015

Availability
Purchase

Language
Fortran

Computer
Prime 300

032

Program name
CLUSTER

Abstract
This program is designed for local authorities and similar bodies to enable them to create, maintain and analyse land-use and employment files. Data is sorted and presented in tabular form

References

Source
Hoskyns Systems Limited
91–93 Farringdon Road
London EC1M 3LB
UK
Telephone 01–242 1951

Availability
Bureau service, purchase, hire

Language
Cobol

Computer
IBM 360, 370
ICL 1900, System 4

033

Program name
LAMSAC Application code 32125460041A

Abstract
This program deals with the control of empty property. Slow peripheral units used are a card reader, tape reader and line printer. The program has been in use since 1976

References
LAMSAC

Source
LOLA (London On-Line Local Authorities)
Computer Bureau
6 Southgate Road
London N1
Telephone 01–249 2171 and 2608

Availability

Language

Computer
IBM 370/158
512K core

034

Program name
LAMSAC Application code 32124122300A

Abstract
This program deals with property file manipulation. Slow peripheral units used are a card reader and line printer. The program was first used in 1974

References
LAMSAC

Source
Architect's Department, Nottinghamshire
County Council
County Hall
West Bridgford, Nottingham NG2 7QP
Telephone Nottingham 863366

Availability

Language
Fortran

Computer
ICL 1903T/1904S
20K core
2 magnetic tape units
1 disc drive

035

Program name
LAMSAC Application code 32125422380A

Abstract
This program provides a property enquiry system. The slow peripheral unit used is a vdu. The program was first used in 1974

References
LAMSAC

Source
Architect's Department, West Sussex County Council
County Hall, West Street
Chichester, West Sussex PO19 1RQ
Telephone Chichester 85100

Availability

Language
PL/1 Assembler

Computer
IBM 370/155
198K core
1 disc drive

036

Program name
LAMSAC Application code 32123252190A

Abstract
This program for land agents deals with pool property management. Slow peripheral units used are a tape reader and line printer. The program has been in use since 1976

References
LAMSAC

Source
Architect's Department, Hertfordshire County Council
County Hall
Hertford SG13 8DE
Telephone Hertford 54242

Availability

Language
Cobol

Computer
NCR Century 251
58K core
1 magnetic tape unit
3 disc drives

037

Program name
LAMSAC Application code 32125460042A

Abstract
This program provides an index of property linked to on-line files. Slow peripheral units used are a card reader, tape reader and line printer. The program has been in use since 1972

References
LAMSAC

Source
LOLA (London On-Line Local Authorities) Computer Bureau
6 Southgate Road
London N1
Telephone 01–249 2171 and 2608

Availability

Language
DL/1, PL/1
Assembler

Computer
IBM 370/158
512K core

038

Program name
LAMSAC Application code 32125460040A

Abstract
This program deals with the acquisition of property. Slow peripheral units used are a card reader, tape reader and line printer. The program was first used in 1975

References
LAMSAC

Source
LOLA (London On-Line Local Authorities) Computer Bureau
6 Southgate Road
London N1
Telephone 01–249 2171 and 2608

Availability

Language
DL/1, PL/1
Assembler

Computer
IBM 370/158
512K core

039

Program name
URBAN

Abstract
This program simulates urban growth over yearly periods

References

Source
University of Arizona, College of Architecture
Tempe
Arizona
USA

Availability

Language

040

Program name
Selective mailing

Abstract
Addresses of customers, contacts or prospective buyers may be classified according to buying pattern, potential or any other factor upon which selection is to be made. Selections may be made upon request or automatically, through a pre-set pattern of contact. Output may be in the form of personal letters, adhesive or Cheshire labels, print-out of details, filing cards or reminders to make telephone contact

References

Source
Jaserve Limited
225 Frimley Green Road
Camberley, Surrey
UK
Telephone Deepcut 6331

Availability
Bureau service

Language
Assembler

Computer
IBM 360

041

Program name
LAMSAC Application code 32125527040A

Abstract
This program compiles a register of property. Slow peripheral units used are a card reader and line printer

References
LAMSAC

Source
Architect's Department, Lothian Regional Council
Regional Headquarters
George IV Bridge, Edinburgh EH1 1UQ
Telephone 031–229 9292

Availability

Language
Cobol

Computer
ICL 4/70
80K core
3 disc drives
1 magnetic tape unit

042

Program name
SNIP

Abstract
This is an interactive system used for monitoring service networks. Information on non-spatial aspects of the network may be added to the initial data base. Typical applications are sewerage, water, gas or electricity supply, district heating and telephone networks

References

Source
ARC Limited
4 Jesus Lane
Cambridge CB5 8BA
UK
Telephone 0223 65015

Availability
Purchase

Language
Fortran

Computer
Prime 300

043

Program name
EASYPLAN

Abstract
This is a flexible system designed to assist where tables of data need to be built and manipulated, often in planning or budgeting

References

Source
Atkins Computing Services Limited
Woodcote Grove, Ashley Road
Epsom, Surrey
UK
Telephone Epsom 40421

Availability
Bureau service, time-sharing. Available in Netherlands

Language
APL

Computer
Honeywell Sigma 9

044

Program name
GPOS

Abstract
This program was developed from the FAPS (Financial Analysis Planning System) program by decisions taken on-line in the United States. GPOS is a comprehensive interactive corporate modelling system and is in use throughout the world. It has been specifically designed for sophisticated modelling of large companies with complex organisations and operating structures

References

Source
Atkins Computing Services Limited
Woodcote Grove, Ashley Road
Epsom, Surrey
UK
Telephone Epsom 40421

Availability
Bureau service, time-sharing. Available in Netherlands

Language
Fortran and Assembler

Computer
Honeywell Sigma 9

Program name
EDMS

Abstract
This is a software system which can be used to organise, sort, retrieve, update and delete information stored in a central data base. It includes a language which allows the user to specify the structure of the data base

References

Source
Atkins Computing Services Limited
Woodcote Grove, Ashley Road
Epsom, Surrey
UK
Telephone Epsom 40421

Availability
Bureau service, time-sharing. Available in Netherlands

Language
Fortran
Cobol
Assembler
APL

Computer
Honeywell Sigma 9

046

Program name
Linear programming system (LP)

Abstract
This program, developed from the RAND Corporation code, uses the product form of the inverse method and is particularly fast because the computation is carried out in the computer core. In time-sharing mode, the program can handle approximately 140 rows, 560 columns and up to 1700 matrix entries and the user can control and amend the data during the run: in batch mode, larger problems may be processed

References

Source
Atkins Computing Services Limited
Woodcote Grove, Ashley Road
Epsom, Surrey
UK
Telephone Epsom 40421

Availability
Bureau service, time-sharing. Available in Netherlands

Language
Fortran

Computer
Honeywell Sigma 9

047

Program name
FORTRAN data-file handling

Abstract
This program handles and edits data for FORTRAN programs

References
Program made available by ICL

Source
Computel Limited
Eastern Road
Bracknell, Berkshire
UK
Telephone Bracknell 23031

Availability

Language

Computer

048

Program name
SPEC

Abstract
A text-editing program currently applied to standard architectural specifications. It can be used to extract, augment and edit text from a standard specification (currently, the National Building Specification) producing copies either on punched tape for use with automatic typewriters, or on a line-printer. Editing commands are comprehensive but simple: the program is controlled by mnemonic single-letter commands

References

Source
Computer Unit, School of Architecture and Landscape
Leeds Polytechnic, Brunswick Terrace
Leeds
UK
Telephone 0532 462222

Availability
Purchase and bureau service

Language
Data General Nova Assembler

Computer
Data General Nova 1200

049

Program name
Sperry preventative maintenance

Abstract
This program automatically processes activities associated with the preventative maintenance of equipment

References

Source
COSMIC
University of Georgia
Athens, Georgia 30602
USA
Telephone 404 542 3265

Availability
Purchase

Language
Fortran IV

Computer
IBM 360

050

Program name
Mark III program library

Abstract
This library includes programs which perform single operations, elaborate systems, routines which can be called from running programs and special language functions. Subjects covered include civil and electrical engineering, heating, lighting, ventilation, inventory and parts control, investment analysis, planning and management

References

Source
Honeywell Information Systems Limited
114 to 118 Southampton Row
London WC1B 5AB
UK
Telephone 01–242 5725

Availability
Bureau service

Language
Basic
Fortran

Computer
Honeywell 6000 series

051

Program name
PR

Abstract
A suite of programs used in managing large text data bases for use in preparing publications. Files are organised in chapters and paragraphs numbered sequentially for identification and editing and by a descriptive code such as SfB or the CIB Master List numbering for retrieval. Commands for string insertion, replacement, deletion and transposition operate on the codes or the text in either batch or interactive mode

References
Production of this book

Source
Hutton + Rostron
Netley House
Gomshall, Nr Guildford
Surrey
Telephone Shere 3221

Availability
Bureau service or sale

Language
PAL, NEAT

Computer
Digital PDP8, ICL 4120

052

Program name
QBANK

Abstract
A program for handling structured data in the form of schedules, with or without text, for the assembly of data bases. Data can be Boolean, real numbers or text. Descriptive data can be inserted by program. Data can be sorted, searched or combined by program. Output can be via a range of devices

References

Source
Hutton + Rostron
Netley House
Gomshall, Nr Guildford
Surrey
Telephone Shere 3221

Availability
Bureau or sale

Language
PAL

Computer
Digital PDP8

053

Program name
SELECT

Abstract
A suite of programs for selectively printing out records from a coded text file and for assembling and formatting sub-files for use in publications, schedules, directories, indexes and labelling. Output can be arranged to operate any suitable device

References
Used to structure the contents of this book

Source
Hutton + Rostron
Netley House
Gomshall, Nr Guildford
Surrey
Telephone Shere 3221

Availability
Bureau or sale

Language
PAL

Computer
Digital PDP8

054

Program name
SORT

Abstract
A program for rearranging records on a file by reference to any desired table of character values

References

Source
Hutton + Rostron
Netley House
Gomshall, Nr Guildford
Surrey
Telephone Shere 3221

Availability
Bureau or sale

Language
PAL

Computer
Digital PDP8

055

Program name
DES

Abstract
This program is used for data editing and validation. The program can edit up to any level of complexity, using simple control statements. User-specified messages are output during the editing to speed correction of input data, which may be edited only, or output for further processing

References

Source
Libra Computing Ltd
29 to 30 Brook Mews North
London W2 3BW
UK
Telephone (01) 402 7479

Availability
Bureau service

Language
Fortran IV
IBM assembler

Computer
IBM 360, 370

056

Program name
EASYTAB

Abstract
This program is used for research analysis and report writing, and produces flexible layout tables. Complex tabulations may be produced by combining previously defined tables

References

Source
Libra Computing Ltd
29 to 30 Brook Mews North
London W2 3BW
UK
Telephone (01) 402 7479

Availability
Bureau service

Language
Fortran IV
IBM assembler

Computer
IBM 360, 370

057

Program name
LAMSAC Application code 32124121230A

Abstract
This program deals with building inspections. Slow peripheral units used are a tape reader and 3 line printers. It has been in use since 1974

References
LAMSAC

Source
Architect's Department, Leeds City Council
Selectapost 13
Dudley House, Albion Street
Leeds LS2 8PS
Telephone Leeds 31301

Availability

Language
Cobol

Computer
ICL 1904S 22K core
4 magnetic tape units
3 disc drives

058

Program name
SIRK

Abstract
This program offers a labour-saving system for the circulation of periodicals by small libraries. It is used in the library of the Norwegian Building Research Institute, where 350 periodicals are circulated to 160 staff members. Six separate print-outs can be produced, giving circulation lists, alphabetical lists of periodicals and information on the number and titles of periodicals circulated to staff members. 440 periodicals and 220 users can be handled

References

Source
Norwegian Building Research Institute
POB 322 Blindern
Oslo 3
Norway
Telephone 46 98 80

Availability
Purchase, bureau service

Language
Fortran IV

Computer
Univac 1100
IBM 360, 370

059

Program name
Sparse matrix handling sub-routines

Abstract
This set contains sub-routines for storing and retrieving sparse matrix elements in a common buffer array. The system is dynamic, in that values subsequently made zero delete the reference to the element from the chain-list of values and free that storage location for use by the same or another matrix. A program written and de-bugged in non-sparse form can be readily translated into

References
Power systems analysis library

Source
Electrical Research Association Ltd
Cleeve Road, Leatherhead
Surrey KT22 7SA
UK
Telephone Leatherhead 74151 Telex 264045

Availability
Purchase, hire

Language
Fortran IV

Computer
Available for most machines

060

Program name
ESOP

Abstract
This program is for the analysis and evaluation of integrated systems supplying communities of limited size with energy, water and waste disposal services. These systems are intended to make the best use of resources. Water requirements, waste water, disposal of solid waste, heating and cooling loads, energy use and economics are all taken into consideration

References

Source
Urban Systems Project, NASA
Johnson Space Center
Houston, Texas
USA

Availability
Available at nominal cost

Language
Fortran V

Computer

061

Program name
PROBE (T)

Abstract
This interactive program allows the compiling and editing of a data base. Once compiled, this data base can be examined and information retrieved in the form of lists, sorted selectively

References

Source
Ove Arup and Partners
13 Fitzroy Street
London W1
UK
Telephone 01–636 1531

Availability
Bureau service

Language
Fortran

Computer

Quantities and stock control

062

Program name
SPECS

Abstract
This program allows a user to edit selectively a master specification, either by reference to pre-determined key-words or by location, to produce final contractual specifications for a particular project. The master specification may be modified as required, and safeguards are incorporated to prevent accidental or unauthorised alterations to the master file

References

Source
APEC Executive Office
Grant-Deneau Tower, Suite M–15
Dayton, Ohio 45402
USA
Telephone 513 228 2602

Availability

Language

Computer
IBM 360, 1130

063

Program name
Bills of quantity, analysis and valuation

Abstract
This program provides a link between the estimated rates set out in a bill of quantities, network analysis or bar-chart plan and periodic valuations. It enables the bill, on which the original cost estimate was based, to be used in planning the work to be done

References

Source
Boeing Computer Centres Limited
31–35 Clarendon Road, Watford
Herts WD1 1JA
UK
Telephone Watford 38321

Availability
Bureau service

Language
Cobol

Computer
ICL 1900

064

Program name
Coded quantities

Abstract
A library system with standard phraseology for quantity surveyors. Each code facet represents a phase of description. The insertion of variable descriptions within standard 'skeleton' items has been incorporated. The coding manual has been designed to reduce 'look-up' time to a minimum; it deals with specific natural groups of items within a trade. Automatic pricing of bills is possible

References
Specified by the Development Group of Chartered Quantity Surveyors

Source
Centre-File (Northern) Limited
Westinghouse Road, Trafford Park
Manchester M17 1PY
UK
Telephone 061 872 1982

Availability
Bureau service

Language
Cobol

Computer
ICL 1900

065

Program name
Autobill

Abstract
This program converts taking-off data into abstracts, priced or unpriced bills of quantities, cost analyses, financial accounts and other associated reports. The system may be used with a library of standard descriptions in Fletcher and Moore phraseology, to suit the user's own requirements, or the surveyor's descriptions. Alternatively, an existing standard library may be used

References

Source
Centre-File (Northern) Limited
Westinghouse Road, Trafford Park
Manchester M17 1PY
UK
Telephone 061 872 1982

Availability
Bureau service

Language
Plan

Computer
ICL 1900

066

Program name
IMACE

Abstract
This system provides an interim certificate in a form that can be submitted direct to the client together with associated cost reports for internal use. It consists of item number, including bill, section and new item references; description containing up to 400 characters, unit of measurement, estimated quantity, quantity measured to date, bill rate, up to eight cost rates and two sort codes that can be used to link similar items in the bill.

References

Source
Computer Services (South West) Limited
Millbay Road
Plymouth PL1 3NG
UK
Telephone 0752 68814

Availability
Bureau service

Language

Computer

Program name
General scheduling program (GSP)

Abstract
This program provides a language for creating, interrogating and updating schedules which have a fixed number of characteristics associated with each item. Two basic forms of schedule are produced: item schedules which contain some or all characteristics ordered on the item identifier; and type schedules which contain the different combinations in the data, together with a list of all identifiers sharing a combination

References

Source
Cusdin Burden and Howitt
Greencoat House, 5th Floor
Francis Street, London
SW1P 1DB, UK
Telephone 01–828 4051/7

Availability
Purchase or hire on a royalty basis

Language
Fortran

Computer
CDC 6000, Cyber

068

Program name
FACEMS

Abstracts
This suite calculates a sequential bill of quantities for civil-engineering work. Descriptions are constructed from a phrase library on a four-level code, and are checked against a standard permutation library, then filed under the appropriate work portion or building. The phrase library is also available in French, and facilities exist to interpolate manuscript or rogue descriptions where these cannot be constructed from the phrase library

References

Source
Faber Computer Operations Limited
Upper Marlborough Road
St Albans
Herts AL1 3UT
Telephone St Albans 61222

Availability
Bureau service

Language

Computer
IBM 1130, System 7

069

Program name
Bautext

Abstract
This program system is designed to produce bills of quantities, to evaluate and compare tenders, and to print the bills of quantities contract. The system includes a library of standard descriptions which conform to DIN or other standards, and can be modified to meet different job requirements. A coding system facilitates the selection of descriptions. Bills can be translated automatically into foreign languages

References
Futterer, E, G Lang and H Wessiepe, Die Bautechnik, 51, 1974, pp 13–16

Source
Friedrich Uhde GmbH
Dortmund, Deggingstrasse 10–12
Postfach 262
W Germany
Telephone (0231) 5471 Telex 0822187

Availability

Language

Computer

070

Program name
ISOPEDAC

Abstract
This program prepares estimates of quantities of materials needed for all phases of a process pipework project. Detailed orders, costs, labour requirements and isometric drawings can be prepared from a final run of data: facilities for control of materials are also included

References

Source
ICI Limited
Central Management Services
Fulshaw Hall
Wilmslow, Cheshire
UK
Telephone Alderley Edge (0625) 582828

Availability

Language
Fortran

Computer
IBM 370–145

071

Program name
LAMSAC Application code 32035122030A

Abstract
This program calculates bills of quantity for architects. Slow peripheral units used are a tape reader and line printer

References
LAMSAC

Source
Architect's Department, Berkshire County Council
Wilton House, Parkside Road
Reading, Berkshire RG3 2DR
Telephone Reading 585101

Availability

Language
Cobol

Computer
ICL 1904S, 15K core
2 magnetic tape units
1 disc drive

072

Program name
LAMSAC Application code 32033432170A

Abstract
This program calculates bills of quantity for architects. Slow peripheral units used are a card reader, tape reader and line printer. It was first used in 1971

References
LAMSAC

Source
Architect's Department, Hampshire County Council
The Castle
Winchester, Hampshire SO23 8UJ
Telephone Winchester 4411

Availability

Language
PL/1

Computer
IBM 370/135 and 145, 100K core
1 magnetic tape unit
3 disc drives

073

Program name
LAMSAC Application code 32034112040A

Abstract
This program calculates bills of quantity for county architects. Slow peripheral units used are a tape reader and line printer

References
LAMSAC

Source
Architect's Department, Buckinghamshire County Council
County Hall
Aylesbury, Buckinghamshire HP20 1UA
Telephone Aylesbury 5000

Availability

Language
Plan Cobol

Computer
ICL 1903T, 12K core
4 magnetic tapes
1 disc drive

074

Program name
LAMSAC Application code 32035122140A

Abstract
This program calculates bills of quantity for architects. Slow peripheral units used are a tape reader and line printer. It has been in use since 1975

References
LAMSAC

Source
Architect's Department, East Sussex County Council
County Hall, St Anne's Crescent
Lewes, East Sussex BN7 1SW
Telephone Lewes 5400

Availability

Language
Plan Cobol

Computer
ICL 1904A, 15K core
2 magnetic tape units
1 disc drive

075

Program name
LAMSAC Application code 32035257100A

Abstract
This program calculates bills of quantity for architects. Slow peripheral units used are a tape reader, line printer and MT encoder

References
LAMSAC

Source
Architect's Department, Renfrew District Council
Municipal Buildings, Cotton Street
Paisley, Strathclyde Region PA1 1BU
Telephone 0411–889 5400

Availability

Language
Cobol

Computer
NCR Century 200
32K core
2 magnetic tape units
4 disc drives

076

Program name
LAMSAC Application code 32037835530A

Abstract
This program provides quantity surveying services for county architects. Slow peripheral units used are a tape reader and a line printer

References
LAMSAC

Source
Architect's Department, Hertfordshire County Council
County Hall
Hertford SG13 8DE
Telephone Hertford 54242

Availability

Language
Cobol

Computer
NCR Century 251
64K core
1 magnetic tape unit
3 disc drives
1 cram unit

Program name
LAMSAC Application code 32033432131A

Abstract
This program calculates bills of quantities and an activity costing and planning system. Slow peripheral units used are a card reader and line printer

References
LAMSAC

Source
Architect's Department, Durham County Council
County Hall
Durham DH1 5UL
Telephone Durham 64411

Availability

Language
PL/1

Computer
IBM 370/145; 60K core; 2 magnetic tape units; 3 disc drives

078

Program name
LAMSAC Application code 32025422380A

Abstract
This program calculates bills of quantity for the SCOLA building system. Slow peripheral units used are a card reader, line printer and card punch. It was first used in 1975

References
LAMSAC

Source
Architect's Department, West Sussex County Council
County Hall, West Street
Chichester, West Sussex, PO19 1RQ
Telephone Chichester 85100

Availability

Language
Cobol Assembler

Computer
IBM 370/155; 90K core; 3 magnetic tape units; 2 disc drives

079

Program name
LAMSAC Application code 32032842150A

Abstract
This program calculates bills of quantities for the CLASP system. Slow peripheral units used are a card reader and line printer. It was first used in 1971

References
LAMSAC

Source
Architect's Department, Essex County Council
County Hall
Chelmsford, Essex CM1 1LX
Telephone Chelmsford 67222

Availability

Language
Cobol

Computer
Honeywell 6060; 18K core; 3 magnetic tape units; 1 disc drive

---

080

Program name
LAMSAC Application code 32034122300A

Abstract
This program calculates bills of quantities for the CLASP system. Slow peripheral units used are a tape reader and line printer. It was first used in 1971

References
LAMSAC

Source
Architect's Department, Nottinghamshire County Council
County Hall, West Bridgford
Nottingham NG2 7QP
Telephone Nottingham 863366

Availability

Language
Cobol

Computer
ICL 1903T/1904S
16K core
2 magnetic tape units
1 disc drive

081

Program name
LAMSAC Application code 32035121140A

Abstract
This program calculates bills of quantity for the CLASP system. Slow peripheral units used are a card reader and tape reader. It has been in use since 1972

References
LAMSAC

Source
Architect's Department, Bradford City Council
City Hall
Bradford, W Yorkshire BD1 1HY
Telephone Bradford 29577

Availability

Language
Cobol

Computer
ICL 1904A; 12K core
2 disc drives

082

Program name
LAMSAC Application code 32035442280A

Abstract
This program calculates bills of quantities for the CLASP system. Slow peripheral units used are a card reader, tape reader, line printer and card punch

References
LAMSAC

Source
Architect's Department, Northumberland County Council
Arden House
Gosforth, Newcastle-upon-Tyne
Telephone Newcastle-upon-Tyne 859021

Availability

Language
Cobol

Computer
IBM 370/135; 20K core; 4 disc drives

083

Program name
LAMSAC Application code 32036436010A

Abstract
This program calculates bills of quantities for the CLASP system, for use by architects. Slow peripheral units used are a card reader and line printer

References
LAMSAC

Source
Architect's Department, Clwyd County Council
Shire Hall,
Mold, Clwyd CH7 6NH
Telephone Mold 2121

Availability

Language
Cobol

Computer
IBM 370/145; 47K core; 1 magnetic tape unit; 3 disc drives

084

Program name
LAMSAC Application code 32031122230A

Abstract
This program calculates bills of quantities. Slow peripheral units used are a card reader, tape reader, line printer and tape punch

References
LAMSAC

Source
Architect's Department, Lancashire County Council
PO Box 78, County Hall
Preston, Lancashire PR1 8XJ
Telephone Preston 54868

Availability

Language

Computer
ICL 1904A; 16K core 4 magnetic tape units; 1 disc drive

085

Program name
LAMSAC Application code 32031400010A

Abstract
This program calculates bills of quantities. Slow peripheral units used are a card reader and line printer. It was first used in 1970

References
LAMSAC

Source
Architect's Department, Greater London Council
The County Hall
London SE1 7PB
Telephone 01–633 5000

Availability

Language
Basic assembler

Computer
IBM 370/158; 70K core; 4 magnetic tape units; 1 disc drive

086

Program name
LAMSAC Application code 32032122220A

Abstract
This program calculates bills of quantities. Slow peripheral units used are a card reader, tape reader and line printer. It was first used in 1968

References
LAMSAC

Source
Architect's Department, Kent County Council
Springfield
Maidstone, Kent
Telephone Maidstone 54371

Availability

Language
Plan

Computer
2 x ICL 1904S; 16K core; 6 magnetic tape units; 1 disc drive

087

Program name
LAMSAC Application code 32033432100A

Abstract
This program calculates bills of quantities. Slow peripheral units used are a card reader and line printer. It has been in use since 1969

References
LAMSAC

Source
Architect's Department, Derbyshire County Council
County Offices, Matlock
Derbyshire DE4 3AG
Telephone Matlock 3411

Availability

Language
Cobol

Computer
IBM 370/145; 32K core; 2 disc drives

088

Program name
LAMSAC Application code 32035537040A

Abstract
This program calculates bills of quantity. Slow peripheral units used are a card reader and line printer

References
LAMSAC

Source
Architect's Department, Lothian Regional Council
Regional Headquarters
George IV Bridge, Edinburgh EH1 1UQ
Telephone 031–229 9292

Availability

Language
Cobol

Computer
ICL 4/70; 47K core; 4 magnetic tape units; 2 disc drives

089

Program name
LAMSAC Application code 32037442050A

Abstract
This program calculates bills of quantities. Slow peripheral units used are a card reader and line printer

References
LAMSAC

Source
Architect's Department, Cambridgeshire County Council
Shire Hall, Castle Hill
Cambridge CB3 0AP
Telephone Cambridge 58811

Availability

Language
Cobol

Computer
IBM 370/135; 27K core; 3 disc drives

090

Program name
LAMSAC Application code 32037835530A

Abstract
This program calculates contract remeasurement for quantity surveyors. Slow peripheral units used are a card reader, tape reader and line printer. It was first used in 1972

References
LAMSAC

Source
Architect's Department, Telford Development Corporation
Priorslee Hall
Telford, Salop
Telephone Telford 613131

Availability

Language
APS TAB Cobol

Computer
Honeywell G–115; 16K core; 2 disc drives

091

Program name
Numeric

Abstract
This system provides abstracts for quantity surveyors and engineers. Dimensions are coded by the user and processed to give an abstract for each coded item. Codes refer to descriptions in either a firm's standard bill or old bills of quantities

References

Source
Oldacres Computers Limited
110 St Martin's Lane
London
WC2N 4BH
Telephone 01–240 5329

Availability
Bureau service

Language
PL1

Computer
IBM 360, 370

092

Program name
Bills of quantities, price re-analysis

Abstract
These programs, which are used in conjunction with a suite for producing bills of quantities, allow prices to be added to the items generated in the bills of quantities. The priced items are then re-sorted to give cost data for elements, operations, locations, etc for the proposed building

References

Source
Oldacres Computers Limited
110 St Martin's Lane
London
WC2N 4BH
Telephone 01–240 5329

Availability
Bureau service

Language
PL1

Computer
IBM 360, 370

093

Program name
Bills of quantities

Abstract
This suite of programs calculates dimensions taken off architects' drawings. The dimensions are sorted into trade or other order and a draft bill of quantities is produced by extracting phrases from various standard libraries. Amendments can be incorporated automatically to produce a final bill and detailed abstracts are provided. Sophisticated code techniques are available

References

Source
Oldacres Computers Limited
110 St Martin's Lane
London
WC2N 4BH
Telephone 01–240 5329

Availability
Bureau service

Language
PL1

Computer
IBM 360, 370

094

Program name
Specifications

Abstract
This system stores standard specification clauses on the computer and allows the user to select and extract those clauses required for a particular project. Non-standard words, phrases or whole clauses may be inserted, as necessary. The program may include the user's own standard specifications or others which are more generally used (eg National Building Specification)

References

Source
Oldacres Computers Limited
110 St Martin's Lane
London
WC2N 4BH
Telephone 01–240 5329

Availability
Bureau service

Language
PL1

Computer
IBM 360, 370

095

Program name
MTO requisition

Abstract
With no additional input, this program sorts the lists of the cables and glands in the bill of quantities generated in MTO design and prints out order requisitions and amendments when changes occur

References
Cable drumming, MTO design programs

Source
Electrical Research Association Ltd
Cleeve Road, Leatherhead
Surrey KT22 7SA
UK
Telephone Leatherhead 74151 Telex 264045

Availability
From owner

Language

Computer

096

Program name
MTO design

Abstract
This program is used for producing priced bills of quantities covering the cost of cables, glands, labour and installation, including installation accessories. Labour costs are estimated in man-hours per operation and price per man-hour can be used to arrive at an estimated cost

References
Cable drumming, MTO requisition programs

Source
Electrical Research Association Ltd
Cleeve Road, Leatherhead
Surrey KT22 7SA, UK
Telephone Leatherhead 74151 Telex 264045

Availability
From owner

Language

Computer

Program name
ECOLE 1

Abstract
This program is used to design secondary school accommodation. It generates a schedule of accommodation which can form part of a brief or investigate alternative strategies of operation. Input comprises: school data, including curricula for each year and subject; allocation data, including areas for pupils and teacher and non-teaching areas; teaching data, including school organisation and shared accommodation; and cost data

References
ABACUS Occasional Paper No 40

Source
ABACUS studies
University of Strathclyde
131 Rottenrow, Glasgow G4 ONG
UK
Telephone 041–522 4400 ext 3021

Availability
Purchase, hire, interactive bureau service

Language
Fortran IV

Computer
Univac 1108
Tektronix graphics terminal

098

Program name
SPACES 3

Abstract
This program gives an appraisal of the performance of buildings such as schools. Input consists of geometry of the building, site description, interdepartmental associations, construction, cost, and environmental and climatic data. Output gives floor and wall areas, wall-to-floor ratios, compactness and planning efficiency indices, figures for heat loss or gain, lighting requirements, boiler plant size, costs, and drawings

References
SPACES 1, 2 and 3, ABACUS Occasional Papers No 21

Source
ABACUS studies
University of Strathclyde
131 Rottenrow, Glasgow G4 ONG
UK
Telephone 041–552 4400 ext 3021

Availability
Purchase, hire, interactive bureau service

Language
Fortran IV

Computer
Univac 1108
Tektronix graphics terminal

099

Program name
ECOLE 3

Abstract
This package models and appraises buildings at the scheme/detail design stage. The designer builds up a scheme description in terms of the geometry, site data, block and room layout, structural form and cladding arrangement. This data can be input on-line or by paper tape together with the cost and planning input data. Functional appraisals relating to planning efficiency, environmental performance and cost are also performed

References
SITE, ESP, ECOLE 1, ABACUS Occasional Papers Nos 40, 48, 61 and 63

Source
ABACUS studies
University of Strathclyde
131 Rottenrow, Glasgow G4 ONG
UK
Telephone 041–552 4400 ext 3021

Availability
Purchase, hire, interactive bureau service

Language
Fortran IV

Computer
Univac 1108
Tektronix graphics terminal

100

Program name
PHASE

Abstract
This program models the built form of a hospital at the design stage and extracts information enabling a large set of measures to be appraised. Graphic output shows site boundary with ground floor, any one floor, axonometric view, or section through site and/or model. Appraisal output is a synoptic table of measures concerning department and boilerhouse location, heat gain/loss diagnostics, and capital and energy costs

References
ACTNET, SERNET, HLE

Source
ABACUS studies
University of Strathclyde
131 Rottenrow, Glasgow G4 ONG
UK
Telephone 041–552 4400 ext 3021

Availability
Purchase, hire, interactive bureau service

Language
Fortran IV

Computer
Univac 1108
Tektronix graphics terminal

101

Program name
HELP (Housing Evaluation Layout Package)

Abstract
This program is a design aid to modelling a housing layout. Input comprises five files: site file, house file, development file, layout file and network file. Graphic output gives site, layout model showing roads and footpaths, and stepped elevations for a given terrace. Tabular output appraises costs, area provision, densities and access. Daylight, sunlight and privacy can be assessed for the complete layout or any individual house

References
SITE
ABACUS Occasional Paper No 64 (HELP)

Source
ABACUS studies
University of Strathclyde
131 Rottenrow, Glasgow G4 ONG
UK
Telephone 041–552 4400 ext 3021

Availability
Purchase, lease, bureau service

Language
Fortran IV

Computer
Univac 1108
Tektronix graphics terminal

102

Program name
PACE 1

Abstract
This on-line program is used for evaluating a particular building design at the outline proposal stage. The designer submits full details of his proposed scheme and the computer produces a series of cost and performance data. The scheme may then be modified and reappraised as many times as required

References

Source
ABACUS studies
University of Strathclyde
131 Rottenrow, Glasgow G4 ONG
UK
Telephone 041–552 4400 ext 3021

Availability
Purchase, lease, interactive bureau service

Language
Fortran

Computer
Univac 1108
Tektronix graphics terminal

103

Program name
ASSIGN/TRANSP

Abstract
ASSIGN can be used to solve assignment problems. Given n functions, n spaces and the matrix for costs of allocating each one, it assigns the functions to the spaces with the minimum cost. It can be used for allocating room positions in an envelope, or functions to room, depending on serving load. TRANSP is used to solve the related transport problem

References

Source
ABACUS studies
University of Strathclyde
131 Rottenrow, Glasgow G4 ONG
UK
Telephone 041–552 4400 ext 3021

Availability
Purchase, lease, interactive bureau service

Language
Fortran

Computer
Univac 1108
Tektronix graphics terminal

104

Program name
SPACES 1

Abstract
This program explores the spatial implications of alternative curricula, teaching methods and educational policies. Data is collected for each subject in the curriculum. Each form records the number and size of groups and time spent in various settings. Minimum space standards appropriate to each setting within each subject are also input. Output gives detailed schedules of accommodation, seat– and room-utilisation indices and summaries

References
SPACES 2 and 3, ECOLE 1, ABACUS Occasional Paper No 21 (SPACES)

Source
ABACUS studies
University of Strathclyde
131 Rottenrow, Glasgow G4 ONG
UK
Telephone 041–552 4400 ext 3021

Availability
Purchase, hire, interactive bureau service

Language
Fortran

Computer
Univac 1106
Tektronix graphics terminal

105

Program name
SIMSTRAT

Abstract
This program is an interactive corporate modelling and project evaluation system which has been designed for use by planners without specialised knowledge. Facilities include sensitivity analysis, aggregation, logical tests, profitability criteria. File handling facilities enable the user to link sub-systems together and to other programs

References

Source
Atkins Computing Services Limited
Woodcote Grove, Ashley Road
Epsom, Surrey
UK
Telephone Epsom 40421

Availability
Bureau service, time-sharing. Available in Netherlands

Language
Fortran + Assembler

Computer
Honeywell Sigma 9

106

Program name
Investment appraisal

Abstract
This program provides an analysis of returns on capital invested and proposed hire rates for purchases of capital equipment. The system operates by using discounted cash flow and other techniques

References

Source
Boeing Computer Centres Limited
31–35 Clarendon Road, Watford
Herts WD1 1JA
UK
Telephone Watford 38321

Availability
Bureau service

Language
Cobol

Computer
ICL 1900

Program name
Plant and asset accounting

Abstract
This system maintains the plant register, calculates hire charges, produces invoices for clients and gives information on the utilisation and profitability of plant. All kinds of plant and capital equipment can be handled

References

Source
Boeing Computer Centres Limited
31–35 Clarendon Road, Watford
Herts WD1 1JA
UK
Telephone Watford 38321

Availability
Bureau service

Language
Cobol

Computer
ICL 1900

108

Program name
COBA

Abstract
COBA (Cost Benefit Analysis) is a progam for applying discounting methods to the appraisal of road schemes. The data bank includes figures for expected growth in traffic, and financial figures for deaths, accidents and environmental damage

References
Program made available by the Department of the Environment

Source
Computel Limited
Eastern Road
Bracknell, Berkshire
UK
Telephone Bracknell 23031

Availability

Language

Computer

109

Program name
PRELAN

Abstract
This program performs simple preliminary economic analyses of building projects using discounted cash flows. Any number of building projects can be analysed in one run

References

Source
CSIRO, Division of Building Research
Graham Road, Highett
Victoria 3190
Australia
Telephone 95 0333

Availability
CSIRONET

Language
Fortran 4·4 extended

Computer
CDC 7600

110

Program name
CSIROCA

Abstract
This program handles all technical, commercial and financial factors which are required to determine the commercial feasibility of proposed buildings. Up to 2000 factors can be used to describe a project. The program handles building proposals with up to three sites and up to fifty accommodation areas, with construction times of up to ten years and investment periods up to forty-five years

References

Source
CSIRO, Division of Building Research
Graham Road, Highett
Victoria 3190
Australia
Telephone 95 0333

Availability
CSIRONET

Language
Fortran

Computer
CDC 7600, Cyber 74

111

Program name
ECONFES

Abstract
This program determines the feasibility of developing a defined site for a defined purpose. It takes into account not only council regulations, architectural requirements, construction times and financing but also effects of risk due to changes in interest rates, inflation rates and marketing. The solution specifies the number of floors and the distribution of space for activities among the floors and the concomitant ancillary and public areas

References

Source
Department of Architectural Science
The University of Sydney
Sydney
New South Wales 2006
Australia

Availability
Sale, bureau service

Language
Fortran IV

Computer
CDC Cyber 72

112

Program name
DIMENSION/DP4

Abstract
This program analyses and sizes room layouts to satisfy any defined restrictions or room aspect ratios, and to minimise construction costs, heat inflows or energy requirements. In addition to calculating the optimum dimensions, the program indicates the sensitivity of the solution

References

Source
Department of Architectural Science
The University of Sydney
Sydney
New South Wales 2006
Australia

Availability
Sale, bureau service

Language
Fortran IV

Computer
CDC Cyber 72

113

Program name
INVAPP

Abstract
This program calculates the economics of alternative proposals for a building. The calculation involves initial expenditure, receipts, and prediction of running costs and the future value of the building

References
PSA program library

Source
Directorate of General Management/Architects' Services
Property Services Agency
Lunar House, 40 Wellesley Road
Croydon CR9 2EL, UK
Telephone 01–686 3499

Availability

Language
Fortran

Computer
Honeywell MK III

114

Program name
MQCOST

Abstract
This program calculates the cost limits for married quarters projects, using the DoE (PSA) Housing Cost Yardstick

References

Source
Directorate of General Management
Property Services Agency
Lunar House, 40 Wellesley Road
Croydon CR9 2EL
UK
Telephone 01–686 3499

Availability
TSL Bureau

Language
Fortran

Computer

115

Program name
INSUL

Abstract
This program compares the cost of insulating new or existing rectangular detached houses with the resulting savings in energy and heating costs

References
PSA program library

Source
Directorate of Engineering Services
Property Services Agency
Lunar House, 40 Wellesley Road
Croydon CR9 2EL
UK
Telephone 01–686 3499

Availability
TSL Bureau

Language
Fortran

Computer

116

Program name
Housing-site layout

Abstract
This system compares costs of alternative housing layouts on a given site. Elements such as housing and garage blocks, roads, services and landscape features can be manipulated interactively. A digitiser is used to input site topography and sketch plans. Output may appear on the dual-screen display, digital plotter, teletype or lineprinter, and it includes plans and sections displayed at selected scales, lists of quantities and costs

References

Source
University of Edinburgh, Department of Architecture
55 George Square
Edinburgh EH8 9JU
UK
Telephone 031–667 3825

Availability
Contact owner

Language

Computer
Nova minicomputer
PDP–10
Tektronix graphics terminal

117

Program name
MACP–301

Abstract
This program for financial analysis is designed to interface with the MACP 100 and 200 series (or act independently) to establish more efficient combinations of heating and cooling equipment. It can simultaneously evaluate a number of investments, revenue sources, costs, effects of tax and discount rates and depreciation, and cash flow options. MACP–301 can be used for any kind of financial analysis

References

Source
Envirodyne Energy Services
421 E Cerritos Ave
Anaheim
California 92805
USA

Availability

Language

Computer

118

Program name
MTWELVE

Abstract
This program calculates the total cost of owning and operating a building as a function of initial cost, annual fixed charges, annual maintenance and costs of building services. The monthly energy requirements of the building are also calculated from design criteria

References

Source
Giffels Associates Incorporated
Marquette Building
243 W Congress
Detroit, Michigan 48226
USA
Telephone 313 961 2084

Availability
Purchase negotiable

Language
Fortran V

Computer
Univac 1108

119

Program name
CEIAPS (Capital equipment investment analysis program)

Abstract
This program compares the probable cash flow resulting from a proposed new method with one or more current production methods. It can also be used to compare two existing methods of production

References
Mark III software library
User manual 5103·10

Source
Honeywell Information Systems Limited
114 to 118 Southampton Row
London WC1B 5AB
UK
Telephone 01–242 5725

Availability
Bureau service

Language
Basic

Computer
Honeywell 6000 series

120

Program name
Building valuations

Abstract
This is a program for interim valuations and it enables a surveyor to obtain a copy of any valuation within a few days of measuring. It takes measured quantities and prepares a priced valuation for building contracts. Facilities exist for collecting totals of money for various parts of the bills and for a predetermined percentage to be applied to these totals

References

Source
Oldacres Computers Limited
110 St Martin's Lane
London
WC2N 4BH
Telephone 01–240 5329

Availability
Bureau service

Language
PL1

Computer
IBM 360, 370

121

Program name
Production and work schedules

Abstract
This suite of programs deals with the production of work schedules, for repair and alteration, on building contracts

References

Source
Oldacres Computers Limited
110 St Martin's Lane
London
WC2N 4BH
Telephone 01–240 5329

Availability
Bureau service

Language
PL1

Computer
IBM 360, 370

122

Program name
Economic Comparison of Systems/B

Abstract
This program combines energy costs for a typical year, and other annual operating costs, with initial investment and the associated costs of ownership, to find the total cost of each system, year-by-year, for a period of up to thirty years

References
Meriwether analysis series

Source
Ross F Meriwether and Associates
Northwood Executive Building
1600 Northeast Loop 410
San Antonio, Texas
Telephone 512–824 5302

Availability
Bureau service, purchase

Language

Computer
Univac 1108

123

Program name
Monthly utility costs

Abstract
This program calculates the monthly energy costs of air-distribution systems using the local utility rate schedules

References
Meriwether analysis series

Source
Ross F Meriwether and Associates
Northwood Executive Building
1600 Northeast Loop 410
San Antonio, Texas
Telephone 512–824 5302

Availability
Bureau service, purchase

Language

Computer
Univac 1108

124

Program name
PLANT

Abstract
The program maintains a file of information for management and accounting of a plant depot or hire company. Reports are produced on utilisation and profitability, including costs, repairs, breakdown time and idle time. These figures are compared with budgets for similar items. Accounting information produced includes revenue accounts, asset accounts and invoicing

References

Source
UCC (GB) Ltd
1258 London Road
London
SW16 4EG UK
Telephone 01–679 1766

Availability
Bureau service, remote batch

Language
Cobol

Computer
Univac 1106

125

Program name
REAP 4

Abstract
This is an interactive program for the economic analysis of property. It calculates, in tabular form, interest against amortisation, cash flow after tax, discount rate of return and an equity revision sheet from various factors keyed-in by the user. Any variables may be changed and re-entered, giving new calculations for comparison

References

Source
University of Arizona, College of Architecture
Tempe
Arizona
USA

Availability

Language

Computer
DEC 10

126

Program name
PROJCT

Abstract
This is an interactive program for assessing the economic feasibility of a building project. From various factors, such as land cost, type of buildings, operating expenses, costs of building and mortgage conditions, are calculated total income, operating expenses, cash flows and return on investment. Analysis of projects may be printed in tabular form, giving comparisons of each variable, as well as calculated results

References

Source
University of Arizona, College of Architecture
Tempe
Arizona
USA

Availability

Language

Computer
DEC 10

Program name
REAP3

Abstract
This is an interactive program for assessing the economic feasibility of a building project. It operates on the same basis as PROJCT, but is tailored specially for the analysis of residential housing developments

References

Source
University of Arizona, College of Architecture
Tempe
Arizona
USA

Availability

Language

Computer
DEC 10

128

Program name
SHOPCE

Abstract
This is an interactive program for assessing the economic feasibility of a building project. It operates on the same basis as PROJCT, but is tailored specially for the analysis of shopping-centre development

References

Source
University of Arizona, College of Architecture
Tempe
Arizona
USA

Availability

Language

Computer
DEC 10

129

Program name
CARBS

Abstract
This program gives capital costs, costs in use and thermal analyses from alternative sketch designs. It produces working plan and elevation drawings and a schedule of components and bills, together with layout drawings, cost estimates and schedules of mechanical services. It also produces pipework isometrics, fabrication and erection lists, cost estimates and instrument and engineering line diagrams for process plant

References

Source
Clwyd County Council
Shire Hall
Mold, Clwyd CH7 6NH
UK
Telephone 0352 2121, Telex 61454

Availability
Purchase, lease

Language
Fortran IV

Computer
IBM 360, 370
ICL
Univac
CDC
Conversions for PDP 10 and Prime

130

Program name
IBES

Abstract
This system, developed at the East Anglian Regional Health Authority, is for the collection, retrieval, modification and re-use of briefing information for buildings. Amendments to the brief during the design process are continually monitored. A large number of catalogues and schedules can be produced, for example, of room data, components, furniture and equipment

References

Source
ARC Limited
4 Jesus Lane
Cambridge CB5 8BA
UK
Telephone 0223 65015

Availability
Purchase

Language
Fortran

Computer
Prime 300

131

Program name
Summation of bending schedules

Abstract
This program sums the lengths and weights of each type of bar, for each diameter, from standard reinforcement bending schedules

References

Source
Camutek
39 Newnham Road
Cambridge CB3 9EY
UK
Telephone Cambridge (0223) 69686

Availability
From owner

Language
Basic

Computer
Hewlett-Packard 9830 (2k) or (6k)

132

Program name
Management information

Abstract
One of a set of integrated programs for management information purposes in all types of organisation. It includes the following features: production of analysis reports from data input on a single document; five processing modes, namely cumulative, comparative, standards, schedule and budget. The system will process simultaneously in as many modes as required

References

Source
Computel Limited
Eastern Road
Bracknell, Berkshire
UK
Telephone Bracknell 23031

Availability

Language

Computer

133

Program name
CUBES

Abstract
This program maintains records of concrete cube crushing test results and performs statistical calculations producing listing, histograms and cumulative-frequency distribution diagrams

References
PSA program library

Source
Directorate of Civil Engineering Services
Property Services Agency
Lunar House, 40 Wellesley Road
Croydon CR9 2EL
UK
Telephone 01–686 3499

Availability

Language
Fortran

Computer

134

Program name
Concrete cube test analysis (Imperial units version)

Abstract
This is a suite of programs designed to organise the storage of results of cube crushing tests for concrete from any number of different sites, and to analyse a requested group of results in any of a number of different ways. Results include statistical parameters arrived at from different types of analysis and the overall trend from a regressional analysis of the whole of the requested group

References

Source
Laing Computing Services
Elstree Way
Borehamwood
Hertfordshire
WD6 1NF UK
Telephone 01–207 2000

Availability
Sale, bureau service

Language
Fortran

Computer
IBM 370–50

135

Program name
LAMSAC Application code 32055422380A

Abstract
This program provides information retrieval for quantity surveyors. Slow peripheral units used are a card reader, line printer and vdu. It was first used in 1975

References
LAMSAC

Source
Architect's Department, West Sussex
County Council
County Hall, West Street
Chichester, West Sussex PO19 1RQ
Telephone Chichester 85100

Availability

Language

Computer
IBM 370/155; 90K core; 2 magnetic tape units; 1 disc drive

136

Program name
Inventory management

Abstract
This program is is a three-level system for recording, controlling and managing stock in different situations

References

Source
Atkins Computing Services Limited
Woodcote Grove, Ashley Road
Epsom, Surrey
UK
Telephone Epsom 40421

Availability
Bureau service, time-sharing. Available in Netherlands

Language
Cobol

Computer
Honeywell Sigma 9

Program name
CAMPARTS

Abstract
This suite is for breakdown of parts lists and schedules of materials. The basic breakdown calculates the gross requirements for all parts and assemblies in the greatest possible detail

References

Source
Cambridge Computer Services Limited
Jupiter House, Station Road
Cambridge
UK
Telephone 0223 66111

Availability
Bureau service

Language
Plan

Computer
ICL 1903A

138

Program name
CUTSHED

Abstract
A program for obtaining the best results in cutting and bending reinforcement bars to BS 4466:1969. It is one of a suite of detailing programs. It is intended for use by bar suppliers or contractors who cut and bend bars on site. It will calculate the most economical permutation of cuts and thus minimise the size of off-cuts. Outputs include cutting instructions, stock reports and bending instructions

References

Source
Computer Consortium Services Ltd
5 Windmill Street
London W1P 1HF
UK
Telephone 01–638 3118

Availability
Bureau service

Language
Fortran

Computer
CDC
IBM

139

Program name
WATE

Abstract
This program abstracts from standard bar schedules the reinforcement weights of straight and bent bars in either Imperial or metric units. Output consists of weight tables for mild steel and high-tensile steel. Each table gives the weight of straight links and bent bars for each diameter

References

Source
Faber Computer Operations Limited
Upper Marlborough Road
St Albans
Herts AL1 3UT
Telephone St Albans 61222

Availability
Bureau service

Language

Computer
IBM 1130, System 7

140

Program name
Inventory control

Abstract
This package allocates inventory status, a re-order report to indicate parts which are below the minimum quantity and an activity report to indicate month-by-month issues and receipts of parts. It also provides reports for requirements, customer orders, vendor orders and processed transactions for an audit

References
Pt no 09830–73030. Part of Financial control and information system (09830–73085)

Source
Hewlett-Packard Limited
King Street Lane, Winnersh
Wokingham, Berks RG11 5AR, UK
Telephone Wokingham 784774

Availability
Purchase

Language
Basic

Computer
HP 9830A with 3808–word memory
11274B strings ROM
9880B mass memory
9866A thermal printer

141

Program name
LMCPLS

Abstract
This program prepares an optimum cutting plan for businesses which cut fixed-length stock, such as seamless tubing, metal bars and timber, into intermediate lengths. It relates the cutting plan to the customer's order

References
Mark III software library
User manual 5302·01

Source
Honeywell Information Systems Limited
114 to 118 Southampton Row
London WC1B 5AB
UK
Telephone 01–242 5725

Availability
Bureau service

Language
Basic

Computer
Honeywell 6000 series

142

Program name
WKSAMS

Abstract
This program is used to solve three major work-sampling problems. It determines how many samples to take, it generates random schedules indicating when sampling should be made and it reports the results. It is also useful for analysing and setting idle-time allowances

References
Mark III software library
User manual 5301·02. Run WSIND

Source
Honeywell Information Systems Limited
114 to 118 Southampton Row
London WC1B 5AB
UK
Telephone 01–242 5725

Availability
Bureau service

Language
Basic

Computer
Honeywell 6000 series

143

Program name
Cable drumming

Abstract
This program is used for calculating convenient drum lengths into which cables can be sorted. Data is printed out for each requisition. (For use with MTO design program and MTO requisition program)

References

Source
Electrical Research Association Ltd
Cleeve Road, Leatherhead
Surrey KT22 7SA
UK
Telephone Leatherhead 74151 Telex 264045

Availability
From owner

Language

Computer

144

Program name
SIM 25

Abstract
This is a program for evaluating the effects of various re-order quantities and re-order levels of prepared timber products. The user provides historic order/sales data over a period for a selection of stock items. Lineprinter output shows input parameters (policy alternatives) and the associated consequences. A range of safety levels may be applied in relation to setting of re-order levels

References

Source
TRADA
Chiltern House, Hughenden Valley
High Wycombe, Buckinghamshire
UK
Telephone Naphill 3091

Availability
For sale as part of consultancy

Language
Fortran

Computer

145

Program name
HASTY (Handling and storage in timber yards)

Abstract
This suite of programs analyses the operation of any timber-yard business, either existing or planned, and evaluates the most cost-efficient handling and storage system

References

Source
TRADA
Chiltern House, Hughenden Valley
High Wycombe, Buckinghamshire
UK
Telephone Naphill 3091

Availability

Language

Computer

146

Program name
TRAID (Timber records, analysis)

Abstract
A suite of programs for order analysis and stock recording. The programs are designed specifically for softwood, hardwood or board materials, in either metric or Imperial units, and used for planning, purchasing and production

References

Source
TRADA
Chiltern House, Hughenden Valley
High Wycombe, Buckinghamshire
UK
Telephone Naphill 3091

Availability

Language

Computer

147

Program name
CARDS (Create and access random data-base system)

Abstract
This program provides a flexible and easily-learnt language of ten basic commands for creating, interrogating and updating information. It may be used interactively or in a batch mode. It produces immediate answers to questions, in a terse form, or tabulated and titled reports suitable for issue. Input is free-form and may be via a terminal or on cards

References

Source
Cusdin Burden and Howitt
Greencoat House, 5th Floor
Francis Street, London
SW1P 1DB, UK
Telephone 01–828 4051/7

Availability
Purchase or hire on a royalty basis

Language
Fortran

Computer
CDC 6000, Cyber

148

Program name
Scheduling program system (SPS)

Abstract
This program provides a language for creating, interrogating and updating schedules where the number of discrete items associated with identifiers varies, for example, room equipment schedules. Thirty-four outputs are available including a list of items present in each room, a summary of items and a schedule showing where each item is to be found. Input is free-form and may have up to eighty columns

References

Source
Cusdin Burden and Howitt
Greencoat House, 5th Floor
Francis Street, London
SW1P 1DB, UK
Telephone 01–828 4051/7

Availability
Purchase or hire on a royalty basis

Language
Fortran

Computer
CDC 6000, Cyber

149

Program name
FORPA

Abstract
This program is designed to compute price adjustments for building contracts based on NEDO Series 2 indices. Both the Work Group and Work Category methods are available, including Fix Only items and the specialist formulae

References
DOC

Source
Design Office Consortium
Guildhall Place
Cambridge CB2 3QQ
Telephone 0223 311246

Availability

Language
Fortran

Computer
Machine independent

150

Program name
REVOP 2

Abstract
This is an interactive program for fluctuations in building contracts based on the NEDO formula. Using the 13 Work Groups, including Fix Only but not specialist indices, the program outputs a valuation page with which the surveyor modifies his valuation by the calculated factors. Early availability of the indices permits the factors to be produced before the valuation is carried out

References
DOC

Source
Design Office Consortium
Guildhall Place
Cambridge CB2 3QQ
Telephone 0223 311246

Availability
See DOC Report No 3

Language
Fortran

Computer
Honeywell

151

Program name
LAMSAC Application code 3212810640A

Abstract
This program relates to housing repairs. Slow peripheral units used are a tape reader and line printer

References
LAMSAC

Source
Architect's Department, Wrexham Maelor Borough Council
Guildhall
Wrexham, Clwyd LL11 1AY
Telephone Wrexham 4611

Availability

Language
Plan

Computer
ICL 1902T; 8K core 2 magnetic tape units; 1 disc drive

152

Program name
LAMSAC Application code 32125121270A

Abstract
This program calculates property valuations for insurance purposes. Slow peripheral units used are a card reader and line printer. The program has been in use since 1976

References
LAMSAC

Source
Architect's Department,
Newcastle-upon-Tyne City Council
1 Civic Centre
Newcastle-upon-Tyne, Tyne and Wear
NE99 2BM
Telephone Newcastle-upon-Tyne 28520

Availability

Language
Cobol

Computer
ICL 1904S; 6K core
1 magnetic tape unit; 1 disc drive

153

Program name
LAMSAC Application code 32125432390A

Abstract
This program forms a register of property in the county for insurance purposes. Slow peripheral units used are a card reader and line printer. The program was first used in 1976

References
LAMSAC

Source
Architect's Department, Wiltshire County Council
County Hall
Trowbridge, Wiltshire BA14 8JG
Telephone Trowbridge 3641

Availability

Language
PL/1 and total data base

Computer
IBM 370/145; 256K core; 1 disc drive

154

Program name
LAMSAC Application code 32504112040A

Abstract
This program provides a commitment system and calculates repairs and MTCE expenditure. Slow peripheral units used are a tape reader and line printer. The program was formulated in 1975

References
LAMSAC

Source
Architect's Department, Buckinghamshire County Council
County Hall
Aylesbury, Buckinghamshire HP20 1UA
Telephone Aylesbury 5000

Availability

Language
Cobol

Computer
ICL 1903T; 12K core
1 disc drive

155

Program name
LAMSAC Application code 32205112330A

Abstract
This program makes an analysis of Method-building quotations. Slow peripheral units used are a card reader and line printer. The program was first used in 1974

References
LAMSAC

Source
Architect's Department, Somerset County Council
County Hall
Taunton, Somerset TA1 4DY
Telephone Taunton 3451

Availability

Language
Cobol

Computer
ICL 1903T; 14K core
2 magnetic tape units; 1 disc drive

Accounting

156

Program name
Sales ledger

Abstract
This program records all steps in a typical sales transaction, such as invoices, cash receipts and credit notes. After checking for errors, it can provide statement, information on customer's activity, analysis of debtors by age of debt and automatic credit control using either open-item or brought-forward methods. It also gives a data base from which other analyses may be made

References

Source
Atkins Computing Services Limited
Woodcote Grove, Ashley Road
Epsom, Surrey
UK
Telephone Epsom 40421

Availability
Bureau service, time-sharing. Available in Netherlands

Language
Cobol

Computer
Honeywell Sigma 9

157

Program name
Purchase ledger system

Abstract
This program is a bought ledger system for producing remittance advice and maintaining ledger accounts in open-item format. A report showing future commitments is also produced. Available as an option are VAT audit lists and cost analysis

References

Source
Atkins Computing Services Limited
Woodcote Grove, Ashley Road
Epsom, Surrey
UK
Telephone Epsom 40421

Availability
Bureau service, time-sharing. Available in Netherlands

Language
Cobol

Computer
Honeywell Sigma 9

158

Program name
Purchase and nominal accounting

Abstract
This system controls invoices for purchases and aids cash flow. Financial controls are provided, together with cheques, cheque listings and remittance advices. The system automatically produces cost input to the nominal ledger

References

Source
Boeing Computer Centres Limited
31–35 Clarendon Road, Watford
Herts WD1 1JA
UK
Telephone Watford 38321

Availability
Bureau service

Language
Cobol

Computer
ICL 1900

159

Program name
CAMBOUGHT

Abstract
This program is a financial package for bought ledger. It processes details of a period of transactions, including purchases, invoices and credits, journal entries, cheques, trader credits and cash received

References

Source
Cambridge Computer Services Limited
Jupiter House, Station Road
Cambridge
UK
Telephone 0223 66111

Availability
Bureau service

Language
Plan

Computer
ICL 1903A

160

Program name
CAMSALES

Abstract
This program is a sales accounting package for customer records, preparation of statements, management control reports and sales analysis. The program will deal with an open-item ledger, a non-open-item ledger, or a non-open-item ledger with an analysis of dated balances by month of invoice

References

Source
Cambridge Computer Services Limited
Jupiter House, Station Road
Cambridge
UK
Telephone 0223 66111

Availability
Bureau service

Language
Plan
Cobol

Computer
ICL 1903A

161

Program name
SCAN

Abstract
A set of interrelated programs for inventory analysis and control, by a variable order-point control system, using short-term forecasting techniques

References
Program made available by ICL

Source
Computel Limited
Eastern Road
Bracknell, Berkshire
UK
Telephone Bracknell 23031

Availability

Language

Computer

162

Program name
Purchase ledger

Abstract
One of a set of integrated programs for accounting purposes with the following features: segregation of payment of accounts from purchase ledger; open-item or balance-brought-forward ledger records for all suppliers with balances outstanding, and showing all transactions in current period; creditors' control list showing suppliers' balances over five months and in total; control accounts for the month; and a VAT summary

References

Source
Computel Limited
Eastern Road
Bracknell, Berkshire
UK
Telephone Bracknell 23031

Availability

Language

Computer

163

Program name
Sales ledger

Abstract
One of an integrated set of programs for accounting purposes in all types of organisation. It has the following features: open-item or balance-brought-forward ledger records, production of statements, maintenance of up-to-date information on credit control, sales analysis, VAT summary and other options

References

Source
Computel Limited
Eastern Road
Bracknell, Berkshire
UK
Telephone Bracknell 23031

Availability

Language

Computer

164

Program name
Invoicing

Abstract
One of an integrated set of programs for invoicing in all types of organisation. Users may select their own invoice layout and the program includes facilities for the calculation of VAT, the provision of information for the sales ledger and access to the Management Information System for the analysis of invoices

References

Source
Computel Limited
Eastern Road
Bracknell, Berkshire
UK
Telephone Bracknell 23031

Availability

Language

Computer

165

Program name
GLII

Abstract
This system performs most of the work associated with traditional general ledger accounting. It is readily adaptable to the requirements of large companies, operating a number of divisions in many locations, or to the relatively simple needs of smaller businesses

References
NBRI (South Africa) abstract
X/BOU-COMP 6

Source
Computer Sciences Sigma Limited
PO Box 31497
Braamfontein, Transvaal
South Africa
Telephone 724–9301

Availability
Bureau service

Language

Computer

166

Program name
Valuation system

Abstract
A system designed to provide, with a minimum of clerical effort, a full internal valuation of the work completed on a contract, and, when necessary, an interim application to the client for payment. The form of the valuation varies with the amount of detail required. A bill of quantities or a consolidated bill is used to create a file, together with LPM rates. Only the monthly measure of work done is then required to produce certificates

References

Source
Construction Computing Limited
Matlock
Derbyshire DE4 3AF
UK
Telephone 062 983 4257

Availability
Bureau service, purchase or hire

Language

Computer

167

Program name
COMPUNET

Abstract
A program for estimating cash-flow patterns for a contracting organisation and its various projects. It has facilities for on-line working, interrogation of weekly cash flows and subsequent high-speed printing at the computer centre. Input consists of week number at start of project, its duration, price of tender or total value of sales, cumulative value of work as function of time, expected profits as percentage on net cost and breakdown of cost

References
Program made available by Compunet Limited

Source
CRC Engineering Services
83 Clerkenwell Road
London
EC1R 5HP
Telephone 01-242 0747

Availability

Language

Computer

168

Program name
COMPASS

Abstract
A program for job-costing, accounting and management reporting for labour-intensive practices or organisations where the financial control of individual projects is important. The system contains three sub-systems, using time sheets, project files, or invoices or bought ledgers. Each of these may be used separately. Additional whole or part sub-systems can be used in conjunction with the basic form of the program's sub-systems

References

Source
Cybernet Time Sharing Limited
83 Clerkenwell Road
London
EC1R 5HP
Telephone 01-242 0747

Availability
Time sharing

Language

Computer

169

Program name
Accounts payable

Abstract
This program provides reports for anticipating liabilities and reflecting early payment discounts. The cash-requirements report shows either the outstanding invoices up to a specified date or all the invoices at present on file. A check register is generated after payments are made to reconcile the user's bank balance. The program also generates disbursement reports and vendor records

References
Pt no 09830–73020. Part of Financial control and information system (09830–73085)

Source
Hewlett-Packard Limited
King Street Lane, Winnersh
Wokingham, Berks RG11 5AR, UK
Telephone Wokingham 784774

Availability
Purchase

Language
Basic

Computer
HP 9830A with 3808–word memory
11274B strings ROM
9880B mass memory
9866A thermal printer

170

Program name
Accounts receivable/billing

Abstract
This program can accommodate 800 outstanding invoices and 800 customers per disc of the mass memory. It provides reports of all outstanding invoices, sub-totalled accounts by customer, customer's credit limit and status, and reports of partially paid invoices. It also creates customer statements

References
Pt no 09830–73025. Part of Financial control and information system (09730–73085)

Source
Hewlett-Packard Limited
King Street Lane, Winnersh
Wokingham, Berks RG11 5AR, UK
Telephone Wokingham 784774

Availability
Purchase

Language
Basic

Computer
HP 9830A with 3808–word memory
11274B strings ROM
9880B mass memory
9866A thermal printer

171

Program name
Financial control and information system

Abstract
This package includes programs for general ledger, accounts receivable/billing, accounts payable, mass memory payroll and inventory control

References
Pt no 09830–73085, 09830–73060, 09830–73025, 09830–73020, 09830–73001, 09830–73032

Source
Hewlett-Packard Limited
King Street Lane, Winnersh
Wokingham, Berks RG11 5AR, UK
Telephone Wokingham 784774

Availability
Purchase

Language
Basic

Computer
HP 9830A

172

Program name
General ledger

Abstract
This package provides a complete financial report for up to 500 general ledger accounts, and ninety-nine sub-accounts and control accounts. Data from sub-systems is automatically transferred to the general ledger. Up to 27 900 financial-year transactions are stored and are accessible via the account-analysis report. Comparative current-year balance/income statements are available for the current period or for a previous month-end

References
Pt no 09830–73060. Part of Financial control and information system (09830–73085)

Source
Hewlett-Packard Limited
King Street Lane, Winnersh
Wokingham, Berks RG11 5AR, UK
Telephone Wokingham 784774

Availability
Purchase

Language
Basic

Computer
HP 9830A

173

Program name
Consultants' cost accounting

Abstract
This package generates detailed cost reports for firms with up to eighty employees and 100 active projects. Each project may be divided into seven separate phases. Employee time and labour costs are shown for each of the seven phases. Up to nine direct charges may be allocated to projects for costing. Hours, labour costs and charges for the current reporting period are printed out, together with the totals to date

References
Part number 09830–73037

Source
Hewlett-Packard Limited
King Street Lane, Winnersh
Wokingham, Berks RG11 5AR
UK
Telephone Wokingham 784774

Availability
Purchase

Language
Basic

Computer
HP 9830A with
3808–word memory
11274B strings
ROM
9865A tape cassette
9866A thermal
printer

174

Program name
ACCSYS

Abstract
An accounts system for use with time and expenses sheets for invoicing or cost control. Data is stored on clients' instructions, budgets, amounts outstanding, charging rates, percentage additions or discounts, VAT, lump sums or periodic payments. Output is in the form of invoices, job and budget statements, work analyses and summaries for management. The program also produces input for an income and expenditure system, CASHUP

References
In use by three firms since 1968

Source
Hutton + Rostron
Netley House
Gomshall, Nr Guildford
Surrey
Telephone Shere 3221

Availability
Bureau service or sale

Language
PAL, ALGOL 68

Computer
Digital PDP8, ICL 4120

175

Program name
CASHUP

Abstract
A system for preparing a cash book and analysis from coded income and expenditure. Input can be taken direct from vouchers or cheque stubs or be in the form of a cash book with a seven-column expenditure analysis and running balance or by use of a terminal. Over 900 subheadings can be analysed. Entries can be split between columns automatically. VAT is analysed separately

References

Source
Hutton + Rostron
Netley House
Gomshall, Nr Guildford
Surrey
Telephone Shere 3221

Availability
Bureau service or sale

Language
PAL

Computer
Digital PDP8

176

Program name
Nominal ledger

Abstract
This program provides fully analysed nominal-ledger, balance-sheet and trading summaries. Also avaiable are operating statements by cost centre, or group cost centres, giving current and cumulative comparisons between actual and budgeted values. Budgets may be fixed or flexible, or phased monthly values may be generated from annual budgets according to predetermined patterns

References

Source
Jaserve Limited
225 Frimley Green Road
Camberley, Surrey
UK
Telephone Deepcut 6331

Availability
Bureau service

Language
Assembler

Computer
IBM 360

177

Program name
Purchase ledger

Abstract
This program produces remittance advices with the optional facility of automatic production of cheques, either for full amounts or for selected items. Purchase and VAT analysis is provided. Automatic posting to the nominal ledger can be made

References

Source
Jaserve Limited
225 Frimley Green Road
Camberley, Surrey
UK
Telephone Deepcut 6331

Availability
Bureau service

Language
Assembler

Computer
IBM 360

178

Program name
Sales ledger

Abstract
This program provides for the input of standard sales and accounts documents, for example, invoices, credit notes and cash receipts. It produces statements analysed by date and analysis of debtors. Sales analysis for the current month and records of sales to customers may be output

References

Source
Jaserve Limited
225 Frimley Green Road
Camberley, Surrey
UK
Telephone Deepcut 6331

Availability
Bureau service

Language
Assembler

Computer
IBM 360

179

Program name
CAP

Abstract
This program is used to keep an up-to-date record of the movement of money within a contract. Limitations are as follows: number of elements, 287; number of transfers, 8000; number of instructions, 4800; and number of estimates, 1500. Any of the following reports may be selected: element and account analysis, cost plan report, special report, interim statement of account, cost control, instruction listing, final statement of account

References

Source
Ove Arup and Partners
13 Fitzroy Street
London W1
UK
Telephone 01–636 1531

Availability
Bureau service

Language
Fortran

Computer
DEC 10

180

Program name
Construction industry payroll and job costing

Abstract
This system is designed for use by companies in the construction industry to calculate and analyse payrolls for site offices. A high standard of analysis is possible and the reports of costs provide comparisons with budgets. Labour and plant costs may be allocated individually or to groups

References

Source
Boeing Computer Centres Limited
31–35 Clarendon Road, Watford
Herts WD1 1JA
UK
Telephone Watford 38321

Availability
Bureau service

Language
Cobol

Computer
ICL 1900

181

Program name
Cost and nominal ledger

Abstract
This system allows costs from other accounts systems to be accumulated under various cost headings. These costs can be compared with budgets or targets fed into the system

References

Source
Boeing Computer Centres Limited
31–35 Clarendon Road, Watford
Herts WD1 1JA
UK
Telephone Watford 38321

Availability
Bureau service

Language
Cobol

Computer
ICL 1900

182

Program name
Stock control

Abstract
One of an integrated set of programs suitable for all types of company. The system may be used in a variety of ways to control raw material, finished goods or work-in-progress stocks. The following modes are available: simple, for record of stock balances; allocations, for known forward demand; forecasting, for expected forward demand; replenishment; purchase order progressing; invoice pricing; stock analysis; and movement analysis

References

Source
Computel Limited
Eastern Road
Bracknell, Berkshire
UK
Telephone Bracknell 23031

Availability

Language

Computer

183

Program name
JCP

Abstract
A job-costing program for firms whose principal costs are staff time, and fees for architects and civil engineers. The program provides an analysis of the time-sheets, staff costs, expenses and budget control for each project. Facilities are available to extract or categorise separate information so that each project controller can monitor his own particular costs

References

Source
Computer Consortium Services Ltd
5 Windmill Street
London W1P 1HF
UK
Telephone 01–638 3118

Availability
Bureau service

Language
Fortran

Computer
CDC
IBM
PDP

184

Program name
Purchases application

Abstract
This financial control system includes the following facilities: purchase ledger details, including VAT for current month, details of imports and items excluded from VAT, purchase ledger controls with VAT summary, list of creditors, production of cheques and list of purchase ledger balances. General financial and cost expenditure analysis is also available

References

Source
Computerskills Limited
Blue Bridge Lane
York YO1 4AS
UK
Telephone 0904 20555

Availability
Bureau service

Language

Computer

185

Program name
ULYSSE

Abstract
This program is suitable for budgeting and controlling costs on building sites. It provides plans and schedules of operators and machines and can be used for financial planning and co-ordination

References

Source
CSTC
41 Rue du Lombard
1000 Bruxelles
Belgium
Telephone 02–511 06 83

Availability
Bureau service

Language
Fortran

Computer
PDP 10

186

Program name
COST

Abstract
This program allows a quantity surveyor to re-calculate quickly the effects of design changes on the distribution of project costs. Different projects and versions of a project can be stored and cost comparisons made between them. The program uses costs of each element and presents results in the usual way. Operation is interactive

References

Source
Data Processing Department
London Transport Executive
London W1
UK
Telephone 01–242 2890

Availability
By negotiation

Language
Cobol

Computer
ICL 19045

187

Program name
FORECAST

Abstract
This program predicts the monthly expenditure on building projects of value between £10 000 and £12 000 000. The program may be used to indicate to what extent the construction is ahead or behind the target completion date

References

Source
Directorate of General Management/Architects' Services
Property Services Agency
Lunar House, 40 Wellesley Road
Croydon CR9 2EL, UK
Telephone 01–686 3499

Availability

Language
Basic

Computer
Honeywell MK III

188

Program name
Expense/budget monitor

Abstract
This program keeps accurate and detailed records of costs incurred, and compares them with budget amounts. The difference between them (spending variance) and the percentage of variance are calculated for each item of expenditure. The amounts for the reporting period are printed out, together with the accounts for the year to date

References
Part number 09830–73051

Source
Hewlett-Packard Limited
King Street Lane, Winnersh
Wokingham, Berks RG11 5AR
UK
Telephone Wokingham 784774

Availability
Purchase

Language
Basic

Computer
HP 9830A with 3808–word memory
11274B strings ROM
9866A thermal printer

189

Program name
LAMSAC Application code 32901141120A

Abstract
This program calculates professional fee control for architects. Slow peripheral units used are a tape reader and line printer

References
LAMSAC

Source
Architect's Department, Birmingham City Council
Baskerville House
Broad Street, Birmingham B1 2NE
Telephone Birmingham 235 2749

Availability

Language
Plan Cobol

Computer
ICL 1906A 24K core
2 disc drives

190

Program name
Job costing

Abstract
In this program time and expense details are fed into the computer, which arrives at a cost for each item and allocates it to the appropriate job number. The program can be modified to suit an individual firm's particular requirements. Additional facilities include budget allocation, profitability of jobs, apportioning of overheads, forecasting of fees, indication of cash flow, general forward planning and an extension to ledger work

References

Source
Oldacres Computers Limited
110 St Martin's Lane
London
WC2N 4BH
Telephmne 01–240 5329

Availability
Bureau service

Language
PL1

Computer
IBM 360, 370

191

Program name
SCORE (System for costing research expenditure)

Abstract
This suite of programs analyses expenditure of resources against cost centres, and produces information for project management

References

Source
TRADA
Chiltern House, Hughenden Valley
High Wycombe, Buckinghamshire
UK
Telephone Naphill 3091

Availability

Language

Computer

192

Program name
CAMBUILD

Abstract
This program is a complete job-costing and payroll package for the building industry. It takes time sheets and produces the complete payroll, and allocates weekly costs and monthly labour costings

References

Source
Cambridge Computer Services Limited
Jupiter House, Station Road
Cambridge
UK
Telephone 0223 66111

Availability
Purchase, bureau service

Language
Plan

Computer
ICL 1903A

193

Program name
CAMPAY

Abstract
This program will process payrolls, allowing for overtime, sick pay, holding pay, bonuses, etc. The program will produce payslips, personnel record forms, coinage reports, credit transfers, company totals and end-of-year tax forms

References

Source
Cambridge Computer Services Limited
Jupiter House, Station Road
Cambridge
UK
Telephone 0223 66111

Availability
Purchase, bureau service

Language
Plan

Computer
ICL 1903A

194

Program name
Payroll

Abstract
This program is designed to operate on a weekly or four-weekly cycle. Payslips can show name of company, basic weekly information, and a breakdown of gross pay and deductions. Cumulative tax returns for all employees can be processed at the end of the year to give an analysis, by occupation code, to show average rates of pay, average payment and overtime

References

Source
Computel Limited
Eastern Road
Bracknell, Berkshire
UK
Telephone Bracknell 23031

Availability

Language

Computer

195

Program name
COMPANY ID

Abstract
A program for use as a standard payroll system with provision for year-end tax returns

References
Program made available by ICL

Source
Computel Limited
Eastern Road
Bracknell, Berkshire
UK
Telephone Bracknell 23031

Availability

Language

Computer

196

Program name
Payroll package

Abstract
This financial control system includes the following facilities: generation of pay-slips, cheques, credit transfers, or magnetic tape for submission to the Bankers' Automated Clearing Service, analysis of notes and coins, National Insurance quarterly schedules, tax certificates, cost analysis of gross pay and allowances, and a pay-roll summary, providing details for posting to the nominal ledger

References

Source
Computerskills Limited
Blue Bridge Lane
York YO1 4AS
UK
Telephone 0904 20555

Availability
Bureau service

Language

Computer

197

Program name
General payroll

Abstract
This program can handle the particulars of up to eighty employees per data cassette with any number of data cassettes allowable. It can deduct up to ten taxes and make up to six voluntary deductions based on a percentage of gross pay, entered amounts or amount per hour. It writes cheques and prepares 941A reports and W-2 forms (USA). It provides employee summaries, payroll-register reports and tax-distribution reports

References
Part number 09830-73001

Source
Hewlett-Packard Limited
King Street Lane, Winnersh
Wokingham, Berks RG11 5AR
UK
Telephone Wokingham 784774

Availability
Purchase

Language
Basic

Computer
HP 9830A with
3808-word memory
11274B strings
ROM
9865A tape cassette
9881A line printer

198

Program name
Mass memory payroll processing

Abstract
This program can accommodate information on 500 employees per disc of the mass memory. It can deduct ten different city and state taxes, and make up to six voluntary deductions. It prints W-2 information (USA) on six-part forms, cheques and cheque stubs

References
Pt no 09830-73035. Part of Financial control and information system (09830-73085)

Source
Hewlett-Packard Limited
King Street Lane, Winnersh
Wokingham, Berks RG11 5AR, UK
Telephone Wokingham 784774

Availability
Purchase

Language
Basic

Computer
HP 9830A with
3808-word memory
11274B strings
ROM
9880B mass memory
9881A line printer

199

Program name
Payroll system

Abstract
The program calculates pay and produces individual documents and records. A weekly input of ministry number, hours worked and other items, such as subscriptions and sick time, is used to produce a pay-slip for each employee. Tax, National Insurance, holiday stamps and inclement weather are all provided for, and a coin analysis is also produced

References

Source
UCC (GB) Ltd
1258 London Road
London
SW16 4EG UK
Telephone 01-679 1766

Availability
Bureau service, remote batch

Language
Cobol

Computer
Univac 1106

200

Program name
Salary system

Abstract
The program produces a detailed individual pay-slip, complete with name and address. Details include cost allocation of salary to the appropriate department or cost centre, income-tax deductions, allowances, ledgers for staff savings, loans, mortgages and end-of-year tax returns

References

Source
UCC (GB) Ltd
1258 London Road
London
SW16 4EG UK
Telephone 01-679 1766

Availability
Bureau service, remote batch

Language
Cobol

Computer
Univac 1106

201

Program name
Assets application

Abstract
This financial control system includes: calculation of depreciation by the straight-line or reducing-balance methods, automatic cessation of depreciation when the asset has been written down to its residual value, grouping of low-value assets as one composite asset and various options for treatment of profits or losses on sales of assets. Non-standard routines cover selected assets, hire-purchase agreements and projected depreciation

References

Source
Computerskills Limited
Blue Bridge Lane
York YO1 4AS
UK
Telephone 0904 20555

Availability
Bureau service

Language

Computer

202

Program name
LAMSAC Application code 32504122270A

Abstract
This program provides a commitments account for architects. Slow peripheral units used are a tape reader and line printer. The program was first used in 1969

References
LAMSAC

Source
Architect's Department, Northamptonshire County Council
Wootton Hall Park
Northampton NN4 9BQ
Telephone Northampton 34833

Availability

Language
Plan

Computer
ICL 1904S; 7K core
5 magnetic tape units

203

Program name
LAMSAC Application code 32502842150A

Abstract
This program makes an analysis of the work record of architects. Slow peripheral units used are a card reader and line printer. The program has been in use since 1969

References
LAMSAC

Source
Architect's Department, Essex County Council
County Hall
Chelmsford, Essex CM1 1LX
Telephone Chelmsford 67222

Availability

Language
Cobol

Computer
Honeywell 6060; 16K core; 1 magnetic tape unit; 1 disc drive

204

Program name
LAMSAC Application code 32505102250A

Abstract
This program makes an analysis of job/staff time in the Architect's Department. Slow peripheral units used are a tape reader and line printer. The program was first used in 1968

References
LAMSAC

Source
Architect's Department, Lincolnshire County Council
County Offices
Lincoln LN1 1YL
Telephone Lincoln 29931

Availability

Language
Plan

Computer
ICL 1904A; 9K core

205

Program name
LAMSAC Application code 32506965510A

Abstract
This program produces a salary allocation system. Slow peripheral units used are a card reader and line printer

References
LAMSAC

Source
Architect's Department, Redditch Development Corporation
Holmwood, Plymouth Road
Redditch, Worcestershire
Telephone Redditch 64200

Availability

Language
RPG BAL

Computer
ICL 1906A; 16K core
2 disc drives

Design, graphics

206

Program name
PARTIAL

Abstract
This program enables a non-professional to generate sketch designs and compare them with existing designs. Graphic output gives: a 'drawing' of the design; bar-charts showing the percentage of deviation of the performance of the design from that of similar designs; and information showing, for each room type, the area selected by the operator, the area required to meet minimum requirements and optimum area

References
ECOLE 3
ABACUS Occasional Paper No 63

Source
ABACUS studies
University of Strathclyde
131 Rottenrow, Glasgow G4 ONG
UK
Telephone 041–552 4400 ext 3021

Availability
Purchase, lease, bureau service

Language
Fortran

Computer
Univac 1108
Tektronix graphics terminal

207

Program name
SPACES 2

Abstract
This program is an aid to producing a diagrammatic layout of a proposed building at the outline proposal stage. From a schedule of accommodation and the relationships between spaces, the program produces bubble diagrams. With standard routines the designer can manipulate the bubbles to satisfy given constraints. Each time a layout is produced, an appraisal of the planning efficiency and the constraints affecting the building are given

References
SPACES 1, SPACES 3. ABACUS Occasional Paper No 21 (SPACES)

Source
ABACUS studies
University of Strathclyde
131 Rottenrow, Glasgow G4 ONG
UK
Telephone 041–552 4400 ext 3021

Availability
Purchase, hire, interactive bureau service

Language
Fortran IV

Computer
Univac 1106
Tektronix graphics terminal

208

Program name
GRAMP

Abstract
This package produces a two-dimensional sketch of a proposed scheme at an early stage of planning and/or design. It consists of a set of routines with which the designer can operate on the layout to produce sketches quickly

References

Source
ABACUS studies
University of Strathclyde
131 Rottenrow, Glasgow G4 ONG
UK
Telephone 041–552 4400 ext 3021

Availability
Purchase, lease, interactive bureau service

Language
Fortran

Computer
Univac 1108
Tektronix graphics terminal

209

Program name
HLE

Abstract
This program displays perspective views of rectilinearly-built forms, and eliminates lines hidden from view. Two versions are available: one draws the view on a graph plotter, the other on a direct-view storage tube display terminal. The input must describe the form in terms of co-ordinates, surfaces, viewing point and angle of vision

References

Source
ABACUS studies
University of Strathclyde
131 Rottenrow, Glasgow G4 ONG
UK
Telephone 041–552 4400 ext 3021

Availability
Purchase, lease, interactive bureau service

Language
Fortran

Computer
Univac 1108
Tektronix graphics terminal

210

Program name
OXSYS

Abstract
This is a general-purpose, computer-aided design system suitable for buildings constructed from co-ordinated components laid out on an orthogonal grid. The program was originally developed for use with the Oxford Method of construction

References
See program description

Source
ARC Limitep
4 Jesus Lane
Cambridge CB5 8BA
UK
Telephone 0223 65015

Availability
Purchase

Language
Fortran

Computer
Prime 300

211

Program name
SESAME

Abstract
This is a design and analysis system comprising a data base and a series of application programs, controlled by a plain English language. The structure is defined by the engineer and stored in the data base so that selective details and analyses can subsequently be extracted. General arrangement drawings can be produced on the plotter and various designs can be produced, ie solid, rib or waffle slabs and columns.

References

Source
Building Computer Services Limited
Bush House
72 Prince Street
Bristol BS1 4HU
Telephone 0272 290651

Availability
Bureau service

Language

Computer

212

Program name
DRAW

Abstract
The program produces conventionally-styled general arrangement drawings to a scale and on a grid specified by the user. All common structural elements can be drawn. The drawing can be fully-dimensioned and elements like walls may be hatched in section. An axis layout relating the axes is used to reference all elements and produce the input data. The drawing is produced on normal tracing or detail paper

References

Source
Building Computer Services Limited
Bush House
72 Prince Street
Bristol BS1 4HU
Telephone 0272 290651

Availability
Bureau service, hire

Language

Computer

213

Program name
Photomontage

Abstract
The function of the program is to aid the production of perspectives for photomontage. The program computes and draws a wire-line perspective of a structure from a file containing co-ordinates of points visible in a photograph of the structure. It is one of a suite of detailing programs which uses DYNADATA to define a structure as a digital model and DYNASHADE and DYNADRAW to display and manipulate that model

References

Source
Computer Aided Design Centre
Madingley Road
Cambridge CB3 0HB
Cambridgeshire UK

Availability
Sale, hire

Language
Fortran

Computer
Prime 3000

214

Program name
BUILD

Abstract
This program allocates activities to spaces in a multi-storey building. It assumes that the building is prismatic or in the form of a set of stepped prisms, eg a tower on a podium, with a single core. Allocations are made on the basis of present value of rentals, less costs, including initial and further costs of the structure, envelope, lifts, air-conditioning, costs in use and various associated expenses, including land, fees and services

References

Source
CSIRO, Division of Building Research
Graham Road, Highett
Victoria 3190
Australia
Telephone 95 0333

Availability
CSIRONET

Language
Fortan IV

Computer
CDC 7400, 7600, Cyber 76

215

Program name
TOPAZ

Abstract
This program indicates the most efficient layouts for activities in urban, regional and institutional building complexes. Up to seventy-five development zones can be handled. The program performs economic evaluations over multiple time periods. Graphic output, of allocation of activities, is optional

References
An Urban Systems Study. Royal Australian Planning Institute Journal, Vol 10, 1972

Source
CSIRO, Division of Building Research
Graham Road, Highett
Victoria 3190
Australia

Availability
CSIRONET, University of Western Australia

Language
Fortran 4·4 extended

Computer
CDC Cyber 76

216

Program name
DESIGN

Abstract
This is an interactive layout planning program which employs a simple language, allowing a user with little or no computing experience to manipulate and lay out spaces. It comprises two sections: the first concerns itself with the layout problem and is a sequential heuristic algorithm, the second provides the interface between the architect and the layout algorithm

References

Source
Department of Architectural Science
The University of Sydney
Sydney
New South Wales 2006
Australia

Availability
Sale, bureau service, time-sharing

Language
APL

Computer
IBM 360–67
CDC Cyber 72

217

Program name
Site layout

Abstract
This program uses the plotter to draw a standard drawing of any layout which is defined by a co-ordinate system in straight lines and circular curves. Card output from COGO (a linked program) may be used directly as data. The drawing is produced on tracing paper or film of variable size, and to any scale, using lines from 0·2mm thick upwards. There is the choice of a grid, and the drawing may be plotted with or without annotations

References

Source
Laing Computing Services
Elstree Way
Borehamwood
Hertfordshire
WD6 1NF UK

Availability
Sale, bureau service

Language
Fortran

Computer
IBM 370–50

218

Program name
LAMSAC Application code 32205121140A

Abstract
This architectural design program enables a graphical manipulation of housing sites to be made. Slow peripheral units used are a tape reader, line printer, nova term, graphic term and teletype. The program was first used in 1975

References
LAMSAC

Source
Architect's Department, Bradford City Council
City Hall
Bradford, West Yorkshire BD1 1HY
Telephone Bradford 29577

Availability

Language
Fortran DG Nova Code

Computer
ICL 1904A
32K core

219

Program name
CADRAW

Abstract
This is a suite of programs designed to produce working drawings through a drum plotter or a storage tube screen. The process is such that grid lines and zones are initially set up, followed by combinations of macros (frequently used shapes) and basic shapes, positioned relative to the grid. Information is entered and altered by batch runs (using punched cards), interactively (using a typewriter terminal), or via the storage tube screen

References

Source
Ove Arup and Partners
13 Fitzroy Street
London W1
UK
Telephone 01–636 1531

Availability
Bureau service

Language
Fortran

Computer
DEC 10

220

Program name
HIDDEN LINES

Abstract
Enables objects defined by use of the THINGS software to be viewed from specific locations with lines for construction only suppressed. Perspective views are greatly enhanced by this technique. It is particularly suitable for bridge and highway design

References
THINGS

Source
Scicon Computer Services Limited
Brick Close, Kiln Farm
Milton Keynes MK11 3EJ
UK
Telephone 0908 565656 Telex 826171

Availability
Bureau service. Available in USA

Language
Fortran

Computer
Univac 1108

221

Program name
SPEED

Abstract
This suite of programs examines the effect of building construction, room size, and orientation on the thermal and visual conditions. The program dealing with daylight evaluation is based on an approximation of the CIE Standard Overcast Sky. A simplified form of the BRE split-flux method is used for the calculation of the reflected component and the luminance of outside surfaces is assumed to be 20 per cent of that of the sky

References
DOC Evaluation Report No 3

Source
Dr A J Baxter, Department of Building
Sheffield Polytechnic, Pond Street
Sheffield S1 1WB
Telephone 0742 20911

Availability
See DOC Report No 3

Language
Fortran IV

Computer
Honeywell Mk III

222

Program name
ROOMS

Abstract
This program generates plans for layouts of rooms in spaces where circulation is predetermined

References

Source
University of Arizona, College of Architecture
Tempe
Arizona
USA

Availability

Language

Computer
DEC 10

223

Program name
SOM

Abstract
This program generates plans of modular spaces within a fixed area of a building

References

Source
University of Arizona, College of Architecture
Tempe
Arizona
USA

Availability
Remote batch

Language

Computer
CDC 6400

224

Program name
HLEIN

Abstract
This program simplifies the definition of an object in a form intelligible to a program for perspective drawing. It provides a conversational means of data input and allows definition of a body and repetition of it as many times as required, shifting and scaling it in all directions and rotating it about a vertical axis. Up to eleven different bodies can be so defined

References
DOC

Source
ABACUS Services
University of Strathclyde
131 Rottenrow
Glasgow
Telephone 041–552 4400 ext 3021

Availability

Language
Univac Fortran V

Computer
UNIVAC 1106

225

Program name
AO15

Abstract
This program produces true perspective drawings from building dimensions. True isometric drawings may also be produced

References

Source
Albert Kahn Associates
New Center Building
Detroit, Michigan 48202
USA
Telephone 313 871 8500

Availability

Language
Fortran IV

Computer
IBM 1130

226

Program name
2–DG

Abstract
This is a set of standard routines which provide simple graphics facilities for Tektronix storage tubes and a range of plotters

References

Source
ARC Limited
4 Jesus Lane
Cambridge CB5 8BA
UK
Telephone 0223 65015

Availability
Purchase

Language
Fortran

Computer
Prime 300

227

Program name
GINO-F

Abstract
This is a library of routines for plotting. Suitable for commercial, architectural and engineering applications, and capable of driving most types of graphic device, including Tektronix screens, flatbed and drum plotters, and various time-sharing plotters

References

Source
Atkins Computing Services Limited
Woodcote Grove, Ashley Road
Epsom, Surrey
UK
Telephone Epsom 40421

Availability
Bureau service, time-sharing. Available in Netherlands

Language
Fortran

Computer
Honeywell Sigma 9

228

Program name
DYNADRAW

Abstract
One of a suite of detailing programs, this program is used to display and manipulate designs stored as digital models by DYNADATA. Hidden lines can be removed partially or completely and the model may be viewed in perspective from any point. Outputs may be directed to various graphics devices. The company (or its agents) will undertake implementation, testing, maintenance and updating of the program

References

Source
Computer Aided Design Centre
Madingley Road
Cambridge CB3 0HB
Cambridgeshire UK

Availability
Hire

Language
Fortran

Computer

229

Program name
GINOGRAF

Abstract
A graph, histogram, bar and pie charting system, using GINO-F for displaying data. The program is capable of both single-call routines and multiple-graph choices of axes, raster and scales. These facilities can be extended by the use of GINO-F transformation and viewing routines. The company (or its agents) will undertake the implementation, testing, maintenance and updating of the program

References

Source
Computer Aided Design Centre
Madingley Road
Cambridge CB3 0HB
Cambridgeshire UK

Availability
Hire (to GINO-F licensees only)

Language
Fortran

Computer

230

Program name
DYNASHADE

Abstract
The program computes and outputs perspective views of three-dimensional objects, imparting grey-tone shaded areas as required. The user controls the data-defining angles, vanishing points, grey tones and light source. The viewing angle can be varied so that a 'filmed' effect may be produced. Output can be directed to any suitable graphics device with at least sixteen levels of shading. DYNADATA output is used for input data

References

Source
Computer Aided Design Centre
Madingley Road
Cambridge CB3 0HB
Cambridgeshire UK

Availability
Hire

Language
Fortran

Computer

Program name
GINO-F

Abstract
A library of routines for building batch or interactive graphics programs. The program is used to display data prepared by related programs, GINOZONE and GINOGRAF, and is in general use throughout the construction industry where graphic output is required. Viewing features include two-dimensional, three-dimensional and perspective viewing. The company (or its agents) will undertake the implementation and updating of the program

References

Source
Computer Aided Design Centre
Madingley Road
Cambridge CB3 0HB
Cambridgeshire UK

Availability
Hire

Language
Fortran

Computer

232

Program name
VIEW

Abstract
This program is designed to plot isometric and perspective views of three-dimensional structures. Viewing points and centres of vision are variable. The drawing is output entirely on the plotter, and there are options to label nodes, joints, lines and members with their respective numbers. There is, however, no way of specifying where plane surfaces of solids exist and therefore no suppression of hidden lines

References

Source
Faber Computer Operations Limited
Upper Marlborough Road
St Albans
Herts AL1 3UT
Telephone St Albans 61222

Availability
Bureau service

Language

Computer
IBM 1130, System 7

233

Program name
FIBS

Abstract
The programs COLO (cooling load/temperature prediction), CPCON (continuous beam analysis), DAFA (daylighting) and VIEW (perspective viewing) have been linked to create an interactive building design program. The geometry of any building is input via a graphic tablet and may be viewed from any position on the visual display unit. Subsequently, any room in the building may be analysed for cooling temperatures, ventilation or daylight

References

Source
Faber Computer Operations Limited
Upper Marlborough Road
St Albans
Herts UK
Telephone St Albans 61222

Availability
Bureau service

Language

Computer
IBM 1130, System 7

234

Program name
PERS

Abstract
This program is part of a computer-based architectural modelling system. It draws perspectives from user-defined eye point, focus point and angle of view. The perspective drawn can have hidden lines removed or shown. In addition, surfaces can have half-tone shading, and shadows for a specific time of day, day of year and latitude. The object is defined in terms of distinct polyhedra

References
DOC

Source
Computer Unit, School of Architecture and Landscape
Leeds Polytechnic
Brunswick Terrace
Leeds 2
Telephone 0532 462222

Availability
By arrangement

Language
Fortran

Computer
Nova 1200

235

Program name
SUE

Abstract
This system produces drawings from simple instructions based on English words (or initials) and measurements. The system draws what the user has previously drawn, and can then draw it in any form with differing dimensions and scale. The system is particularly appropriate for drawings with some degree of repetition, such as working drawings. Each drawing is stored in the computer's version of the instruction language

References

Source
Liverpool Polytechnic, Department of Architecture
53 Victoria Street
Liverpool L1 6EY
UK
Telephone 051–709 0571

Availability
Purchase or hire

Language

Computer
Data General

236

Program name
AUTOPROD

Abstract
This program provides an instrument for three-dimensional presentation of objects, showing perspective or axonometric views on to any defined plane. Obscured lines are shown dotted or are omitted. Sections can also be drawn. The results are drawn on a storage tube or plotter

References
DOC Evaluation Report No 1

Source
Department of Land Surveying
North-East London Polytechnic
Forest Road
London E17 4JB
Telephone 01–527 2272

Availability

Language
Fortran

Computer
Univac 1108 and others

237

Program name
DISSPLA (Display Integrated Software System and Plotting Language)

Abstract
This program is a library of sub-routines (costing, statistics, planning and control, data analysis) for general-purpose graphic representation of data. Its features include linear, log, polar axes and curve interpolation, as well as 3–D surface plotting. A program calling DISSPLA produces a diagram plus a self-explanatory line-printer summary. Input data is usually visible graphically on output diagram

References

Source
Repko bv
van Blankenburgstraat 58
The Hague
Netherlands
Telephone 070–608425

Availability
License; monthly rental; also from SIA London, CDC Kronos and Comshare

Language
Fortran
Can be linked as for Fortran

Computer
IBM 360, 370
Univac 1100
PDP 10
CDC 6000, 7000, Cyber

238

Program name
THINGS

Abstract
A collection of sub-routines using Fortran, held in a library, which allows the user to define simply a three-dimensional model. Basic shapes (eg box, cylinder, sphere, pyramid, cone) can be scaled and positioned at particular locations in a three-dimensional co-ordinate system

References
HIDDEN LINES

Source
Scicon Computer Services Limited
Brick Close, Kiln Farm
Milton Keynes MK11 3EJ
UK
Telephone 0908 565656 Telex 826171

Availability
Bureau service. Available in USA

Language
Fortran

Computer
Univac 1108

239

Program name
Terminal control system

Abstract
A software package used in the operation of Tektronix graphics terminals. It enables a programmer to produce elementary computer graphics immediately, and also to develop sophisticated interactive systems. It is also a suitable basis for applications programs

References

Source
Tektronix UK Limited
PO Box 69, Harpenden
Herts AL5 4UP
UK
Telephone Harpenden 63141 Telex 25559

Availability
Contact owner. Also available in USA, Holland, Japan, Australia, Canada

Language
Fortran IV

Computer
Available for most computers with a minimum of 2K core

240

Program name
OTOTROL

Abstract
This program produces perspective drawings on a plotter. Plans, elevations and isometric drawings can all be handled. Lines which would be hidden are eliminated from the drawings

References

Source
University of Arizona, College of Architecture
Tempe
Arizona
USA

Availability
Remote batch

Language

Computer
CDC 6400

Program name
SYMVU

Abstract
This program produces two-dimensional drawings on a plotter

References

Source
University of Arizona, College of Architecture
Tempe
Arizona
USA

Availability
Remote batch

Language

Computer
CDC 6400

242

Program name
FORMS

Abstract
This program transforms irregular forms into regular

References

Source
University of Arizona, College of Architecture
Tempe
Arizona
USA

Availability

Language

Computer
DEC 10

243

Program name
GRADIS-F, GRADIS-A

Abstract
This is a package of sub-routines, providing a large number of functions, which allow the user to display shapes on a visual display unit. With slight modifications, graphic output may be produced

References

Source
User Group Software, CTL
Eaton Road, Hemel Hempstead
Hertfordshire HP2 7EQ
UK

Availability
Purchase

Language
GRADIS-F, Fortran
GRADIS-A, Algol 68S

Computer

244

Program name
DHIST

Abstract
This system produces three-dimensional drawings of histograms and surfaces which are defined as two-dimensional matrices. Data will be accepted as a matrix or as values at random points. Continuous or angular surface representations may be produced

References

Source
ARC Limited
4 Jesus Lane
Cambridge CB5 8BA
UK
Telephone 0223 65015

Availability
Purchase

Language
Fortran

Computer
Prime 300

245

Program name
CIIS (Contouring, Interpolation and Integration System)

Abstract
This is a system for manipulating functions of two variables which are specified only at randomly spaced points. General-purpose graphic representation of the function is produced in the form of contour maps. Specific purposes depend on the function being manipulated. For example, when the function is a description of ground levels over a building site, cut and fill volumes can be calculated

References

Source
ARC Limited
4 Jesus Lane
Cambridge CB5 8BA
UK
Telephone 0223 65015

Availability
Purchase

Language
Fortran

Computer
Prime 300

246

Program name
NETMAP

Abstract
This system is for manipulation, analysis and mapping of network-based data. A basic data file is created, which may be manipulated, checked or restructured. Shortest routes or critical paths through the network can be isolated. Maps of selected parts of the network can be output

References

Source
ARC Limited
4 Jesus Lane
Cambridge CB5 8BA
UK
Telephone 0223 65015

Availability
Purchase

Language
Fortran

Computer
Prime 300

247

Program name
OVERLAY

Abstract
This system allows a user to overlay a square grid on a map of polygonal areas. This is created using POLYMAP. The scale of the grid is defined by the user

References

Source
ARC Limited
4 Jesus Lane
Cambridge CB5 8BA
UK
Telephone 0223 65015

Availability
Purchase

Language
Fortran

Computer
Prime 300

248

Program name
POINTMAP

Abstract
This system is for the manipulation and mapping of point-referenced data. Information about the objects can be merged with the file containing the point-references. Objects with values that satisfy user-defined conditions, or which lie within particular rectangles, polygons or circles, or on a particular path, can be selectively retrieved. These can be tabulated or displayed as a map

References

Source
ARC Limited
4 Jesus Lane
Cambridge CB5 8BA
UK
Telephone 0223 65015

Availability
Purchase

Language
Fortran

Computer
Prime 300

249

Program name
POLYMAP

Abstract
This is a system for the manipulation and mapping of data referenced to polygonal areas. This information can be displayed on computer-drawn maps. Display routines enter numerical data or symbolic markers, shade the map according to values given, map flows between areas or isolate an area of special interest

References

Source
ARC Limited
4 Jesus Lane
Cambridge CB5 8BA
UK
Telephone 0223 65015

Availability
Purchase

Language
Fortran

Computer
Prime 300

250

Program name
Frame analysis graphics

Abstract
This program enables the user to check and edit design data visually before running a frame analysis program, and to display results using GINO-F. Input is the data file for ICL PLANE, FRAME and GRIDS programs. The program gives editable and graphic representation of frame geometry, support conditions, loadings, moments, shears and deflections

References

Source
Computer Aided Design Centre
Madingley Road
Cambridge CB3 0HB
Cambridgeshire UK

Availability
Sale, hire

Language
Fortran

Computer
ICL 1904A

251

Program name
GINOZONE

Abstract
A zonal and interzonal desired-line mapping program which can produce a display of traffic flows or area data. The program is used to prepare fixed input data for display by GINO-F, used in conjunction with GINOZONE. The Company (or its agents) will undertake the implementation, testing, maintenance and updating of the program

References

Source
Computer Aided Design Centre
Madingley Road
Cambridge CB3 0HB
Cambridgeshire UK

Availability
Hire

Language
Fortran

Computer

252

Program name
General Purpose Contouring Program

Abstract
This program displays, in the form of contour maps on a plotter, functions or surfaces which are dependent on two independent variables. Applications include surveying and stress mapping. The function or surface can be specified in grid form or at random points. Areas can be specified in which the contours are not to be plotted or in which they are to be plotted as special lines. Skewed, rotated and inverted co-ordinate systems can be specified

References
NBRI (SA) abstract X/BOU-COMP 4. The program was developed by CALCOMP

Source
Computer Centre, University of the Witwatersrand, Milner Park
Johannesburg
South Africa
Telephone Johannesburg 724–7009

Availability
Bureau service

Language

Computer

253

Program name
CARTA

Abstract
This program analyses random-point data gathered by field surveying or aerial photogrammetry in order to produce plotted contour maps. Maps are based on a triangulation algorithm rather than a 'best fit' or grid transformation method and the program ensures that each contour line passes on the correct side of each data point. The results are output with the original data included

References

Source
Idan Computers Ltd
3A Yitzhak Sadeh Street
PO Box 33390
Tel-Aviv, Israel
Telephone 30726 39419

Availability
Bureau service

Language
Fortran IV

Computer

254

Program name
MEDALS

Abstract
A graphics system which allows high-quality engineering and architectural drawings to be produced from user-defined data inputs. The system provides control of reference axes, scales and units, and the manipulation of pre-defined draughting modules. Basic modules provide elementary draughting facilities. User-defined routines are used to express repeated units. The program may be operated from batch, teletype or graphics terminal

References
Developed by CADC, incorporating GINO-F graphics package

Source
Scicon Computer Services Limited
Brick Close, Kiln Farm
Milton Keynes MK11 3EJ
UK
Telephone 0908 565656 Telex 826171

Availability
Bureau service. Available in USA

Language
Fortran

Computer
Univac 1108

255

Program name
SYMAP

Abstract
These programs produce three types of map: conformant, contour and proximal. Conformant or choropleth (SYM 1) are best suited to quantitative or qualitative data, the area limits of which are significant. Contour or isoline maps consist of closed curves which connect all points with the same value. In proximal maps the spatial units are defined by 'nearest neighbour' methods

References
Developed at NW University and Harvard

Source
The National Computing Centre Limited
Oxford Road
Manchester M1 7ED
UK
Telephone 061–228 6333Telex 668962

Availability
Conformant, purchase; contour and proximal, bureau service

Language

Computer
Conformant mapping only:
ICL 1900, System 4
IBM 360, 370
Honeywell
CDC
Univac

256

Program name
SITE

Abstract
This package gives a graphic representation of a given site which can be used to calculate the net site area. It is intended for use with appraisal programs ECOLE 3 and HELP. Input comprises a site file containing co-ordinates of spot heights, soil tests, services and other features, and a network file containing co-ordinates of roads and footpaths. Graphic output includes site boundary, soil-condition indices, contours and road networks

References
ECOLE 3, HELP
ABACUS Occasional Paper No 61 (SITE)

Source
ABACUS studies
University of Strathclyde
131 Rottenrow, Glasgow G4 ONG
UK
Telephone 041–552 4400 ext 3021

Availability
Purchase, hire, bureau service

Language
Fortran IV

Computer
Univac 1108
Tektronix graphics terminal

257

Program name
Traverse computation

Abstract
This program corrects angular measurements made in traverse and calculates co-ordinates of stations in traverse

References
Program made available by ICL

Source
Computel Limited
Eastern Road
Bracknell, Berkshire
UK
Telephone Bracknell 23031

Availability

Language

Computer

258

Program name
CHART

Abstract
A set of programs for calculating and plotting positions of survey paths

References
GEOCOMP

Source
Computel Limited
Eastern Road
Bracknell, Berkshire
UK
Telephone Bracknell 23031

Availability

Language

Computer

259

Program name
COGO

Abstract
A program, for use by civil engineers, surveyors, etc who have no previous experience with computers, to assist in survey calculations, design of roads and highways, setting out of sites, and subdivision and adjustment of areas. The command language requires no knowledge of exact command forms on the part of the user, who may request detailed instructions from the program. The language includes capabilities for a variety of applications

References

Source
CRC Engineering Services
83 Clerkenwell Road
London
EC1R 5HP
Telephone 01–242 0747

Availability

Language

Computer

260

Program name
GEONET

Abstract
A program for the determination and adjustment of medium– to large-scale surveying networks. The program computes the approximate co-ordinates of new points, based upon known points in a COGO data table. Computation may be based on one of four methods. Data may be input interactively or from a data file

References
Based on IBM 1130 Geodetic Network Adjustment program

Source
CRC Engineering Services
83 Clerkenwell Road
London
EC1R 5HP
Telephone 01–242 0747

Availability

Language

Computer

Program name
PROPX

Abstract
The program calculates the combined section properties of any area specified by the co-ordinates of its corner points. By numerical integration the program calculates properties for the total area specified about the given axes, about axes through the centroid parallel to those given, and about the principal axes

References

Source
Faber Computer Operations Limited
Upper Marlborough Road
St Albans
Herts AL1 3UT
Telephone St Albans 61222

Availability
Bureau service

Language

Computer
IBM 1130, System 7

262

Program name
COCA

Abstract
This program calculates the co-ordinates of the vertices of a quadrilateral triangulation. It ensures (by correction) that the sum of the angles is equal to 360°, that the sum of the outer two angles of opposite triangles are equal and then makes the log (sine) correction. The co-ordinates of the vertices are then calculated and the lengths of all the sides are computed. The input form is a single self-explanatory pro-forma sheet

References

Source
Faber Computer Operations Limited
Upper Marlborough Road
St Albans
Herts AL1 3UT
Telephone St Albans 61222

Availability
Bureau service

Language

Computer
IBM 1130, System 7

263

Program name
PACE

Abstract
This program calculates the closing error of a close traverse survey by the Bowditch method, and deals with SI or Imperial units. It will accept up to 20 stations for a survey which may be open or closed. The final closing error is output along with the position of the survey in the overall grid system. Both uncorrected and corrected co-ordinates are given along with the closing error

References

Source
Faber Computer Operations Limited
Upper Marlborough Road
St Albans
Herts AL1 3UT
Telephone St Albans 61222

Availability
Bureau service

Language

Computer
IBM 1130, System 7

264

Program name
COGO

Abstract
This program makes co-ordinate geometry calculations. A problem is specified by the engineer in terms of a set of instructions, which are printed out with the results. These results may also be plotted and labelled as a supplement to the printed results

References

Source
Faber Computer Operations Limited
Upper Marlborough Road
St Albans
Herts AL1 3UT
Telephone St Albans 61222

Availability
Bureau service

Language

Computer
IBM 1130, System 7

265

Program name
NST

Abstract
This suite of programs is designed for applications which require the quantitative description of surfaces. By making numerical or analytical approximations to a set of co-ordinate values defining a surface, contour maps can be plotted. Real or hypothetical surfaces may be dealt with. These may include geographical heights, illuminated surfaces, temperatures, stress distributions and strata thicknesses

References

Source
Faber Computer Operations Limited
Upper Marlborough Road
St Albans
Herts UK
Telephone St Albans 61222

Availability
Bureau service

Language

Computer
IBM 1130, System 7

266

Program name
XSECS

Abstract
This program calculates the area of cross-section from rod readings

References
Mark III software library
User manual 5202·18

Source
Honeywell Information Systems Limited
114 to 118 Southampton Row
London WC1B 5AB
UK
Telephone 01–242 5725

Availability
Bureau service

Language
Basic

Computer
Honeywell 6000 series

267

Program name
TRAVRS

Abstract
This program analyses all problems associated with survey traverses. It provides closure error, linear precision, length of traverse, station co-ordinates, error distribution and traverse area. It also analyses traverses where the bearing or distance of one or two of the courses is unknown. Versions are also available which solve traverses with up to 150 curved courses (TRAV1S) and which calculate errors of closure for curved courses (TRCLO and TRADJS)

References
Mark III software library
User manuals 5202·01 and 5202·21

Source
Honeywell Information Systems Limited
114 to 118 Southampton Row
London WC1B 5AB
UK
Telephone 01–242 5725

Availability
Bureau service

Language
Basic

Computer
Honeywell 6000 series

268

Program name
TERRA

Abstract
This program is designed to retrieve longitudinal and cross-sectional data along given horizontal alignments, based on the contoured ground model calculated by CARTA, a linked land-survey program. Optional facilities are grid evaluation and plotting of perspective and axonometric views of the terrain

References

Source
Idan Computers Ltd
3A Yitzhak Sadeh Street
PO Box 33390
Tel-Aviv, Israel
Telephone 30726 39419

Availability
Bureau service

Language
Fortran IV

Computer

269

Program name
Grid transformation

Abstract
A grid, on which the known co-ordinates of a number of survey stations are based, is rotated, though not necessarily about its origin. This program calculates the new co-ordinates of the stations from one of three given cases

References

Source
Laing Computing Services
Elstree Way
Borehamwood
Hertfordshire
WD6 1NF UK
Telephone 01–207 2000

Availability
Sale, bureau service

Language
Fortran

Computer
IBM 370–50

270

Program name
Station setting out

Abstract
This program calculates the angle and distance from a number of reference lines to each of several field stations. Each reference line is defined by two points for which co-ordinates are known. The co-ordinates of each field station must be given

References

Source
Laing Computing Services
Elstree Way
Borehamwood
Hertfordshire
WD6 1NF UK
Telephone 01–207 2000

Availability
Sale, bureau service

Language
Fortran

Computer
IBM 370–50

271

Program name
COGO

Abstract
Starting with one or more known points, the co-ordinates of other points can be established. The new co-ordinates are stored by the program and may be used, in turn, to locate further points. The program will handle linear and angular relationships, circular arcs and transitional curves (spirals), vertical curves (parabolas), the evaluation of areas, and adjustment of traverse. The results can be printed or output using a data-plotting program

References

Source
Laing Computing Services
Elstree Way
Borehamwood
Hertfordshire
WD6 1NF UK
Telephone 01–207 2000

Availability
Sale, bureau service

Language
Fortran

Computer
IBM 370–50

272

Program name
Land Survey

Abstract
This program accepts and validates measurements made during a site survey, and performs the calculations and corrections necessary to produce a printed listing of all the stations, their co-ordinates and, in some cases, levels, bearings and lengths. The results are also available for use by a data-plotting program, and as a punched paper tape for transmission

References

Source
Laing Computing Services
Elstree Way
Borehamwood
Hertfordshire
WD6 1NF UK
Telephone 01–207 2000

Availability
Sale, bureau service

Language
Fortran

Computer
IBM 370–50

273

Program name
LAMSAC Application code 32164952240A

Abstract
This is an interactive program for setting out co-ordinates for civil engineers and surveyors

References
LAMSAC

Source
Architect's Department, Leicestershire County Council
County Hall, Glenfield
Leicester LE3 8RA
Telephone Leicester 871313

Availability

Language
Fortran

Computer
UNIVAC 1106; 8K core; 1 disc drive

274

Program name
LAMSAC Application code 32155422380A

Abstract
This program provides a site recording and plotting system. The slow peripheral unit used is a graph plotter. The program was implemented in 1974

References
LAMSAC

Source
Architect's Department, West Sussex County Council
County Hall, West Street
Chichester, West Sussex PO19 1RQ
Telephone Chichester 85100

Availability

Language
Fortran PL/1

Computer
IBM 370/155; 90K core; 1 magnetic tape unit; 1 disc drive

275

Program name
RGSP (Rothamsted general survey program)

Abstract
A program for the construction, manipulation and printing of multi-way tables from survey data. Hierarchical data structures can be handled. Data can be accepted at one time or in successive batches, and late returns and amendments accommodated. Data may be input from cards, paper tape or existing computer files. All common types of card coding, including multiple punching, are acceptable

References

Source
RGSP Secretariat, Computer and Statistics Department
Rothamsted Experimental Station
Harpenden, Herts AL5 2JQ
UK
Telephone 058 2762271

Availability
On lease

Language
Fortran

Computer
ICL Sytem 470, 370
CDC 6600, 7600
Version for ICL 1900 and 2900 under development

276

Program name
FASTPLOT

Abstract
A graphics system for the operation of incremental plotters at high speed via a low-speed Post Office line

References
Developed by the Production Engineering Research Association

Source
Scicon Computer Services Limited
Brick Close, Kiln Farm
Milton Keynes MK11 3EJ
UK
Telephone 0908 565656 Telex 826171

Availability
Bureau service. Available in USA

Language
Fortran

Computer
Univac 1108

Civil engineering

Bridges
Continuous beams
Foundations, retaining walls
Earthworks
Highways
Waterways
Other

277

Program name
PRELOAD

Abstract
This program generates values for the equivalent loading on a bridge decking member to represent the pre-stressing force. It is one of a suite of analysis programs. It will take friction losses and wobble factors into account, if required. Output provides load data for LEAP

References

Source
Computer Consortium Service Ltd
5 Windmill Street
London W1P 1HF
UK
Telephone 01–638 3118

Availability
Bureau service

Language
Fortran

Computer
CDC
IBM
PDP

278

Program name
GMESH

Abstract
This program provides automatic generation of data on grillage mesh for bridge deck analysis. It is one of a suite of analysis programs. It is used to prepare data for LEAP from a concise statement of bridge geometry, thereby giving the LEAP user a pre-processing data check

References

Source
Computer Consortium Services Ltd
5 Windmill Street
London W1P 1HF
UK
Telephone 01–638 3118

Availability
Bureau service

Language
Fortran

Computer
CDC
IBM
PDP

279

Program name
HLOAD

Abstract
This bridge design program is one of a suite of analysis programs. It calculates influence lines and critical positions of vehicles along continuous beams or plane frames. Outputs include maximum moments with related shears (and vice versa) at one-tenth centres along each beam, plots and reactions. Calculations are to BS 153:1972

References

Source
Computer Consortium Services Ltd
5 Windmill Street
London W1P 1HF
UK
Telephone 01–638 3118

Availability
Bureau service

Language
Fortran

Computer
CDC
IBM
PDP

280

Program name
Bridge suite

Abstract
These programs solve the erection conditions for the following bridge types: continuous beams; slabs, using finite-element, grillage and space-frame techniques; box girders and suspension and curved bridges. Pre-processors generate structure geometry, support conditions and loading. Post-processors can be used for creating and merging files, combining loading conditions and producing maximum forces

References
ECLIPSE program library

Source
Electronic Calculus Limited
344 to 350 Euston Road
London NW1 3BJ UK
Telephone 01–388 7705, Telex 27192

Availability
Purchase, hire, bureau service

Language
Fortran V

Computer
Univac 1106, 1108
CDC 6600, 7600
DEC System 10
IBM
ICL

281

Program name
Bridge/1

Abstract
This sub-system enables an engineer to analyse bridges which, when the effect of the distribution of transverse loads is ignored, can be considered as continuous beams. A bridge may be of constant or varying cross-section, with an inclined or horizontal surface. Any degree of stiffness can be applied to elastic supports, to meet site and construction requirements

References
GENESYS program library

Source
GENESYS Limited
Pennine House, Lemyngton Street
Loughborough, Leicestershire
LE11 1XA UK
Telephone 0509 39185 Telex 341747

Availability
Bureau service, hire

Language
Gentran

Computer
CDC 6500, 6600, 7600
DEC 10
Honeywell 6000
IBM 360, 370
ICL 1900, System 4
Philips P1400
PRIME 300
Univac 1100

282

Program name
Slab-bridge/1

Abstract
This sub-system enables an engineer to analyse the finite elements of concrete bridge-slab (or slab-and-beam) structures. It is suitable for most bridges of regular or semi-regular shape, including those with arbitrary support conditions such as elastic bearings

References
GENESYS program library

Source
GENESYS Limited
Pennine House, Lemyngton Street
Loughborough, Leicestershire
Telephone 0509 39185 Telex 341747

Availability
Bureau service, hire

Language
Gentran

Computer
CDC 6500, 6600, 7600
DEC 10
Honeywell 6000
IBM 360, 370
ICL 1900, System 4
Philips P1400
PRIME 300
Univac 1100

283

Program name
Suspension bridge flutter program

Abstract
This program calculates the critical wind speed which induces flutter in suspension bridges

References

Source
UMIST
Department of Civil and Structural Engineering
PO Box 88, Manchester
UK
Telephone 061 236 3311

Availability
Sale or hire negotiable

Language
Fortran

Computer
CDC 7600

284

Program name
Suspension bridge dynamic relaxation program

Abstract
This program calculates natural modes and frequencies of vibration of three-span suspension bridges. Torsional, coupled and both vertical and lateral flexural vibrations can be calculated

References

Source
UMIST
Department of Civil and Structural Engineering
PO Box 88, Manchester
UK
Telephone 061 236 3311

Availability

Language
Fortran

Computer
CDC 7600

285

Program name
Suspension bridge program

Abstract
This program carries out non-linear elastic analysis of suspension bridges and other cable structures (for example, cable roofs and guyed masts). Analysis is three-dimensional. The program takes account of slack hinges and open joints

References

Source
UMIST
Department of Civil and Structural Engineering
PO Box 88, Manchester
UK
Telephone 061 236 3311

Availability
Sale or hire negotiable

Language
Algol 60

Computer
CDC 7600

286

Program name
BADS

Abstract
The program analyses continuous beams (including cantilevers) which must be of prismatic section throughout. Section profiles may be T or rectangular, and dimensions may differ in each span. Input data should include support type and width, span type and length, physical dimensions, loading, and covers to steel. Outputs (in tabular form) give moments and steel requirements for maximum moments, shears, support reactions, warnings and failure indicators

References

Source
Building Computer Services Limited
Bush House
72 Prince Street
Bristol BS1 4HU
Telephone 0272 290651

Availability
Bureau service, hire

Language

Computer

287

Program name
Multi-span beam analysis

Abstract
This program analyses continuous beams by automatically applying the correct combination of load factors for any specified load case without the need for re-entering the loads. The load factors may be standard (to BS CP 110:1972) or specified

References

Source
Camutek
39 Newnham Road
Cambridge CB3 9EY
UK
Telephone Cambridge (0223) 69686

Availability
From owner

Language
Basic

Computer
Hewlett-Packard
9830 (2k) or (6k)

288

Program name
Continuous beam analysis

Abstract
A program to determine the distribution of bending moments, shear force and deflections along a continuous beam subject to specified loads

References
Program made available by ICL

Source
Computel Limited
Eastern Road
Bracknell, Berkshire
UK
Telephone Bracknell 23031

Availability

Language

Computer

289

Program name
PRESBEAM

Abstract
This analysis program will calculate the prestressing forces on continuous beam designs of variable cross-section, enabling the user to check the validity of chosen sections and tendon layouts and arrive at a satisfactory design. Input data includes beam geometry and section properties as well as bending moments and any built-in stresses. Outputs may be directed to a direct-view storage tube, a plotter or a line printer

References

Source
Computer Aided Design Centre
Madingley Road
Cambridge CB3 0HB
Cambridgeshire UK

Availability
Sale, hire

Language
Fortran

Computer
Prime 3000

290

Program name
CONBEM

Abstract
A program for the analysis of continuous beams, up to seven spans, simply supported but with varying cross-sectional areas within any span. The program takes account of settlement at supports and cantilevers at either end, and can be used for on-line input, display and amendment of data. Output may be selected by the user from tables of moments, forces and reactions for up to seven internal points along a span

References
Program developed by Highways Engineering Computer Branch of the Department of the Environment

Source
CRC Engineering Services
83 Clerkenwell Road
London EC1R 5HP
Telephone 01-242 0747

Availability

Language

Computer

291

Program name
CPCON

Abstract
This program analyses and designs continuous beams in accordance with BS CP114:1969. It simulates the load conditions of alternate and adjacent spans, and for any support conditions evaluates the support reactions and the moment and shear force at the end of each span. Bending moment and shear force envelopes are generated along with designated areas of steel reinforcement, calculated at critical stations in each span

References

Source
Faber Computer Operations Limited
Upper Marlborough Road
St Albans
Herts AL1 3UT
Telephone St Albans 61222

Availability
Bureau service

Language

Computer
IBM 1130, System 7

292

Program name
GCPCN

Abstract
This program analyses and designs continuous beams in accordance with BS CP114:1969 and is substantially the same as program CPCON, except that complex live and dead loads may be specified. Any number and combination of point, uniform and trapezoidal loads may be specified on each span for both the dead and live loading conditions. Results are identical in layout to CPCON

References

Source
Faber Computer Operations Limited
Upper Marlborough Road
St Albans
Herts AL1 3UT
Telephone St Albans 61222

Availability
Bureau service

Language

Computer
IBM 1130, System 7

293

Program name
CP110–BEAMS/1

Abstract
This sub-system enables an engineer to analyse and design continuous, reinforced-concrete beams in accordance with BS CP110:Part 1:1972. The method used is one of sub-frame analysis, and includes column lifts. Line loading patterns are automatically applied. Moment redistribution is effected by user control

References
GENESYS program library

Source
GENESYS Limited
Pennine House, Lemyngton Street
Loughborough, Leicestershire
LE11 1XA UK
Telephone 0509 39185 Telex 341747

Availability
Bureau service, hire

Language
Gentran

Computer
CDC 6500, 6600, 7600
DEC 10
Honeywell 6000
IBM 360, 370
ICL 1900, System 4
Philips P1400
PRIME 300
Univac 1100

294

Program name
Continuous beams I

Abstract
This program calculates stress and moments in a continuous beam with a given load. Loads may be horizontal or vertical or trapeze loads

References
Danish Building Research Institute
Abstract 48 11 601

Source
Geodata A/S
Dagmarhus
HC Andersens Boulevard 7
1553 Copenhagen V
Denmark

Availability
Bureau service

Language

Computer

295

Program name
Wheel train and continuous beams

Abstract
This program calculates the maximum stress in a continuous beam with a given load train. Stress contours, to be used as part of input, can be calculated by Continuous Beams II

References
Danish Building Research Institute
Abstract 48 11 603

Source
Geodata A/S
Dagmarhus
HC Andersens Boulevard 7
1553 Copenhagen V
Denmark

Availability
Bureau service

Language

Computer

296

Program name
Continuous beams II

Abstract
This program calculates stress and tension at points in continuous beams for given loads. Stress contours, which may be used as part of input for Wheel train and continuous beams, are also calculated

References
Danish Building Research Institute
Abstract 48 11 602

Source
Geodata A/S
Dagmarhus
HC Andersens Boulevard 7
1553 Copenhagen V
Denmark

Availability
Bureau service

Language

Computer

297

Program name
Influence lines

Abstract
This program calculates influence lines and evaluates shears, moments and support reactions for given loads. Beams may be from two to ten spans. Loads may be trapezoidal or point, live or dead. The program evaluates the influence lines for a moving load, such as a truck or train, comprising trapezoidal and point loads. Influence lines can be allocated a file number and stored on cassette

References

Source
Hewlett-Packard Limited
King Street Lane, Winnersh
Wokingham, Berks RG11 5AR
UK
Telephone Wokingham 784774

Availability
Purchase

Language
Basic

Computer
HP 830A with
3808–word memory
9865A tape cassette

298

Program name
Continuous beams

Abstract
This program deals with continuous beams of up to ten spans. Loads can be trapezoidal or point, live or dead (chequerboard loading is used). Point moments may also be used. It calculates maximum and minimum moments, shears for chosen points and support reactions. It calculates the reinforcement needed for the moments and shears to certain national standards. Sections may be slab, rectangular or T beam

References

Source
Hewlett-Packard Limited
King Street Lane, Winnersh
Wokingham, Berks RG11 5AR
UK
Telephone Wokingham 784774

Availability
Purchase

Language
Basic

Computer
HP 9830A with
3808–word memory

299

Program name
CONBEM

Abstract
This program, which is maintained by the DoE, is for the elastic analysis of continuous beams using the flexibility- or influence-coefficient method. It can handle up to seven spans, which may have constant or variable section members with any combination of point loads, distributed loads, applied moments, varying prestressing forces and temperature differentials. Prescribed displacements at the supports can also be included

References
CALL, IBM United Kingdom Limited

Source
Highway Engineering Computer Branch
Department of the Environment
St Christopher House
Southwark Street
London SE1, UK
Telephone 01–928 7999

Availability
Also available from IBM offices

Language

Computer

300

Program name
GIRDRS

Abstract
This program calculates reactions, shears and bending moments in continuous beams and girders subjected to unit loads. Beams of up to five spans can be dealt with

References
Mark III software library
User manual 5202·26

Source
Honeywell Information Systems Limited
114 to 118 Southampton Row
London WC1B 5AB
UK
Telephone 01–242 5725

Availability
Bureau service

Language
Basic

Computer
Honeywell 6000
series

301

Program name
CONDEFO

Abstract
This program calculates the deformation of a continuous beam of either constant or variable inertia. The left-hand end may be supported in one of the following ways, pin-jointed end, clamped end, shear-free clamped end or free end (cantilever). It calculates, at each end, the displacement of the point, the angle of the slope of the tangent at this point, the bending moment and the shear stress

References
CALL library

Source
IBM United Kingdom Limited
40 Basinghall Street
London EC2P 2DY
UK
Telephone 01–628 7700 Telex 884382

Availability
Also available from IBM offices
throughout the world

Language

Computer

Program name
CONBEAM

Abstract
This program analyses multiple-span continuous beams. Either prismatic or non-prismatic spans are admissible. Cantilevers may also be considered as part of the continuous beam. Uniform, partial or concentrated dead and live loads may be specified. Output consists of maximum and minimum column beam moments, maximum and minimum beam shears and information concerning the applied dead and live loads at each station

References
CALL library

Source
IBM United Kingdom Limited
40 Basinghall Street
London EC2P 2DY
UK
Telephone 01–628 7700 Telex 884382

Availability
Also available from IBM offices throughout the world

Language
Basic

Computer

303

Program name
Continuous beams 1

Abstract
This program analyses and designs continuous beams. It accepts as input the member properties of a multi-span continuous beam, together with the various loading conditions. Output gives the bending moments and shear forces, and their maximum and minimum envelope values, at each of a given number of equally spaced points along each member of the beam. The program accepts any combination of live loads and variable moments of inertia for each span

References

Source
Laing Computing Services
Elstree Way
Borehamwood
Hertfordshire
WD6 1NF, UK
Telephone 01–207 2000

Availability
Sale, bureau service

Language
Fortran

Computer
IBM 370–50

304

Program name
Continuous beams II

Abstract
This program accepts as input the member properties of a multi-span continuous beam, together with the various loading conditions. It calculates the deflection, rotation, bending moment and shear forces at all the following points along its length: at each support; at all points at which either a concentrated load or moment is applied; at each change of section; at specified intervals of length along the beam

References

Source
Laing Computing Services
Elstree Way
Borehamwood
Hertfordshire
WD6 1NF, UK
Telephone 01–207 2000

Availability
Sale, bureau service

Language
Fortran

Computer
IBM 370–50

305

Program name
Strip footing on elastic foundation

Abstract
This program performs an analysis of multi-span continuous beams resting on an elastic, discontinuous foundation material. A solution for the differential equation of the elastic line is obtained for each member together with the values of deflection, rotation, bending moment and shear forces at equally spaced points along the beam

References

Source
Laing Computing Services
Elstree Way
Borehamwood
Hertfordshire
WD6 1NF, UK
Telephone 01–207 2000

Availability
Sale, bureau service

Language
Fortran

Computer
IBM 370–50

306

Program name
AO1 Multispan beam

Abstract
This program calculates support moments for a continuous beam of up to fifteen main spans. The beam may have cantilevers at each end, or the ends may be fixed or pinned. All other supports (including those at cantilever ends) are treated as being simply supported. Each span may vary in length and stiffness, but is assumed to be prismatic. Any practical arrangement of vertical point loads and/or uniformly-distributed loads can be handled

References
A02 Simply supported beam with end moments. NBRI (South Africa) abstract X/BOU-COMP 5

Source
Metricomp Programmes (Pty) Limited
PO Box 4, Johannesburg
South Africa
Telephone Johannesburg 41-8501

Availability
Subscription service

Language

Computer
Hewlett-Packard 9820

307

Program name
PILE-3D/1

Abstract
This program analyses groups of piles, in three dimensions. Piles may be vertical or raked to any pattern. For each pile, the output gives the axial and shear forces, and bending and twisting moments, and a full listing of input data

References
Developed by GENESYS Ltd

Source
UCC, University Computing Company
344–350 Euston Road
London NW1
UK
Telephone 01–387 9661

Availability
Bureau service

Language
Fortran
Gentran

Computer

308

Program name
DSIGN

Abstract
The program comprises a series of linked sub-systems to process beams, columns and foundations, producing reports on final design, steel fixing details, bar schedules and steel, concrete and shuttering quantities. Data may be prepared using related programs. Outputs for beams and columns comprise a table of design requirements, while pad foundation fixing details are in tabular form and bar schedules are as for beams and columns

References

Source
Building Computer Services Limited
Bush House
72 Prince Street
Bristol BS1 4HU
Telephone 0272 290651

Availability
Bureau service, hire

Language

Computer

309

Program name
Concrete-pad foundation design

Abstract
This program designs reinforced-concrete pad-foundations to resist specified vertical loads and bending moments and maintain the bearing pressure within specified limits

References

Source
Camutek
39 Newnham Road
Cambridge CB3 9EY
UK
Telephone Cambridge (0223) 69686

Availability
From owner

Language
Basic

Computer
Hewlett-Packard
9830 (2k) or (6k)

310

Program name
Angled retaining walls

Abstract
This program calculates the strength of angled retaining walls with given geometry where soil conditions are specified

References

Source
CE-data
Lundtoftevej 1G
2800 Lyngby
Denmark

Availability
Bureau service

Language

Computer

311

Program name
Foundations

Abstract
This program calculates dimensions of foundations and, where applicable, reinforcement necessary to carry given columns or walls. Calculations are carried out to DS411:1973

References

Source
CE-data
Lundtoftevej 1G
2800 Lyngby
Denmark

Availability
Bureau service

Language

Computer

312

Program name
RETWALL

Abstract
RETWALL 1 is a design program for simple retaining walls
RETWALL 2 is a program for the analysis of a finite-element retaining wall with non-linear soil springs

References
GEOCOMP

Source
Computel Limited
Eastern Road
Bracknell, Berkshire
UK
Telephone Bracknell 23031

Availability

Language

Computer

313

Program name
GROUP

Abstract
A set of programs, based on the integration of Mindlin's Solution, for considering the lateral, vertical and applied moments on a pile group

References
GEOCOMP

Source
Computel Limited
Eastern Road
Bracknell, Berkshire
UK
Telephone Bracknell 23031

Availability

Language

Computer

314

Program name
PILEBR

Abstract
A program designed to assist in the determination of the most economical geometric dimensions for a pile to be driven through a number of soil strata. The program calculates the vertical load-bearing capacity of a vertical pile from information input interactively or from a data file. A maximum of ten soil strata can currently be handled

References
Program made available by Foundata Computer Services Limited

Source
CRC Engineering Services
83 Clerkenwell Road
London
EC1R 5HP
01–242 0747

Availability
Low rates available for remote batch

Language

Computer

315

Program name
SLIPCIRC

Abstract
A program to analyse the stability of earth slopes by calculating the factor of safety mobilised on a circular-arc slip plane. The weight of each slice is calculated, considering soil densities, piezometric level and/or pore-water ratio in combination with specified drawdown level. Output consists of a table of co-ordinates of the centre of curvature and radius for each arc, together with the calculated factor of safety

References
Program made available by Foundata Computer Services Limited

Source
CRC Engineering Services
83 Clerkenwell Road
London
EC1R 5HP
Telephone 01–242 0747

Availability
Overnight or low-cost remote batch

Language

Computer

316

Program name
SHEPILE

Abstract
A program for the analysis of earth-retaining structures, the stability of which relies on ground penetration only, or ground penetration in combination with ties or bracing. The user may specify the factor of safety required in the calculation and the program gives a full analysis of the pressures, forces and bending moments, and the penetration necessary to provide rotational stability

References
Program made available by Foundata Computer Services Limited

Source
CRC Engineering Services
83 Clerkenwell Road
London
EC1R 5HP
Telephone 01–242 0747

Availability

Language

Computer

Program name
PGELV

Abstract
A program for the analysis of the load-displacement behaviour of freestanding pile groups, composed of vertical piles embedded within a soil layer. The pile group may be loaded with axial or eccentric loads but these must be vertical. The pile groups are analysed using the integral-equation method. The program is written for solid cylindrical piles but the input data can be adjusted for hollow tubes and piles of square, rectangular or elliptical cross-section

References
Program made available by Highways Engineering Computer Branch of the Department of the Environment

Source
CRC Engineering Services
83 Clerkenwell Road
London EC1R 5HP, UK
Telephone 01–242 0747

Availability

Language

Computer

318

Program name
PILEGRP

Abstract
A program for the analysis of a group of piles supporting a rigid pile cap which is loaded with any combination of moments and forces. The piles, which are of uniform cross-section, may be in any configuration with either hinged or fixed heads and toes. The properties of each pile may be specified individually or overall for the group. The pile group may be analysed for a number of loading conditions

References
Modification of IBM 1130–CEP pilegroup program

Source
CRC Engineering Services
83 Clerkenwell Road
London
EC1R 5HP, UK
Telephone 01–242 0747

Availability

Language

Computer

319

Program name
LATPILE

Abstract
A program to determine the bending moment and shear forces in a vertical pile subjected to a lateral force and/or moment at the pile head. The user specifies the effective diameter and length of the pile, the loading at the head and the soil strata in which the pile is to be founded. The output gives a tabulation of earth pressures, deflection, shear force and bending moment against depth. The program is currently limited to ten soil strata and 100 divisions

References
Program made available by Foundata Computer Services Limited

Source
CRC Engineering Services
83 Clerkenwell Road
London
EC1R 5HP, UK
Telephone 01–242 0747

Availability

Language

Computer

320

Program name
HOLD

Abstract
This program analyses or designs a concrete cantilevered retaining wall. Only granular soils can be specified, and the pressure distribution behind the wall is assumed trapezoidal according to Rankine's theory. Output consists of permissible stresses, earth forces, moments and shears, soil pressures at toe and heel, quantities of concrete and steel, safety factors and overloading results

References

Source
Faber Computer Operations Limited
Upper Marlborough Road
St Albans
Herts AL1 3UT, UK
Telephone St Albans 61222

Availability
Bureau service

Language

Computer
IBM 1130, System 7

321

Program name
PILE

Abstract
This program analyses a tied or untied sheet-pile retaining wall in uniform ground with a single tie. It calculates the required penetration, soil pressure, bending moment and shear forces at seven critical positions up the pile. Densities of soil and materials, maximum shear forces and the position and angle of tie are included in the input data. All input data is listed in the output

References

Source
Faber Computer Operations Limited
Upper Marlborough Road
St Albans
Herts AL1 3UT, UK
Telephone St Albans 61222

Availability
Bureau service

Language

Computer
IBM 1130, System 7

322

Program name
SHEETPILE/1

Abstract
This sub-system enables an engineer to design single- and multiple-anchor retaining walls of the sheet-pile type for various depths. There are no limits to the numbers of layers or types of soil to be considered

References
GENESYS program library

Source
GENESYS Limited
Pennine House, Lemyngton Street
Loughborough, Leicestershire
LE11 1XA, UK
Telephone 0509 39185 Telex 341747

Availability
Bureau service, hire

Language
Gentran

Computer
CDC 6500, 6600, 7600
DEC 10
Honeywell 6000
IBM 360, 370
ICL 1900, System 4
Philips 1400
PRIME 300
Univac 1100

323

Program name
PILE–2D/1

Abstract
This sub-system enables an engineer to analyse the behaviour of groups of piles in long rows. Forces are considered in two dimensions. Bending, shear and axial forces are determined in vertical or raked piles

References
GENESYS program library

Source
GENESYS Limited
Pennine House, Lemyngton Street
Loughborough, Leicestershire
LE11 1XA, UK
Telephone 0509 39185 Telex 341747

Availability
Bureau service, hire

Language
Gentran

Computer
CDC 6500, 6600, 7600
DEC 10
Honeywell 6000
IBM 360, 370
ICL 1900, System 4
Philips 1400
PRIME 300
Univac 1100

324

Program name
PILE–3D/1

Abstract
This sub-system enables the engineer to analyse the behaviour of groups of piles in long rows. Forces are considered in three dimensions. Bending, shear and axial forces are determined in vertical or raked piles

References
GENESYS program library

Source
GENESYS Limited
Pennine House, Lemyngton Street
Loughborough, Leicestershire
LE11 1XA, UK
Telephone 0509 39185 Telex 341747

Availability
Bureau service, hire

Language
Gentran

Computer
CDC 6500, 6600, 7600
DEC 10
Honeywell 6000
IBM 360, 370
ICL 1900, System 4
Philips 1400
PRIME 300

325

Program name
NON-CIRCULAR SLIP/1

Abstract
This sub-system enables an engineer to examine the stability of a slope, using the Morgernstern and Price method. The number of soils and geometry of slope to be considered are not limited by the sub-system. The size of problem to be handled is limited only by the size and type of computer used

References
GENESYS program library

Source
GENESYS Limited
Pennine House, Lemyngton Street
Loughborough, Leicestershire
LE11 1XA, UK
Telephone 0509 39185 Telex 341747

Availability
Bureau service, hire

Language
Gentran

Computer
CDC 6500, 6600, 7600
DEC 10
Honeywell 6000
IBM 360, 370
ICL 1900, System 4
Philips P1400
PRIME 300
Univac 1100

326

Program name
RETWALL 1

Abstract
This program calculates active and passive pressures, depth of penetration, bending moments and shear stress for retaining walls of sheet-pile type in multi-layered soils. Cantilevered or anchored walls can be analysed. For anchored walls the required tie force is calculated. The effects of water on the active and/or passive side of wall, and of seepage cracks owing to tension, may also be considered

References

Source
Geocomp UK Limited
Eastern Road, Bracknell
Berkshire
UK
Telephone 24567

Availability
Sale or hire negotiable

Language
Fortran IV

Computer
ICL 1900
CDC 6600

Program name
Retaining walls

Abstract
This program deals with retaining walls back-filled with sand. It calculates stability and bearing capacity and examines the possibility of shifting. The terrain behind the wall is assumed to be a non-loaded slope to a given height, and thereafter a loaded horizontal surface. The method is as examined in 'Geotechnic', JB Hansen and H Lundgren

References
Danish Building Research Institute
Abstract 48 13 103

Source
Geodata A/S
Dagmarhus
HC Andersens Boulevard 7
Copenhagen V
Denmark

Availability
Bureau service

Language

Computer

328

Program name
Anchor length for sheet piling

Abstract
This program calculates the distance necessary between anchored sheet piling and its anchor plate

References
Danish Building Research Institute
Abstract 48 13 201

Source
Geodata A/S
Dagmarhus
HC Andersens Boulevard 7
1553 Copenhagen V
Denmark

Availability
Bureau service

Language

Computer

329

Program name
Cellar walls

Abstract
This program calculates stress and deformation in cellar walls from the pressure of surrounding earth. The walls are assumed to be supported both by a floor and ceiling

References
Danish Building Research Institute
Abstract 48 13 104

Source
Geodata A/S
Dagmarhus
HC Andersens Boulevard 7
1553 Copenhagen V
Denmark

Availability
Bureau service

Language

Computer

330

Program name
Bearing capacity of foundations

Abstract
This program calculates the nominal bearing capacity of both block and strip foundations on sand and clay. The effects of short-term and long-term loads can be examined. Calculations are carried out to DS 415

References
Danish Building Research Institute
Abstract 48 13 002

Source
Geodata A/S
Dagmarhus
HC Andersens Boulevard 7
1553 Copenhagen V
Denmark

Availability
Bureau service

Language

Computer

331

Program name
Cantilevered retaining walls

Abstract
This program deals with cantilevered retaining walls back-filled with sand. It calculates stability and bearing capacity and examines the possibility of shifting. Calculations are carried out to DS 415

References
Danish Building Research Institute
Abstract 48 13 101

Source
Geodata A/S
Dagmarhus
HC Andersens Boulevard 7
1553 Copenhagen V
Denmark

Availability
Bureau service

Language

Computer

332

Program name
Sheet piling 1

Abstract
This program calculates dimensions of anchors and anchor plates for sheet piling. The minimum depth to which the anchor must be driven is also calculated

References
Danish Building Research Institute
Abstract 48 13 106

Source
Geodata A/S
Dagmarhus
HC Andersens Boulevard 7
1553 Copenhagen V
Denmark

Availability
Bureau service

Language

Computer

333

Program name
Piling I

Abstract
This program calculates forces in pile foundations under a static load. It assumes that the piles are simply-supported. The program is based on elasticity theory. Foundations with up to 250 piles can be handled

References
Danish Building Research Institute
Abstract 48 13 301

Source
Geodata A/S
Dagmarhus
HC Andersens Boulevard 7
1553 Copenhagen V
Denmark

Availability
Bureau service

Language

Computer

334

Program name
Piling II

Abstract
This program calculates forces in pile foundations under a static load. The program is based on elasticity theory. Fastening of the piles can be taken into consideration. Foundations with up to 300 piles can be handled

References
Danish Building Research Institute
Abstract 48 13 302

Source
Geodata A/S
Dagmarhus
HC Andersens Boulevard 7
1553 Copenhagen V
Denmark

Availability
Bureau service

Language

Computer

335

Program name
RETWLS

Abstract
This program is used for designing gravity-type retaining walls. It verifies the safety of the cantilever and produces a design which will most economically meet input restrictions and considerations

References
Mark III software library
User manual 5202·27

Source
Honeywell Information Systems Limited
114 to 118 Southampton Row
London WC1B 5AB
UK
Telephone 01–242 5725

Availability
Bureau service

Language
Basic

Computer
Honeywell 6000 series

336

Program name
Sheet piling

Abstract
This program calculates the internal forces and deformations in a sheet-piling wall for given loads of earth and water pressure. The wall may be of cantilever construction, or propped with either rigid or elastic anchors

References

Source
Laing Computing Services
Elstree Way
Borehamwood
Hertfordshire
WD6 1NF, UK
Telephone 01–207 2000

Availability
Sale, bureau service

Language
Fortran

Computer
IBM 370–50

337

Program name
Pile group

Abstract
This program analyses a group of any number of piles in any pattern, supporting one pile cap. The output gives the displacement and rotation of the pile cap, moments, shears and axial forces in piles, displacements and rotations, and a full listing of input data

References

Source
Laing Computing Services
Elstree Way
Borehamwood
Hertfordshire
WD6 1NF, UK
Telephone 01–207 2000

Availability
Sale, bureau service

Language
Fortran

Computer
IBM 370–50

338

Program name
XEBESS

Abstract
This program analyses slope stability using Bishop's routine method of 1954 or the Morgenstern and Price method. A wide range of options is available

References

Source
Markworth Design Consultants Limited
Coppers, Pyrford Heath
Surrey GU22 8SR
UK
Telephone Byfleet 41088, 41013

Availability
Bureau service

Language
Fortran

Computer
ICL 1904A

339

Program name
Ground water

Abstract
This program calculates levels and current of ground water. The area to be examined is divided into a large number of sections. Geohydrological characteristics are defined for each. 1600 sections can be handled by the program

References
Danish Building Research Institute
Abstract 48 13 601

Source
Nielsen & Rauschenberger
Radgivende ingeniorer A/S
Lundtoftevej 7
2800 Lyngby
Denmark

Availability

Language

Computer

340

Program name
SHEETPILE/1

Abstract
This program designs single and multiple anchor sheet-pile retaining walls for variable piling depths. Output gives moments, shear forces, deflections and pressures at various nodes, and a full listing of input data

References
Developed by GENESYS Ltd

Source
UCC, University Computing Company
344–350 Euston Road
London NW1
UK
Telephone 01–387 9661

Availability
Bureau service

Language
Fortran
Gentran

Computer

341

Program name
PILE–2D/1

Abstract
This program analyses a group of piles in long rows. Piles may be vertical or raked. Forces on the piles are considered in two dimensions only. Output gives the bending shear and axial force in each pile, and a full listing of input data

References
Developed by GENESYS Ltd

Source
UCC, University Computing Company
344–350 Euston Road
London NW1
UK
Telephone 01–387 9661

Availability
Bureau service

Language
Fortran
Gentran

Computer

Program name
PGROUP

Abstract
This program analyses groups of piles. The geometry of the piles and the loads to which they are subjected are at the discretion of the user. Output gives settlement, moments, shear and axial loads, and a full listing of input data

References
Developed by the computer branch of the DoE (Highway Engineering)

Source
UCC, University Computing Company
344–350 Euston Road
London NW1
UK
Telephone 01–387 9661

Availability
Bureau service

Language
Fortran

Computer

343

Program name
SPILE

Abstract
This program analyses any arrangement of a group of piles supporting one pile cap. Output gives moments, axial shears and forces, and a full listing of input data

References
Developed by the Midland Road Construction Unit

Source
UCC, University Computing Company
344–350 Euston Road
London NW1
UK
Telephone 01–387 9661

Availability
Bureau service

Language
Fortran

Computer

344

Program name
Slip-circle/1

Abstract
This program analyses the stability of earth slopes using Bishop's adaptation of the Swedish method, based on circular arc traces. For each radius and centre of rotation, the position at which the failure surface cuts the profile is given, together with the number of slices and the safety factor

References
Developed by GENESYS Ltd

Source
UCC, University Computing Company
344–350 Euston Road
London NW1
UK
Telephone 01–387 9661

Availability
Bureau service

Language
Fortran
Gentran

Computer

345

Program name
Cut and fill

Abstract
This system converts information on existing site levels and substrata from the site plan, spot-heights and trial holes, into a mathematical representation of surface and underground features. Cut-and-fill volumes related to the topsoil and affected substrata are calculated for a series of proposed locations of buildings and level areas

References

Source
ARC Limited
4 Jesus Lane
Cambridge CB5 8BA
UK
Telephone 0223 65015

Availability
Purchase

Language
Fortran

Computer
Prime 300

346

Program name
STAB

Abstract
This program calculates slope stability, or the factor of safety against circular slip

References

Source
Atkins Computing Services Limited
Woodcote Grove, Ashley Road
Epsom, Surrey
UK
Telephone Epsom 40421

Availability
Bureau service, time-sharing. Available in Netherlands

Language
Fortran

Computer
Honeywell Sigma 9

347

Program name
Sheet piling

Abstract
This program calculates drive-depths and anchor strength required for sheet piling. Calculations are carried out to DS415:1965

References

Source
CE-data
Lundtoftevej 1G
2800 Lyngby
Denmark

Availability
Bureau service

Language

Computer

348

Program name
Pile foundations

Abstract
This program calculates strength and stability of pile foundations of given weight. Two– or three-dimensional frameworks can be considered

References
HANSEN, B, A new design method for pile foundations

Source
CE-data
Lundtoftevej 1G
2800 Lyngby
Denmark

Availability
Bureau service

Language

Computer

349

Program name
GEO 15

Abstract
A program concerned with the stability of three-dimensional wedges

References
GEOCOMP

Source
Computel Limited
Eastern Road
Bracknell, Berkshire
UK
Telephone Bracknell 23031

Availability

Language

Computer

350

Program
SLIPSYST

Abstract
A program concerned with slope stability and which uses the Bishop circular, and Morgenstern and Price non-circular routines

References
GEOCOMP

Source
Computel Limited
Eastern Road
Bracknell, Berkshire
UK
Telephone Bracknell 23031

Availability

Language

Computer

351

Program name
Cut and fill

Abstract
A program for the calculation of cut and fill volumes of different strata. Account is taken of removal of topsoil and resoiling. Output can be in the form of drawings produced on a graph plotter

References
Program made available by ICL

Source
Computel Limited
Eastern Road
Bracknell, Berkshire
UK
Telephone Bracknell 23031

Availability

Language

Computer

Program name
Seepage

Abstract
A program for the analysis of seepage by the finite method of calculation for the distribution of piezometric head and velocity under seepage conditions. Any soil geometry can be dealt with if the complete problem is defined. The program has automatic data-generation for simple shapes, such as dams. It is also capable of solving either transient or steady-state flow, with automatic location of the phreatic surface

References
Program made available by Engineering Programs and Services Limited

Source
CRC Engineering Services
83 Clerkenwell Road
London
EC1R 5HP
Telephone 01–242 0747

Availability

Language

Computer

353

Program name
SITEPREP

Abstract
This program calculates earthwork volumes for a construction site where the desired topography can be described as one or more areas, each consisting of a plane, optionally bounded by sloping sides. For each area, the user provides data describing the existing terrain, four plane-defining points, and the side-slope options and magnitude. The program then computes the cut-and-fill volumes for each area separately and for the entire tract

References
CALL library

Source
Data Center
IBM World Trade Corporation
821 United Nations Plaza
New York 10017
USA

Availability
Also available from IBM offices throughout the world

Language
Basic

Computer
IBM 360

354

Program name
Site excavation

Abstract
A set of six programs to compute volumes of earthworks by comparing original site levels with given levels of buildings or excavated areas. The system allows for comparison of cut-and-fill ratios, and produces contoured final site plans for setting out. It enables a designer to explore the relative cost of placing buildings at different heights or positions

References
Incorporates CAD Centre GINO-F graphics package

Source
Design Office Consortium
6 Green Street
Cambridge CB2 3JU
UK
Telephone 0223 68387

Availability
Bureau service, hire

Language
ASA Fortran IV

Computer

355

Program name
SLOPE

Abstract
This program analyses the stability of earth slopes using Bishop's adaptation of the Swedish method based on circular arc traces. Pore water is taken into account. For each radius and centre of rotation, the position at which the failure surface cuts the profile is given, together with the number of slices and the safety factor

References

Source
Faber Computer Operations Limited
Upper Marlborough Road
St Albans
Herts AL1 3UT
Telephone St Albans 61222

Availability
Bureau service

Language

Computer
IBM 1130, System 7

356

Program name
Slip-circle/1

Abstract
This sub-system enables a designer to examine the stability of slopes by the method of slip-circle failure. The number of soils which may be considered is not limited by the sub-system, and any geometry can be analysed. The size of the problem to be handled is limited only by the size and type of computer used

References
GENESYS program library

Source
GENESYS Limited
Pennine House, Lemyington Street
Loughborough, Leicestershire
LE11 1XA, UK
Telephone 0509 39185 Telex 341747

Availability
Bureau service, hire

Language
Gentran

Computer
CDC 6500, 6600, 7600
DEC 10
Honeywell 6000
IBM 360, 370
ICL 1900, System 4
Philips P1400
PRIME 300
Univac 1100

357

Program name
WEDGE

Abstract
This program calculates the factor of safety against sliding of a wedge of material. Forces required to maintain a specified factor of safety are determined. The program will analyse several planes, at which failure is possible, in one run. Varying properties of soils and effects of cracks owing to tension may also be considered

References

Source
Geocomp UK Limited
Eastern Road, Bracknell
Berkshire
UK
Telephone 24567

Availability
Sale or hire negotiable

Language
Fortran IV

Computer
ICL 1900
CDC 6600

358

Program name
SLIPSYST

Abstract
This program calculates the factor of safety against sliding for either a circular or a non-circular slip surface. The effect of excess water pressure in pores, Ru values, tension cracks, point or uniformly-distributed loads and also earthquake effects may be considered on a section with up to twenty soil types and up to ten phreatic surfaces

References

Source
Geocomp UK Limited
Eastern Road, Bracknell
Berkshire
UK
Telephone Bracknell 24567

Availability
Sale or hire negotiable

Language
Fortran IV

Computer
ICL 1900
IBM 360
CDC 6600

359

Program name
FEAST

Abstract
This program creates a mathematical model of an earth volume with given edge characteristics. The program assumes that the earth volume is of elastic/plastic material. Stress at selected points and tension in the layers of material is calculated

References
Danish Building Research Institute
Abstract 48 13 401

Source
Geoteknisk Institut
Maglebjergvej 1
2800 Lyngby
Denmark

Availability
Bureau service

Language
Fortran IV

Computer
IBM 370

360

Program name
CFVOLS

Abstract
This program calculates cut-and-fill volumes

References
Mark III software library
User manual 5202·17

Source
Honeywell Information Systems Limited
114 to 118 Southampton Row
London WC1B 5AB
UK
Telephone 01–242 5725

Availability
Bureau service

Language
Basic

Computer
Honeywell 6000 series

361

Program name
SOILXS

Abstract
This program gives an analysis of soil stability

References
Mark III software library
List SOIINF

Source
Honeywell Information Systems Limited
114 to 118 Southampton Row
London WC1B 5AB
UK
Telephone 01–242 5725

Availability
Bureau service

Language
Basic

Computer
Honeywell 6000 series

Program name
QUANTA

Abstract
This program calculates accurate cut-and-fill volumes between ground level and design elevations for construction sites, ground levelling, terrace building, open-cast mining and other excavation jobs. The procedure for solving the problem is based on a prismatic cut-out of the volumes between the existing contoured ground model, plotted by CARTA, a linked land-survey program, and the designed lot elevations

References

Source
Idan Computers Ltd
3A Yitzhak Sadeh Street
PO Box 33390
Tel-Aviv, Israel
Telephone 30726 39419

Availability
Bureau service

Language
Fortran IV

Computer

363

Program name
Earth calculations

Abstract
This program calculates the volume of cut-and-fill in a straight trench, particularly where the total area is broken down into different types. It calculates the areas of adjacent sections along the trench, the volume between the sections and the cumulative running total. In suitable circumstances, this program may be used for mass excavations or spoil tips

References

Source
Laing Computing Services
Elstree Way
Borehamwood
Hertfordshire
WD6 1NF, UK
Telephone 01–207 2000

Availability
Sale, bureau service

Language
Fortran

Computer
IBM 370–50

364

Program name
Non-circular slip/1

Abstract
This program examines the stability of a slope, using the method of analysis of general slip surfaces developed by Morgenstern and Price. The output gives an analysis of the state of iteration, the calculated value of the horizontal force at the end of the last slice, the moment about the centre of the failure surface in that slice and a full listing of input data

References
Developed by GENESYS Ltd

Source
UCC, University Computing Company
344–350 Euston Road
London NW1
UK
Telephone 01–387 9661

Availability
Bureau service

Language
Fortran
Gentran

Computer

365

Program name
CONTOUR

Abstract
This system maps noise contours generated from a road. Traffic flow, ground levels and the vertical alignment of the road and associated structures, such as cuttings, embankments and edge barriers, are taken into consideration. Noise levels are calculated in relation to the surrounding topography. These are drawn as a shaded contour map to be laid over the original map

References

Source
ARC Limited
4 Jesus Lane
Cambridge CB5 8BA
UK
Telephone 0223 65015

Availability
Purchase

Language
Fortran

Computer
Prime 300

366

Program name
MWAY

Abstract
This system provides a detailed assessment of a proposed road development. Noise predictions are made, and visual and shading effects assessed, based on a three-dimensional mathematical model of the local terrain, including buildings. Detailed tables or summaries are output, together with the original maps with the results annotated on them

References

Source
ARC Limited
4 Jesus Lane
Cambridge CB5 8BA
UK
Telephone 0223 65015

Availability
Purchase

Language
Fortran

Computer
Prime 300

367

Program name
BIPS–3

Abstract
This is an implementation of the DoE highway design system, which is capable of operation in batch or time-sharing modes. The suite of programs covers all aspects of highway design, including initial alignment, cross sections and earthworks quantities

References

Source
Atkins Computing Services Limited
Woodcote Grove, Ashley Road
Epsom, Surrey
UK
Telephone Epsom 40421

Availability
Bureau service, time-sharing. Available in Netherlands

Language
Fortran

Computer
Honeywell Sigma 9

368

Program name
MTC093

Abstract
This program computes stress at any point inside an elastic, layered structure resting on an elastic half-space, with non-slip or fully slippery interfaces, under a uniform (normal or shear) circular load applied at the surface. Deflections on load axis are also produced

References
Romain, J E, Stresses, strains and deflections in elastic layered systems

Source
Centre de Recherches Routieres
Boulevard de la Woluwe
B–1200 Brussels
Belgium
Telephone 771 20 80

Availability
Purchase, bureau service

Language
Fortran

Computer
GE235
CDC 7000

369

Program name
ORN093

Abstract
This program computes the predictable deformation ('rut depth') of a road, pavement or assimilated system, from the thicknesses and deformation properties of the materials, the traffic and the stress distribution inside the structure. Can be coupled with program MTC093 for stress computation

References
Romain, J E, Rut Depth Prediction in Asphalt Pavements

Source
Centre de Recherches Routieres
Boulevard de la Woluwe
B–1200 Brussels
Belgium
Telephone 771 20 80

Availability
Purchase, bureau service

Language
Basic

Computer
GE235

370

Program name
VALOR

Abstract
VALOR (Vertical Alignment Optimisation of Roads) is used for road design in urban areas where most of the work is confined to re-alignment or widening of existing roads

References
Program made available by the Department of the Environment

Source
Computel Limited
Eastern Road
Bracknell, Berkshire
UK
Telephone Bracknell 23031

Availability

Language

Computer

371

Program name
BIPS

Abstract
BIPS (British Integrated Program System) is a program for carrying out all calculations involved in road design. The program prints out the results in tabulated form. It can also transform numerical output into contract drawings by means of a graph plotter

References
Program made available by the Department of the Environment

Source
Computel Limited
Eastern Road
Bracknell, Berkshire
UK
Telephone Bracknell 23031

Availability

Language

Computer

372

Program name
FREEWAY

Abstract
An alternative program to HOPS or BIPS. It can carry out all calculations involved in road design, including the finding of the optimum vertical alignment when considering the line of the road. The program is suitable for more complex interchanges than is HOPS or BIPS

References
Program made available by the Department of the Environment

Source
Computel Limited
Eastern Road
Bracknell, Berkshire
UK
Telephone Bracknell 23031

Availability

Language

Computer

373

Program name
HOPS

Abstract
HOPS (Highway Optimisation Program Systems) is a program used to refine the calculation of the line of the road and to minimise costs. It is applied to find the optimum vertical alignment

References
Program made available by the Department of the Environment

Source
Computel Limited
Eastern Road
Bracknell, Berkshire
UK
Telephone Bracknell 23031

Availability

Language

Computer

374

Program name
HIGHWAYS/1

Abstract
This sub-system enables an engineer to design highways from preliminary stages through to final quantities and setting-out information. The method used is one of longitudinal and horizontal alignments, with lateral templates. Ground information is in the form of variable digital models or cross-sections

References
GENESYS program library

Source
GENESYS Limited
Pennine House, Lemyngton Street
Loughborough, Leicestershire
LE11 1XA, UK
Telephone 0509 39185 Telex 341747

Availability
Bureau service, hire

Language
Gentran

Computer
CDC 6500, 6600, 7600
Honeywell 6000
IBM 360, 370
ICL 1900, System 4
Philips P1400
PRIME 300
Univac 1100

375

Program name
COGOS

Abstract
This program performs common civil-engineering calculations involving co-ordinate geometry. These include right-of-way, highway ramp designs, subdivision layout and interchange calculations. A more precise version, COGODS, is also available

References
Mark III software library
User manual 5202·14

Source
Honeywell Information System Limited
114 to 118 Southampton Row
London WC1B 5AB
UK
Telephone 01–242 5725

Availability
Bureau service

Language
Basic

Computer
Honeywell 6000 series

376

Program name
MOSS

Abstract
This system enables the engineer to plan the best alignment of a highway, taking into account factors such as visual intrusion, traffic flow and economy of design. It consists of a data base which holds records of traffic flows, accident records and housing information, as well as a digital ground model. Graphic output can be obtained using a plotter or vdu, and can be in the form of annotated plans, three-dimensional views or contoured plans

References
Public Works Congress, Paper 7, 1974

Source
Moss Consortium
Northamptonshire County Council
Northampton NN1 2HZ
UK
Telephone Northampton 34833

Availability
Through bureaux (eg Scicon) throughout the world

Language
Fortran

Computer
IBM (including System 4), ICL, CDC and UNIVAC machines with 32k core

377

Program name
SSLEW

Abstract
Given information relating to road centre-lines, this program produces cross-sectional plotting data, earthworks and pavement quantities, tabulation of finished road profile levels and grades, and slope lengths for single or dual carriageways. Output gives all quantities related to the road cross-section

References

Source
Ove Arup and Partners
13 Fitzroy Street
London W1
UK
Telephone 01–636 1531

Availability
Bureau service

Language
Fortran

Computer
DEC 10

378

Program name
BIPS (British Integrated Program System)

Abstract
Geometric design of highway alignments. A stage-by-stage approach is used, similar to that in a drawing office. Cross and longitudinal sections, plans and earthworks can be output graphically. The system comprises several groups of programs, each of which performs a specific function. At each stage, data is input and intermediate results may be inspected

References

Source
Scicon Computer Services Limited
Brick Close, Kiln Farm
Milton Keynes MK11 3EJ
UK
Telephone 0908 565656 Telex 826171

Availability
Bureau service

Language

Computer
Univac 1108

379

Program name
HOPS

Abstract
A system comprising five programs designed to assist the engineer in generating alignments of highways from ground data, and in planning earthworks and structures at the lowest cost. Any one of the five programs may be used individually. They cover ground-data processing, generation of initial vertical alignments, phasing of horizontal and vertical curves, reduction of costs of earthworks and structures, and analysis of earth-moving

References
Developed by the Transport and Road Research Laboratory

Source
Scicon Computer Services Limited
Brick Close, Kiln Farm
Milton Keynes MK11 3EJ
UK
Telephone 0908 565656 Telex 826171

Availability
Bureau service

Language

Computer
Univac 1108

380

Program name
HYANDRY

Abstract
This program designs large tree-structure drainage schemes, taking account of the storage capacity of the pipes. It uses the hydrograph method of the Road Research Laboratory, and is based on the Colebrook-White equation

References

Source
Atkins Computing Services Limited
Woodcote Grove, Ashley Road
Epsom, Surrey
UK
Telephone Epsom 40421

Availability
Bureau service, time-sharing. Available in Netherlands

Language
Fortran

Computer
Honeywell Sigma 9

381

Program name
Storm sewer design and analysis

Abstract
A program for the design of storm sewerage systems, branch by branch. It is based on the hydrograph techniques of the Road Research Laboratory

References
Program made available by ICL

Source
Computel Limited
Eastern Road
Bracknell, Berkshire
UK
Telephone Bracknell 23031

Availability

Language

Computer

Program name
CULV

Abstract
A program for the automatic design and detailing of a cross section of a unit length of box culvert of reinforced concrete. The user prescribes loading systems to which the culvert would be subjected and the program selects the lowest cost arrangement of roof, wall and floor thicknesses, and associated reinforcement. Consecutive runs of the program can be made, with amended data as required

References
Highways Engineering Computer Branch of the DoE

Source
CRC Engineering Services
83 Clerkenwell Road
London
EC1R 5HP
Telephone 01–242 0747

Availability
Remote batch

Language

Computer

383

Program name
WATERNET

Abstract
A program to solve the flow equations governing the behaviour of a water-distribution network. Input consists of a complete description of the network, including pipes, consumptions, reservoirs and valves. A modified Newton-Ralphson technique is used for the analysis, with pipe resistances represented by the Hazen-Williams empirical formula. Several load conditions for the network can be considered in one run and very large networks can be analysed

References
Program made available by the Water Research Station

Source
CRC Engineering Services
83 Clerkenwell Road
London
EC1R 5HP
Telephone 01–242 0747

Availability

Language

Computer

384

Program name
BACKWATER/1

Abstract
This sub-system enables an engineer to calculate by the standard step method, surface profiles of water, for gradually varied flows in open, non-prismatic waterways

References
GENESYS program library

Source
GENESYS Limited
Pennine House, Lemyngton Street
Loughborough, Leicestershire
LE11 1XA, UK
Telephone 0509 39185 Telex 341747

Availability
Bureau service, hire

Language
Gentran

Computer
CDC 6500, 6600, 7600
DEC 10
Honeywell 6000
IBM 360, 370
ICL 1900, System 4
Philips 1400
PRIME 300
Univac 1100

385

Program name
CULV

Abstract
This program, which is maintained by the DoE, designs the cross-section of a unit length of rectangular reinforced concrete box culvert of given internal dimensions. The unit length considered is analysed as a closed plane frame, which is subject to specified combinations of loads. Both mild and high-tensile steel may be specified, together with two classes of concrete, the twenty-eight-day cube strengths of which are 22·5 and 30N/mm^2

References
CALL, IBM United Kingdom Limited

Source
Highway Engineering Branch
Department of the Environment
St Christopher House
Southwark Street
London SE1, UK
Telephone (01) 928 7999

Availability
Also available from IBM offices

Language

Computer

386

Program name
CULVRS

Abstract
This program determines the size and the number of pipes for a circular culvert which satisfies hydrological data and site conditions for inlet and outlet control. A version is also available with provision for selecting output options, DCOGOS

References
Mark III software library
User manual 5202·10

Source
Honeywell Information Systems Limited
114 to 118 Southampton Row
London WC1B 5AB
UK
Telephone 01–242 5725

Availability
Bureau service

Language
Basic

Computer
Honeywell 6000 series

387

Program name
BOXCUS

Abstract
This program determines the size and the number of barrels of a box culvert which satisfies hydrological data and site conditions for inlet and outlet control

References
Mark III software library
User manual 520·04

Source
Honeywell Information Systems Limited
114 to 118 Southampton Row
London WC1B 5AB
UK
Telephone 01–242 5725

Availability
Bureau service

Language
Basic

Computer
Honeywell 6000 series

388

Program name
SSDP (Storm sewer design)

Abstract
A program for the design of storm sewers. It is based on the TRRL hydrograph method and operates in metric and/or Imperial units. It is capable of analysing networks of up to twenty branches, each of which may consist of up to 99 lengths. One– to twenty-year rain profiles, and circular, rectangular, trapezoidal and egg-shaped sections can be allowed for. The system produces a comprehensive output of network results and hydrographs

References

Source
Scicon Computer Service Limited
Brick Close, Kiln Farm
Milton Keynes MK11 3EJ
UK
Telephone 0908 565656 Telex 826171

Availability
Bureau service

Language

Computer
Univac 1108

389

Program name
CDSS (Computer-draughted sewer sections)

Abstract
This system prepares designs for longitudinal sewer sections. The drawing-frame and title-block required must first be described by the user, and data describing the layout and sections prepared on forms. The data is then submitted to a checking program for verification. The plotting program analyses this data and produces high-quality drawings off-line. Surface profiles, manholes, pipe diameters and type and other details may be plotted

References
Developed by JD and DM Watson, consulting engineers

Source
Scicon Computer Services Limited
Brick Close, Kiln Farm
Milton Keynes MK11 3EJ
UK
Telephone 0908 565656 Telex 826171

Availability
Bureau service

Language

Computer
Univac 1108

390

Program name
CULV

Abstract
This system provides designs for reinforced culverts. It is based on the elastic method of design and provides the cheapest arrangement of roof, wall and floor thicknesses and their associated reinforcement

References

Source
Scicon Computer Services Limited
Brick Close, Kiln Farm
Milton Keynes MK11 3EJ
UK
Telephone 0908 565656 Telex 826171

Availability
Bureau service

Language

Computer
Univac 1108

391

Program name
Backwater/1

Abstract
This program calculates, by the standard step method, the water-surface profiles for gradually varied flows in open non-prismatic waterways. Output is in the form of two tables, one giving water-surface level, flow area and wetted perimeter, the other giving supplementary information on surface and energy gradients, energy and velocity heads and energy losses. There is also a full listing of input data

References
Developed by GENESYS Ltd

Source
UCC, University Computing Company
344–350 Euston Road
London NW1
UK
Telephone 01–387 9661

Availability
Bureau service

Language
Fortran
Gentran

Computer

Program name
CULV

Abstract
This program analyses and designs cross-sections of culverts by the elastic stiffness method. The design process gives the best arrangement of reinforcement for the minimum cost. Output gives moments, shears, thrusts, the diameters and arrangement of bars, plus a full listing of input data

References
Developed by the computer branch of the DoE (Highway Engineering)

Source
UCC, University Computing Company
344–350 Euston Road
London NW1
UK
Telephone 01–387 9661

Availability
Bureau service

Language
Fortran

Computer

393

Program name
AREAS

Abstract
This program calculates areas, moments of inertia, radii of gyration and other important properties of sections of composite geometric figures

References
Mark III software library
User manual 5202·22

Source
Honeywell Information Systems Limited
114 to 118 Southampton Row
London WC1B 5AB
UK
Telephone 01–242 5725

Availability
Bureau service

Language
Basic

Computer
Honeywell 6000 series

394

Program name
Flange design

Abstract
This program was originally developed to design or analyse flanges to ASME VIII or BS 1500–1515 by Whessoe Limited. The time-sharing version designs a single plate, flat, lap or tapered hub flange, and the batch program can process up to four designs, and includes floating head flanges with backing rings

References

Source
Atkins Computing Services Limited
Woodcote Grove, Ashley Road
Epsom, Surrey
UK
Telephone Epsom 40421

Availability
Bureau service, time-sharing. Available in Netherlands

Language
Fortran

Computer
Honeywell Sigma 9

395

Program name
Load tables for storage tanks

Abstract
This program calculates load tables for storage tanks as a function of the depth to which they are filled

References

Source
CE-data
Lundtoftevej 1G
2800 Lyngby
Denmark

Availability
Bureau service

Language

Computer

396

Program name
Storage tanks

Abstract
This program allows the design of steel tanks making the most economical use of types of steel available. The skin construction can be of welded belts of different height, thickness and type of steel

References

Source
CE-data
Lundtoftevej 1G
2800 Lyngby
Denmark

Availability
Bureau service

Language

Computer

397

Program name
Analogue computer simulation

Abstract
A program to facilitate the use of a digital computer to solve problems of dynamic systems. Information is input in terms of an analogue block diagram

References
Program made available by ICL

Source
Computel Limited
Eastern Road
Bracknell, Berkshire
UK
Telephone Bracknell 23031

Availability

Language

Computer

398

Program name
GEO 12

Abstract
A suite of programs for the analysis of dewatering systems

References
GEOCOMP

Source
Computel Limited
Eastern Road
Bracknell, Berkshire
UK
Telephone Bracknell 23031

Availability

Language

Computer

399

Program name
GEO 16

Abstract
A program concerned with pressures in seepage pores of fully saturated media

References
GEOCOMP

Source
Computel Limited
Eastern Road
Bracknell, Berkshire
UK
Telephone Bracknell 23031

Availability

Language

Computer

400

Program name
ECLIPSE (Electronic Calculus Library of Integrated Programs and Services)

Abstract
This library includes programs for analysing and designing offshore structures, commercial and industrial buildings, bridges, stadia, exhibition centres, transmission towers, and mechanical and nuclear engineering projects. Information is given in tabular or graphic form in a format to the client's specification. Results include deflections, member forces and reactions

References

Source
Electronic Calculus Limited
344 to 350 Euston Road
London NW1 3BJ
UK
Telephone 01-388 7705, Telex 27192

Availability
Purchase, hire, bureau service

Language
Fortran V

Computer
Univac 1106, 1108
CDC 6600, 7600
DEC System 10
IBM
ICL

401

Program name
TKI

Abstract
This program is used to analyse cylindrical tanks or silos. A vertical strip of the tank wall is divided up into a maximum of forty separate elements, and calculations on the shear and bending moments at the end of each element are made, together with deflections, circumferential stresses and any support reactions. The program is run and re-run with an increasing number of elements until the results are consistent

References

Source
Faber Computer Operations Limited
Upper Marlborough Road
St Albans
Herts AL1 3UT
Telephone St Albans 61222

Availability
Bureau service

Language

Computer
IBM 1130, System 7

Program name
WINDV

Abstract
This program determines the wind pressure profile on a building in accordance with BS CP3:Chapter V:Part 2:1972. Calculations are made for the wind velocities and pressures from each of the four primary directions at selected positions up the height of the building. Account is taken of the surrounding country (ie proximity of escarpments) and the building life. The results for each wind direction are given

References

Source
Faber Computer Operations Limited
Upper Marlborough Road
St Albans
Herts AL1 3UT
Telephone St Albans 61222

Availability
Bureau service

Language

Computer
IBM 1130, System 7

403

Program name
RC building /1

Abstract
This sub-system enables an engineer to analyse, design and detail reinforced concrete buildings constructed from beams, solid slabs and vertical columns. The overall shape of the building need not be rectangular, and storey heights, bay centres and foundation levels need not be constant. The number of beams, slabs, columns and loading conditions which may be considered is not limited by the sub-system

References
GENESYS program library

Source
GENESYS Limited
Pennine House, Lemyngton Street
Loughborough, Leicestershire
LE11 1XA UK
Telephone 0509 39185Telex 341747

Availability
Bureau service, hire

Language
Gentran

Computer
CDC 6500, 6600, 7600
DEC 10
Honeywell 6000
IBM 360, 370
ICL 1900, System 4
Philips P1400
PRIME 300
Univac 1100

404

Program name
GENESYS

Abstract
This is a library of related programs intended to solve various problems of engineering design. The designer need have no knowledge of computers. Programs in the library cover design and analysis of roads, bridges and buildings. They are described individually elsewhere

References

Source
GENESYS Limited
Pennine House, Lemyngton Street
Loughborough, Leicestershire
Telephone 0509 39185Telex 341747

Availability
Bureau service, hire

Language
Gentran

Computer
CDC 6500, 6600, 7600
DEC 10
Honeywell 6000
IBM 360, 370
ICL 1900, System 4
Philips P1400
PRIME 300
Univac 1100

405

Program name
PNC1

Abstract
This program, for undergraduate teaching, uses a metric version of The Road Research Laboratory's report Road Note 4 to design the cheapest concrete mix, subject to the input of certain criteria including standard supervision, types of cement and aggregates, vibration of sections and reinforcement

References

Source
Ulster College, The Northern Ireland Polytechnic
Shore Road, Newtownabbey
Co Antrim, Northern Ireland
Telephone Whiteabbey (0231) 65131

Availability
At terminal for on-line use

Language
Fortran IV

Computer
ICL 19

406

Program name
RC-Buildings/1

Abstract
This program designs and details reinforced concrete building frames (cast in-situ), in accordance with BS CP114:1969. The output gives bending moments and shear envelopes, sectional moments of resistance, areas of steel, bending schedules, reinforcement weights and a full listing of input data

References
Developed by GENESYS Ltd

Source
UCC, University Computing Company
344–350 Euston Road
London NW1
UK
Telephone 01–387 9661

Availability
Bureau service

Language
Fortran
Gentran

Computer

Structural frames

Two-dimensional frames
Three-dimensional frames
Offshore structures
Other

407

Program name
53–T24

Abstract
This program calculates tensions, deformations and constants in a composite cross-section. The cross-section is assumed to be built up of polygonal or circular parts, corresponding to reinforcement. These parts may overlap. In cases where pull and pressure-resistance are different at the same point as the cross-section, the placing of zero lines is arrived at by repeated calculation

References

Source
A/S Regnecentralen
Falkoneralle 1
2000 Copenhagen F
Denmark

Availability
Bureau service from Geodata A/S

Language

Computer

408

Program name
53–T14 and T23

Abstract
This program calculates frequencies and vibrations or tensions, reactions and deflections in a plane structural frame. It is based on the deformation method. Correct deflection lines for beam elements are used which are not obtained by using the mass-matrix method. Distributed and concentrated masses are permitted

References

Source
A/S Regnecentralen
Falkoneralle 1
2000 Copenhagen F
Denmark
Telephone (01) 10 53 66

Availability

Language

Computer

409

Program name
53–T25

Abstract
This program calculates tensions, reactions and deflections and also cable strengths in a plane frame or a grid construction. It is based on the deformation method. The tightening, loosening and re-tightening of cables, friction and shrinkage may also be taken into consideration

References

Source
A/S Regnecentralen
Falkoneralle 1
2000 Copenhagen F
Denmark
Telephone (01) 10 53 66

Availability

Language

Computer

410

Program name
PLANE

Abstract
This program is for the analysis of plane structural frames for varying loading conditions, sizes, constants etc

References

Source
Atkins Computing Services Limited
Woodcote Grove, Ashley Road
Epsom, Surrey
UK
Telephone Epsom 40421

Availability
Bureau service, time-sharing. Available in Netherlands

Language
Fortran

Computer
Honeywell Sigma 9

411

Program name
FRAME

Abstract
The program analyses two-dimensional orthogonal frames and continuous beams comprising slender prismatic members. Non-prismatic members may be represented by dividing the member into prismatic sub-members and providing 'dummy' joints between each sub-member. Input data should include relationships of members to joints, physical dimensions, moduli of elasticity and loadings

References

Source
Building Computer Services Limited
Bush House
72 Prince Street
Bristol BS1 4HU
Telephone 0272 290651

Availability
Bureau service, hire

Language

Computer

412

Program name
Pin-jointed plane-frame analysis

Abstract
This program analyses statistically-determinate frames

References

Source
Camutek
39 Newnham Road
Cambridge CB3 9EY
UK
Telephone Cambridge (0223) 69686

Availability
From owner

Language
Basic

Computer
Hewlett-Packard
9830 (2k) or (6k)

413

Program name
Plane-frame elastic analysis

Abstract
This program analyses plane frames which are statistically indeterminate. It gives the axial and shear forces and the bending moments at each end of every member. It also gives the deflection at every point on the structure

References

Source
Camutek
39 Newnham Road
Cambridge CB3 9EY
UK
Telephone Cambridge (0223) 69686

Availability
From owner

Language
Basic

Computer
Hewlett-Packard
9830 (2k) or (6k)

414

Program name
SGR2 and SGR3 grillage analysis

Abstract
These programs analyse the effects of normal loading on plane grids, with or without shear deformation. Simple mnemonic loadings exist for self-weight, HA, HB, strip loads, area loads and other loads encountered in bridge-deck analysis. Post-processing programs can combine load conditions with envelopes. These programs are approved by HECB

References
Idealisation manual 46·017
User manuals PS/25, PS/26

Source
Cement and Concrete Association
Wexham Springs
Slough SL3 6PL
UK
Telephone Fulmer 2727 Telex 848352

Availability
Bureau service

Language
Algol
Plan

Computer
ICL 1903A

415

Program name
FRAME

Abstract
This program performs the elastic analysis of plane frames by the stiffness method, with additional features. The version of stiffness analysis used assumes small-deflection theory. Frames are made up of straight uniform members connected at nodal points. Various types of connection can be made between members and loads can be applied horizontally, vertically, rotationally and normal to members

References
Bradshaw, Buckton and Tonge

Source
Civil and Structural Computing (Northern) Limited
14 Bramley Centre
Leeds LS13 2ET
Telephone 0532 563322

Availability
Bureau service, time-sharing, in-house

Language

Computer
Hewlett Packard
9800 and others

416

Program name
DSIGN

Abstract
This program carries out the plastic design of the portal frame defined in DTAIL. The program can be run interactively, allowing the engineer to make pertinent decisions and providing accurate design and estimating information quickly. Foundation reactions, bending moments and restraint information are output, together with section sizes and weights

References
Bradshaw, Buckton and Tonge

Source
Civil and Structural Computing (Northern) Limited
14 Bramley Centre
Leeds LS13 2ET
Telephone Pudsey (0532) 563322

Availability
Bureau service, time-sharing, in-house

Language

Computer

417

Program name
D4 package (DTAIL, DSIGN, DFLEC and DPICT)

Abstract
This is a suite of programs which carries out the plastic design and elastic analysis of multi-bay portal frames, used especially in industrial and agricultural buildings

References
Bradshaw, Buckton and Tonge

Source
Civil and Structural Computing (Northern) Limited
14 Bramley Centre
Leeds LS13 2ET
Telephone Pudsey (0532) 563322

Availability
Bureau service, time-sharing, in-house

Language

Computer

418

Program name
DFLEC

Abstract
This program (part of the D4 package) is used to carry out an elastic deflection analysis under working-load conditions of a portal frame. The program is run interactively and if the deflections of the frame are critical, then the engineer can alter eaves and apex haunches and section sizes to obtain a more acceptable design. In this way, each design can be assessed and the economics of alternative designs compared

References
Bradshaw, Buckton and Tonge

Source
Civil and Structural Computing (Northern) Limited
14 Bramley Centre
Leeds LS13 2ET
Telephone Pudsey (0523) 563322

Availability
Bureau service, time-sharing, in-house

Language

Computer

419

Program name
DTAIL

Abstract
This program forms part of the D4 package. It calculates input frame data-geometry, haunching requirements, feet fixity and loading. The data can be easily corrected or altered and can be stored on disc for future use

References
Bradshaw, Buckton and Tonge

Source
Civil and Structural Computing (Northern) Limited
14 Bramley Centre
Leeds LS13 2ET
Telephone Pudsey (0532) 563322

Availability
Bureau service, time-sharing, in-house

Language

Computer

420

Program name
EVCON

Abstract
This program makes an analysis of a bolted column/beam moment connection. Column/rafter sections, haunch depth/length and bolt details are input by the engineer. Six loadings can be applied and each load can consist of a moment and a vertical shear

References
Bradshaw, Buckton and Tonge

Source
Civil and Structural Computing (Northern) Limited
14 Bramley Centre
Leeds LS13 2ET
Telephone Pudsey (0532) 563322

Availability
Bureau service, time-sharing, in-house

Language

Computer
Hewlett Packard 9800 and others

421

Program name
GRID

Abstract
This program analyses a plane grid of simply-supported beam elements subject to static vertical loading. The loading can be a combination of point loads, moments and uniformly-distributed loads applied directly to members. Axial loading on individual members can also be input. The program calculates the loading on every member due to the loads input and loads transferred from other members. Beam end reactions are output

References
Bradshaw, Buckton and Tonge

Source
Civil and Structural Computing (Northern) Limited
14 Bramley Centre
Leeds LS13 2ET
Telephone 0532 563322

Availability
Bureau service, time-sharing, in-house

Language

Computer
Hewlett Packard 9800 and others

422

Program name
DPICT

Abstract
This program, which is part of the D4 package, plots the deflected forms of a portal frame and the plastic bending moment diagrams. The designs can then be visually assessed

References
Bradshaw, Buckton and Tonge

Source
Civil and Structural Computing (Northern) Limited
14 Bramley Centre
Leeds LS13 2ET
Telephone Pudsey (0532) 563322

Availability
Bureau service, time-sharing, in-house

Language

Computer

423

Program name
Analysis of plane frames and grids

Abstract
This program calculates shear, bending moments, deflections and rotations on a two-dimensional rigidly-jointed frame

References
Program made available by ICL

Source
Computel Limited
Eastern Road
Bracknell, Berkshire
UK
Telephone Bracknell 23031

Availability

Language

Computer

424

Program name
PLANE

Abstract
This frame analysis to BS CP114:1969 is one of a suite of analysis programs. The program will calculate deflection, moments, shear, axial forces and support reactions along continuous beam and plane frames. The program is capable of making the best envelopes to reduce moments. Outputs include moment envelopes at one-tenth centres along each beam

References

Source
Computer Consortium Services Ltd
5 Windmill Street
London W1P 1HF
UK
Telephone 01–638 3118

Availability
Bureau service

Language
Fortran

Computer
CDC
IBM
PDP

425

Program name
Marc-CDC

Abstract
This program is for linear and non-linear finite element analysis of structures under static and dynamic loads. A comprehensive library of elements is available for modelling

References
Danish Building Research Institute
Abstract 48 11 003

Source
Control Data
Sonder Boulevard 35
1720 Copenhagen V
Denmark

Availability
Bureau service

Language

Computer

426

Program name
STARDYNE

Abstract
A suite of programs for the analysis of linear elastic structures exposed to static, dynamic, thermal and other shock loads. The finite element method is used

References
Danish Building Research Institute
Abstract 48 11 006

Source
Control Data
Sonder Boulevard 35
1720 Copenhagen K
Denmark

Availability
Bureau service

Language

Computer

427

Program name
INSTRUCTA

Abstract
This program provides a two-dimensional structural analysis of the majority of plane structures which comprise rod, beam and membrane elements. It can also be used to create data for the program ELAS

References

Source
CRC Engineering Services
83 Clerkenwell Road
London
EC1R 5HP
Telephone 01–242 0747

Availability

Language

Computer

428

Program name
FRAME

Abstract
This program uses the Hardy-Cross method of moment distribution for the analysis of simple rectilinear plane frames. The geometry of a multi-storey frame can be described by specifying the number of bays and the storeys above them, together with their respective dimensions. The program can be extended to allow the input of parameters for automatic calculation of dead load, and will take beam, joint and wind loads

References

Source
CRC Engineering Services
83 Clerkenwell Road
London
EC1R 5HP
Telephone 01–242 0747

Availability

Language

Computer

429

Program name
POPDES 1, POPDES 3

Abstract
This program determines a plastic design for unbraced two-dimensional frames which are orthogonal, (apart from sloping exterior columns ie a tapered framework). Constraints on the horizontal deflection of any floor under working loads can be specified. Particular members in the framework can be specified to be either universal beams or universal columns, and nominated members with the same section may be specified

References

Source
CSIRO, Division of Building Research
Graham Road, Highett
Victoria 3190
Australia
Telephone 95 0333

Availability
ACADS

Language
Fortran IV

Computer
CDC 6600, Cyber 74

430

Program name
PUNDES

Abstract
This program determines a plastic design for unbraced two-dimensional frames which are orthogonal. Design of individual members is to the plastic design requirements of the steel structures code AS 1250–1975. Any available grade of steel can be specified for the individual members, and upper and lower limits placed on their size. The program can handle frameworks of up to eight bays and forty-eight storeys

References

Source
CSIRO, Division of Building Research
Graham Road, Highett
Victoria 3190
Australia
Telephone 95 0333

Availability
ACADS

Language
Fortran IV

Computer
CDC 7400, Cyber 74

431

Program name
MULT

Abstract
This program performs a static linear elastic analysis of framed structures using the stiffness method. It can be used to analyse plane trusses, frames and grids, as well as space trusses. Specific provision is made in the program for repetitive joint and member patterns, so that it can also be used for multi-storey frames in two or three dimensions. Shear walls, as equivalent columns, and rigid in-plane floor systems can be represented

References

Source
CSIRO, Division of Building Research
Graham Road, Highett
Victoria 3190
Australia
Telephone 95 0333

Availability

Language
Fortran

Computer
CDC 7400

Program name
ELAPLA

Abstract
This program is for the analysis of plane frames. The non-linear plasticity method is used, based on the calculation of the most dangerous breaking-point. The program finds the meeting-points and calculates, at every step, the beam strengths and deflections, so that it can be determined whether there is sufficient capacity for rotation in the elements

References

Source
Danmarks Ingeniorakademi
Bygningsafdelingen
Bygning 373
2800 Lyngby
Denmark

Availability

Language
Fortran

Computer
IBM 370/165

433

Program name
201P Plastic analysis

Abstract
This program performs a linear plane-frame analysis with provisions for calculating plastic collapse. It lists the data on the geometry and calculations involved in setting up the initial stiffness matrix for each load. Using an elastic analysis, the given load is applied and the deformations and moments calculated. Values representing the remaining load are applied to the model of the modified structure and the position of new hinges is calculated

References
ECLIPSE program library

Source
Electronic Calculus Limited
344 to 350 Euston Road
London NW1 3BJ
UK
Telephone 01–388 7705, Telex 27192

Availability
Purchase, hire, bureau service

Language
Fortran V

Computer
Univac 1106, 1108
CDC 6600, 7600
DEC System 10
IBM
ICL

434

Program name
FRAME

Abstract
This program analyses plane frames on elastic supports. It employs the same methods as STRESS, but makes its calculations more quickly, can analyse much larger structures and includes many plotting facilities. Loads are imposed on the structure and the resultant output includes nodal displacement, forces at member ends, support reactions and residual joint loads (to corroborate the accuracy of the solution)

References

Source
Faber Computer Operations Limited
Upper Marlborough Road
St Albans
Herts AL1 3UT
Telephone St Albans 61222

Availability
Bureau service

Language

Computer
IBM 1130, System 7

435

Program name
GRID

Abstract
This program makes a grid analysis of plane grillages on elastic supports. It employs similar methods to the grid facilities of STRESS, but will make its calculations more quickly, can analyse larger grillages and includes plotting facilities. Loads are imposed on the grillage and the resultant output includes nodal displacements, forces at member ends, support reactions and residual joint loads (to corroborate the accuracy of the solution)

References

Source
Faber Computer Operations Limited
Upper Marlborough Road
St Albans
Herts AL1 3UT
Telephone St Albans 61222

Availability
Bureau service

Language

Computer
IBM 1130, System 7

436

Program name
PLANE

Abstract
This program analyses in-plane loadings on finite elements. The slice of material is divided into a triangular mesh, each triangle representing a region of constant stress. Loads are imposed and the resultant output gives listings of nodal displacements, stresses and directions in each element, support reactions and residual joint loads (to corroborate the accuracy of the solution). Principal stresses may be plotted, if required

References

Source
Faber Computer Operations Limited
Upper Marlborough Road
St Albans
Herts AL1 3UT
Telephone St Albans 61222

Availability
Bureau service

Language

Computer
IBM 1130, System 7

Program name
SUBFRAME/1

Abstract
This sub-system enables a designer to analyse simple frames consisting of a beam string with column lifts above and below, in accordance with BS CP110:Part 1:1972 or BS CP114:1969

References
GENESYS program library

Source
GENESYS Limited
Pennine House, Lemyngton Street
Loughborough, Leicestershire
LE11 1XA, UK
Telephone 0509 39185 Telex 341747

Availability
Bureau service, hire

Language
Gentran

Computer
CDC 6500, 6600, 7600
Honeywell 6000
IBM 360, 370
ICL 1900, System 4
Philips P1400
PRIME 300
Univac 1100

438

Program name
Plane frame

Abstract
This program analyses stress in plane frames and grids

References
Danish Building Research Institute
Abstract 48 11 505

Source
Geodata A/S
Dagmarhus
HC Andersens Boulevard 7
1553 Copenhagen V
Denmark

Availability
Bureau service

Language

Computer

439

Program name
Plane grids

Abstract
This program calculates static loads in plane grids. Frames with up to thirty nodes can be handled

References
Danish Building Research Institute
Abstract 48 11 801

Source
Geodata A/S
Dagmarhus
HC Andersens Boulevard 7
1553 Copenhagen V
Denmark

Availability
Bureau service

Language

Computer

440

Program name
Modified moment distribution

Abstract
This program solves modified frames or continuous beams which may be coplanar or of prismatic or variable section. They may have up to twenty spans with uniform loads and/or any number of concentrated loads per span for up to twenty-one loading conditions. Beam-column joints may be loaded with concentrated moments to account for cross-beam torsions or end-joint cantilevers

References
Part number 09830–74210. Part number 09830–74211 (faster program)

Source
Hewlett-Packard Limited
King Street Lane, Winnersh
Wokingham, Berks RG11 5AR
UK
Telephone Wokingham 784774

Availability
Purchase

Language
Basic

Computer
HP 9830A

441

Program name
LUCAS (R01041)

Abstract
This is a finite element program for linear static analysis of plane or axisymmetric structures. The following loads are applicable, distributed asymmetric loads, gravity and centrifugal loads, shrinkage, forced deformations and temperature loads

References
R19001 PREALEX and R02013 ALEXANDER

Source
Industridata AB
Fack
Solna, Sweden
171 20
Telephone 08 98 03 50

Availability
Contact owner

Language
Fortran IV

Computer
Honeywell H6080

Program name
LUCAS III (R01044)

Abstract
This is a finite element program dealing with small deformations in plane or axisymmetric structures. Static (elastic/plastic) analysis is carried out. The following loads are applicable, gravity and centrifugal loads, shrinkage, forced deformations and temperature. Temperature dependent properties of materials are allowed

References
R19001 PREALEX and R02013 ALEXANDER

Source
Industridata AB
Fack
Solna, Sweden
171 20
Telephone 08 98 03 50

Availability
Contact owner

Language
Fortran IV

Computer
Honeywell H6080

443

Program name
MATSTR

Abstract
This program calculates maximum tension and points of maximum stress in plane constructions of rectangular cross-section. The mathematical model constructed by the program distinguishes between joints and linear elements

References
Danish Building Research Institute Abstract 48 11 504

Source
Ingeniorfirma FRI
Ny Kongensgade 21
1557 Kobenhavn K
Denmark

Availability
Bureau service

Language
Fortran

Computer
Univac 1106

444

Program name
PLASTE

Abstract
This program analyses plane frames under an arbitrary number of loads. Either linear elastic or elastic/plastic analysis is carried out. The theory of the program is as examined in Plastic Analysis of Structures, PG Hodge, and The Plastic Methods of Structural Analysis, PG Hodge

References
Danish Building Research Institute Abstract 48 11 506

Source
Ingeniorfirma FRI
Ny Kongensgade 21
1557 Kobenhavn K
Denmark

Availability
Bureau service

Language
Fortran

Computer
Univac 1106

445

Program name
Plane-frame analysis

Abstract
This program analyses plane frames (including ring frames and continuous beams) of up to twelve joints and fifteen members. It gives the displacements of joints, reactions of supports and forces on members

References

Source
John FS Pryke and Partners Limited
105 Fonthill Road
London N4 3JH
UK
Telephone 01–272 9144

Availability
From owner

Language
Basic

Computer
Hewlett-Packard 9830

446

Program name
XEBECQ

Abstract
This program performs a finite-element analysis, using curvilinear quadrilateral elements, of plane or axisymmetric linearly elastic bodies. Plate flexure, including shear effects, is also included. Results are presented graphically

References

Source
Markworth Design Consultants Limited
Coppers, Pyrford Heath
Surrey GU22 8SR
UK
Telephone Byfleet 41088, 41013

Availability
Bureau service

Language
Fortran

Computer
ICL 1904A

447

Program name
DAGS

Abstract
This program performs undamped dynamic analysis of beam-type structures, using a general stiffness or displacement method with either lumped or consistent mass. It will determine natural frequencies, node shapes of beam structures, member forces, potential and kinetic energies, buckling loads and displacement shapes for complex structures

References

Source
Structural Dynamics Research Corporation
5729 Dragon Way
Cincinnati, Ohio 45227
USA
Telephone (513) 272 1100

Availability
Time sharing. Available in UK

Language

Computer
CDC 6500

448

Program name
53–T17

Abstract
This program calculates tensions, reactions and deflections in a three-dimensional structural frame, influenced by arbitrary strength and temperature distributions. The program is based on the deformation method. Wholly– or partly-rigid beam elements can be handled, to avoid too large a reduction in the accuracy of the calculation when some beams are more rigid than others. The frame can be drawn in perspective or with spatial effect

References

Source
A/S Regnecentralen
Falkoneralle 1
2000 Copenhagen F
Denmark
Telephone (01) 10 53 66

Availability

Language

Computer

449

Program name
FRAMEM

Abstract
This program makes a static elastic analysis of frames consisting of straight, prismatic members. Six types of frame can be analysed: continuous beam, plane truss, plane frame, grid, space truss and space frame. Facilities are provided for generation of repetitious data to simplify preparation of input. Loads can be applied directly to joints, or as concentrated, uniform or triangular loads to members, along the axis of member or structure

References
ACADS (Melbourne)

Source
The Association for Computer Aided Design Limited
576 St Kilda Road
Melbourne 3004, Victoria
Australia
Telephone (03) 51 9153

Availability
Contact ACADS

Language
Fortran IV

Computer
Univac 1108, CDC 6600, Burroughs 6700, Cyber 72

450

Program name
SPACE

Abstract
This program analyses three-dimensional structural frames under a variety of loading conditions

References

Source
Atkins Computer Services Limited
Woodcote Grove, Ashley Road
Epsom, Surrey
UK
Telephone Epsom 40421

Availability
Bureau service, time-sharing. Available in Netherlands

Language
Fortran

Computer
Honeywell Sigma 9

451

Program name
B & W FINEL

Abstract
This program is for analysis of stress owing to stationary and transient heat conduction in two– and three-dimensional structures. Isotherms and heat-current functions can be output. It is possible to examine structures composed of different materials with various conditions of surface temperature

References
Danish Building Research Institute
Abstract 48 14 010

Source
B & W Engineering
Torvegarde 2
1449 Copenhagen K
Denmark

Availability
Bureau service

Language
Fortran

Computer
Univac 1106

Program name
B & W FINEL

Abstract
This is a general program allowing the calculation of tension and deformation in arbitrary two– and three-dimensional constructions. Isoperimetric elements capable of similar movement are used, which also makes the program suitable for use with curved structures. It can be used as an iterative program to deal with non-linear problems

References
Danish Building Research Institute
Abstract 48 11 002

Source
B & W Engineering
Torvegarde 2
1449 Copenhagen K
Denmark

Availability
Bureau service

Language
Fortran

Computer
Univac 1106

453

Program name
SAP IV

Abstract
This is a general program allowing the calculation of deformation and tension in arbitrary one–, two– or three-dimensional linear elastic structures with different surface temperatures, subject to static and dynamic loads. The program uses elements with compatible fields of movement: the library of elements contains bars, beams, pipes, plates, shells and various symmetrical forms

References
Danish Building Research Institute
Abstract 48 11 005

Source
B & W Engineering
Torvegarde 2
1449 Copenhagen K
Denmark

Availability
Bureau service

Language

Computer
Univac 1106

454

Program name
STRESS

Abstract
The program analyses two– or three-dimensional frames, trusses and plane grids, comprising slender prismatic members. It deals with loadings on members and member joints, the effects of displacements and rotations at support joints, temperature changes and subsequent distortions in members. The form of input is such that the user defines his problem in simple terms by a 'shorthand'. The type and volume of output can be controlled

References

Source
Building Computer Services Limited
Bush House
72 Prince Street
Bristol BS1 4HU
Telephone 0272 290651

Availability
Bureau service, hire

Language

Computer

455

Program name
Structural frames

Abstract
This program calculates stress and tension in plane and space frames

References

Source
CE-data
Lundtoftevej 1G
2800 Lyngby
Denmark

Availability
Bureau service

Language

Computer

456

Program name
Glued-wood frames

Abstract
This program allows the design of wood frames with curved corners such that the volume of wood used is as small as possible. Calculations are carried out to DS413:1974 and DS410:1966

References

Source
CE-data
Lundtoftevej 1G
2800 Lyngby
Denmark

Availability
Bureau service

Language

Computer

457

Program name
Space frame analysis

Abstract
This program calculates shear, bending moments, deflections and rotations on a three-dimensional rigidly-jointed frame

References
Program made available by ICL

Source
Computel Limited
Eastern Road
Bracknell, Berkshire
UK
Telephone Bracknell 23031

Availability

Language

Computer

458

Program name
DYNADATA

Abstract
This program has been designed to prepare finite-element analyses of structures so that they may be stored as digital models in the computer. This enables the user to build up complex shapes from basic ones such as pyramids, prisms and cylinders, and define what may be part or the whole of the completed structure. The digital model created may be viewed and manipulated by the DYNADRAW or DYNASHADE programs

References

Source
Computer Aided Design Centre
Madingley Road
Cambridge CB3 0HB
Cambridgeshire UK

Availability
Hire

Language
Fortran

Computer

459

Program name
STRUDL

Abstract
This sub-system allows a user to specify data concerning two and three-dimensional structures consisting of truss, frame and continuous finite elements. A variety of analyses may then be performed. Information about a structure may be stored, retrieved and manipulated

References
NBRI (SA) abstract X/BOU-COMP 3

Source
Computer Centre, University of the Witwatersrand
Milner Park
Johannesburg
South Africa
Telephone Johannesburg 724–7009

Availability
Bureau service

Language

Computer

460

Program name
LEAP

Abstract
General frame analysis; the basic program in a suite of analysis programs. The program can calculate deflections, member forces, shears, moments, support reactions and stresses for all types of framework, including buildings, bridges, marine structures, portals, boxes, girders etc. This program has been approved by the Department of the Environment

References

Source
Computer Consortium Services Ltd
5 Windmill Street
London W1P 1HF
UK
Telephone 01–638 3118

Availability
Bureau service

Language
Fortran

Computer
CDC
IBM
PDP

461

Program name
RENUMBER

Abstract
This program reduces the joint difference and cost of a LEAP analysis. It is one of a suite of analysis programs

References

Source
Computer Consortium Services Ltd
5 Windmill Street
London W1P 1HF
UK
Telephone 01–638 3118

Availability
Bureau service

Language
Fortran

Computer
CDC
IBM
PDP

Program name
ELAS

Abstract
A general-purpose digital program for solving linear equilibrium problems in structural mechanics. Solutions are obtained by the displacement method and finite-element technique. Almost any geometry and structure may be handled, and for elements which are not linear, a linear interpolation rule is used to compute deflections between mesh-points

References
Program made available by Technical Computer Sharing International Limited

Source
CRC Engineering Services
83 Clerkenwell Road
London
EC1R 5HP
Telephone 01–242 0747

Availability
Time sharing, remote batch

Language

Computer

463

Program name
STRESS

Abstract
A program for the elastic analysis of trussed or frame structures, comprising beams or rods. The analysis may be carried out in two or three dimensions, and applied to pinned, hinged or rigidly-jointed structures. The problem may be described by a series of English-language statements and an unlimited number of load cases may be solved. The program also offers an experimental transient analysis

References

Source
CRC Engineering Services
83 Clerkenwell Road
London
EC1R 5HP
Telephone 01–242 0747

Availability

Language

Computer

464

Program name
VISTA

Abstract
VISTA 2 gives a vibration analysis of space frames by using an eigenvalue technique to determine a specified number of normal modes of vibration and the corresponding frequencies. VISTA 1 is a more comprehensive version of VISTA 2, involving different analyses and types of element. VISTA 1 can undertake the analysis of structures composed of beams and plates, and can determine vibration modes or modes of buckling under excessive load

References
Program made available by Engineering Programs and Services Limited

Source
CRC Engineering Services
83 Clerkenwell Road
London
EC1R 5HP
Telephone 01–242 0747

Availability

Language

Computer

465

Program name
PARBEL

Abstract
This program is used for analysis of finite elements, covering orthotropic conditions of stress between planes. Three types of quadratic edge-displacement element are available: eight-node rectangular, six-node triangular and eight-node isoparametric quadrilateral. A three-node line-element that can resist axial loads only is also included. The program includes orthotropic properties of materials that can vary from element to element

References

Source
CSIRO, Division of Building Research
Graham Road, Highett
Victoria 3190
Australia
Telephone 95 0333

Availability

Language
Fortran

Computer
CDC 7600

466

Program name
BPLUS

Abstract
This program produces a plastic design of traced rectilinear steel frames using the theory of a strong column/weak beam. All loads and moments are assumed to be applied in the plane of the frame. Each adjacent frame linking girders must be simply connected to the web of columns. Beams and columns are chosen to satisfy the plastic design requirements set out in section 10 of the steel structures code AS 1250–1975

References

Source
CSIRO, Division of Building Research
Graham Road, Highett
Victoria 3190
Australia
Telephone 95 0333

Availability
ACADS

Language
Fortran IV

Computer
CDC 6600, Cyber 74

467

Program name
ELFRAME

Abstract
This program produces designs for two- or three-dimensional frames made from prismatic and hollow steel members with up to eight load conditions. Design is on the basis that the allowable stress is approached under at least one loading condition. Members can have pinned or fixed ends. Types of section available for selection include universal beams, universal columns, castellated beams, open-web joists

References

Source
CSIRO, Division of Building Research
Graham Road, Highett
Victoria 3190
Australia
Telephone 95 0333

Availability
ACADS

Language
Fortran IV

Computer
CDC 6600, Cyber 74

468

Program name
SPACE

Abstract
This program, based on the matrix displacement method, can be used for either linear elastic analysis or design of a general space framework, under any number of loading conditions. A maximum of 96 sections can be made available for the design of the steel members. Successive analysis and design cycles are specified as a means of achieving a fully-stressed design of the steel members in the framework

References

Source
CSIRO, Division of Building Research
Graham Road, Highett
Victoria 3190
Australia
Telephone 95 0333

Availability
ACADS

Language
Fortran IV

Computer
CDC 6600, Cyber 74

469

Program name
DYNAMIC

Abstract
This program carries out a linear-elastic dynamic analysis of soil or building structures. The program analyses plane structures and consists of three main parts: STRDYN, FREQ and DYNAM. STRDYN collates the global rigidity matrix and the mass matrix and carries out static analysis. FREQ determines oscillations and bending of the structure. DYNAM decides the response from earthquake accelerations or sine form accelerations

References

Source
Danmarks Ingeniorakademi
Bygningsafdelingen
Bygning 373
2800 Lyngby
Denmark

Availability

Language
Fortran

Computer
IBM 370/165

470

Program name
ASKA

Abstract
This is a general system for conducting static and dynamic analysis of one–, two– and three–dimensional constructions under arbitrary load conditions. Linear elastic, static and elastic/plastic elements can be considered under static loads. Oscillation from dynamic loads on linear and non–linear damped systems can be considered

References
Danish Building Research Institute
Abstract 48 11 001

Source
Danmarks tekniske, Hojskole
Afd f Baerende Konstruktioner
Bygning 118
2800 Lyngby
Denmark

Availability
Bureau service (IKO software)

Language

Computer

471

Program name
FRAME

Abstract
This program is intended for the analysis of structural frames of multi-storey buildings. It is specifically geared to the repetitive construction of multi-storey buildings, so that a twenty-storey building can be defined in less than thirty data statements. The results list the effects of bending deformation throughout, and axial and shear deformations in columns and walls, and give a finite element analysis.

References

Source
Department of Architectural Science
The University of Sydney
Sydney
New South Wales 2006
Australia

Availability
Sale, bureau service

Language
Fortran IV

Computer
Univac 1108
Univac 1106
CDC 6600, Cyber 72

Program name
1441 Three-dimensional finite-element analysis

Abstract
This program determines, for each loading condition or combination, translations and rotations of joints; internal efforts of beams, quadrilateral and triangular panels, and solid elements; tri-axial corner forces and stresses at all nodes of twenty-node and thirty-two-node solid elements; and reactions. The maximum number of joints, elements and loading conditions is limited only by the computer configuration used

References
ECLIPSE program library

Source
Electronic Calculus Limited
344 to 350 Euston Road
London NW1 3BJ
UK
Telephone 01–388 7705, Telex 27192

Availablility
Purchase, hire, bureau service

Language
Fortran V

Computer
Univac 1106, 1108
CDC 6600, 7600
DEC System 10
IBM
ICL

473

Program name
641–602 Static analysis and automatic design of steel structures

Abstract
This program produces lists of those selected members capable of supporting the corresponding governing combinations of loading conditions and satisfying the pertinent requirements of codes of practice and engineering criteria. It also gives the maximum stresses, the ratios of actual and admissible stresses, and the total structural weight of members

References
ECLIPSE program library

Source
Electronic Calculus Limited
344 to 350 Euston Road
London NW1 3BJ
UK
Telephone 01–388 7705, Telex 27192

Availability
Purchase, hire, bureau service

Language
Fortran V

Computer
Univac 1106, 1108
CDC 6600, 7600
DEC System 10
IBM
ICL

474

Program name
201–641C Two– and three-dimensional frame analysis

Abstract
This program determines, for each loading condition or combination, translations and rotations of joints; axial and shear forces on each member; bending and torsional moments; and reactions. The maximum number of joints, members and loading conditions is limited only by the computer configuration used. Members of different materials and with semi-rigid connections are acceptable and, for straight members, variable section

References
ECLIPSE program library

Source
Electronic Calculus Limited
344 to 350 Euston Road
London NW1 3BJ
UK
Telephone 01–388 7705, Telex 27192

Availability
Purchase, hire, bureau service

Language
Fortran V

Computer
Univac 1106, 1108
CDC 6600, 7600
DEC System 10
IBM
ICL

475

Program name
STRESS

Abstract
This program analyses plane frames, trusses and grids, and space frames and trusses. A number of loading conditions may be analysed in one run, and up to six loading conditions may be integrated by a combined instruction. Pins may be inserted, and temperature stresses and displacements may be imposed on the defined structure. Joint displacements, end forces on members and support reactions may be output

References

Source
Faber Computer Operations Limited
Upper Marlborough Romd
St Albans
Herts AL1 3UT
Telephone St Albans 61222

Availability
Bureau service

Language

Computer
IBM 1130, System 7

476

Program name
SPACE

Abstract
This program analyses rigid space frames or elastic supports. It will analyse larger structures and work to greater accuracy than STRESS and can consider spring supports and support displacements. Nodal displacements are listed in the output, together with axial, shear and bending moment forces at member ends, and support reactions. An isometric or perspective diagram can be plotted, numbered or unnumbered

References

Source
Faber Computer Operations Limited
Upper Marlborough Road
St Albans
Herts AL1 3UT
Telephone St Albans 61222

Availability
Bureau service

Language

Computer
IBM 1130, System 7

477

Program name
Frame analysis/2

Abstract
This sub-system enables an engineer to analyse a frame which may be a space frame, a plane frame loaded in its own plane or a grid loaded normal to its own plane. The number of members, joints and loading conditions which may be considered is not limited by the sub-system. The size of problem to be handled is limited only by the size and type of computer used

References
GENESYS program library

Source
GENESYS Limited
Pennine House, Lemyngton Street
Loughborough, Leicestershire
LE11 1XA, UK
Telephone 0509 39185 Telex 341747

Availability
Bureau service, hire

Language
Gentran

Computer
CDC 6500, 6600, 7600
DEC 10
Honeywell 6000
IBM 360, 370
ICL 1900, System 4
Philips P1400
PRIME 300
Univac 1100

478

Program name
ST10

Abstract
This program analyses plane and space frames and grids. Point loads at nodes and stress within each element are calculated. The program can handle up to 250 elements, 125 nodes and six loading cases in one run

References
Danish Building Research Institute
Abstract 48 11 402

Source
Geodata A/S
Dagmarhus
HC Andersens Boulevard 7
1553 Copenhagen V
Denmark

Availability
Bureau service

Language

Computer

479

Program name
Multi-storey moment distribution

Abstract
This program produces final end moments, end shears and axial forces for each member in a given frame of up to twenty storeys (fifty storeys if using peripheral cassette memory) and ten bays. Frames must be orthogonal and have members of constant section. (A program requiring peripheral cassette memory for members with variable cross-sectional properties is also available)

References
Part number 09830–74220. Part number 09830–74221. Part number 09830–74222

Source
Hewlett-Packard Limited
King Street Lane, Winnersh
Wokingham, Berks RG11 5AR
UK
Telephone Wokingham 784774

Availability
Purchase

Language
Basic

Computer
HP 9830A

480

Program name
Space-frame analysis

Abstract
This program provides a linear analysis of three-dimensional structural frames with up to 400 jointed sub-frames. Joint movements, member end forces, moments and reactions are calculated. Total loadings may consist of joint loadings, support settlement and concentrated, uniform, linear or temperature-change loadings on members. Supports may be assumed rigid or in one or all of six degrees of freedom

References
Part number 09830–74225

Source
Hewlett-Packard Limited
King Street Lane, Winnersh
Wokingham, Berks RG11 5AR
UK
Telephone Wokingham 784774

Availability
Purchase

Language
Basic

Computer
HP 9830A with 7904–word memory
11270B matrix ROM
11274B strings ROM
9880B mass memory
9866A thermal printer

481

Program name
STRESS (Structural engineering systems solver)

Abstract
This package is capable of analysing various types of structural system including two– or three–dimensional structures, pin-connected or rigid frames, grids and structures with non-prismatic members. Built-in messages allow the input to be made in engineering terminology

References
Mark III software library
User manual 5202·01

Source
Honeywell Information Systems Limited
114 to 118 Southampton Row
London WC1B 5AB
UK
Telephone 01–242 5725

Availability
Bureau service

Language
Basic

Computer
Honeywell 6000 series

Program name
WINDAS

Abstract
This program uses the slope-deflection method to perform analyses of lateral forces (such as wind stress) in indeterminate structures such as multi-storey rigid-frame buildings

References
Mark III software library
User manual 5202·13

Source
Honeywell Information Systems Limited
114 to 118 Southampton Row
London WC1B 5AB
UK
Telephone 01–242 5725

Availability
Bureau service

Language
Basic

Computer
Honeywell 6000 series

483

Program name
RAMSES (R01054)

Abstract
This is a finite-element program for linear static and dynamic analysis of general frame and shell structures. Dynamic analysis includes modal analysis, time history due to transient and harmonic loads, and response spectrum analysis. Concentrated and distributed loads, temperature loads, forced deformations and loads of inertia are applicable

References

Source
Industridata AB
Fack
Solna, Sweden
171 20
Telephone 08 98 03 50

Availability
Contact owner

Language
Fortran IV

Computer
Honeywell H6080

484

Program name
Shell calculations (R01002, R01023, R01030)

Abstract
The program carries out stress calculations of symmetrical shells asymmetrically loaded. Combined shells can be calculated

References

Source
Industridata AB
Fack
Solna, Sweden
171 20
Telephone 08 98 03 50

Availability
Contact owner

Language
Fortran

Computer
Honeywell 6000

485

Program name
Frame calculation (R01025)

Abstract
This is a program for the calculation of stresses in frames. Loads, temperature changes, springs and deformations are calculated

References

Source
Industridata AB
Fack
Solna, Sweden
171 20
Telephone 08 98 03 50

Availability
Contact owner

Language
Fortran

Computer
Honeywell 6000

486

Program name
SPACE

Abstract
This program analyses space frames under an arbitrary number of loads. The method is as examined in all standard works (eg Analysis of Framed Structures, JM Gene and W Weaver). Stress and tension in all members is calculated

References
Danish Building Research Institute
Abstract 48 11 404

Source
Ingeniorfirma FRI
Ny Kongensgade 21
1557 Copenhagen K
Denmark

Availability
Bureau service

Language
Fortran

Computer
Univac 1106

487

Program name
Structural analysis

Abstract
This program computes the joint rotations and displacements, moments, shear and axial forces in orthogonal frame structures under static loads. The moments, and shear and axial forces, are computed at the ends of members and at equidistant sections in each member. The number of such sections is specified by the user, but must be the same for all members. A structure may contain prismatic or non-prismatic members

References

Source
Laing Computing Services
Elstree Way
Borehamwood
Hertfordshire
WD6 1NF, UK
Telephone 01–207 2000

Availability
Sale, bureau service

Language
Fortran

Computer
IBM 370–50

488

Program name
STRESS

Abstract
This program makes a linear analysis of elastic, statically loaded structures composed of slender prismatic members ie members which can be represented by their centroidal axis and analysed as line elements. The structure may extend in either two or three dimensions and members may be pin-jointed or rigidly connected to each other

References

Source
Laing Computing Services
Elstree Way
Borehamwood
Hertfordshire
WD6 1NF, UK
Telephone 01–207 2000

Availability
Sale, bureau service

Language
Fortran

Computer
IBM 370–50

489

Program name
STRUDL II/1 & 2

Abstract
A suite of programs for solving engineering design problems which can be used for both two– and three-dimensional structural frames. Analysis of reinforced concrete constructions can also be carried out. The stiffness matrix method is used for analysis. The programs can handle frames with an unlimited number of elements

References
Danish Building Research Institute,
Abstract 48 11 008

Source
Maersk data
Titangade 11
2200 Copenhagen N
Denmark

Availability
Bureau service

Language

Computer

490

Program name
THEANER

Abstract
This program gives static and dynamic analyses of two– and three-dimensional frames. Output includes member forces, joint displacements, reactions and equilibrium, member properties, joint loading table, plotted or digital envelope diagrams for bending moments and shear forces, natural-frequency and mode curves, displacements and forces resulting from a forced vibration, and perspectives

References

Source
Markworth Design Consultants Limited
Coppers, Pyrford Heath
Surrey GU22 8SR
UK
Telephone Byfleet 41088, 41013

Availability
Bureau service

Language
Fortran

Computer
CDC 6500

491

Program name
A10

Abstract
This program determines forces in any statically-determinate pin-jointed triangulated frame. Any loading arrangement is acceptable and multiple loads can be applied at nodes. The frame is defined by node co-ordinates and node linking. Loads are defined by node number, magnitude and direction. All errors in input can be corrected by a user-orientated error procedure

References
NBRI (South Africa) abstract
X/BOU-COMP 9

Source
Metricomp Programmes (Pty) Limited
PO Box 4
Johannesburg 2000
South Africa
Telephone Johannesburg 41–8501

Availability
Subscription service

Language

Computer
Hewlett-Packard
9820A

492

Program name
STIN

Abstract
Two- and three-dimensional frameworks can be analysed using the most appropriate of three programs, ALES (developed by Ove Arup), STRESS (IBM), or ECI (Electronic Calculus Inc). The program provides a standard form of input to all three programs and will, if required, select the most suitable program for the problem

References
DOC Bulletin, March 1976

Source
Ove Arup and Partners
13 Fitzroy Street
London W1
UK
Telephone 01–636 1531

Availability

Language

Computer
DEC 10

493

Program name
DAFT

Abstract
This program makes a dynamic analysis of two- and three-dimensional land-based or offshore structures. Earthquakes or wave forces may be considered, if required. Details such as the number of nodes, co-ordinates, number and type of members, load conditions, foundations and type of output are entered, and the program is run. Results may be numerical or graphic (via the plotter). The program assumes rigid soil-structure interfaces

References

Source
Ove Arup and Partners
13 Fitzroy Street
London W1
UK
Telephone 01–636 1531

Availability
Bureau service

Language
Fortran

Computer
DEC 10

494

Program name
STIN-F

Abstract
This program makes linear static, dynamic and buckling analyses of skeletal and finite-element structures. It will accept frameworks, diaphragms, plates, axisymmetric loads, shells and solids, and can take into account various loadings and displacements. Solution is by the stiffness method, coupled with either frontal solution or a variety of banded solutions. Graphic output is available via plotter or terminal display

References

Source
Ove Arup and Partners
13 Fitzroy Street
London W1
UK
Telephone 01–636 1531

Availability
Bureau service

Language
Fortran

Computer
DEC 10

495

Program name
STRESS

Abstract
A program used for the design of framed structures, either space frames or plane frames. It is especially useful for small- to medium-sized structures. Joint displacements, member end forces and moments, member distortions and the reactions at support joints are calculated for a given geometry of structure. The program is capable of handling a wide range of structures, including off-shore platforms

Reference

Source
Scicon Computer Services Limited
Brick Close, Kiln Farm
Milton Keynes MK11 3EJ
UK
Telephone 0908 565656 Telex 826171

Availability
Bureau service

Language

Computer
Univac 1108

496

Program name
GASP (General Analysis of Structural Problems)

Abstract
A program for general analysis of plane and space structures. Frame members, as well as rectangular or triangular plate and shell elements can be considered. Loads can be applied to any part of the structure. Supports may be elastic. The program computes deflections of nodes, forces and moments in individual members. ADGASP processes results and combines individual loadings to produce maximum and minimum values of member reactions

References
NBRI (SA) abstract X/BOU-COMP 6

Source
Scientific and Engineering Division, INFONET
CSSL, PO Box 31497
Braamfontein, Transvaal
South Africa
Telephone Johannesburg 724–9301

Availability
Bureau service

Language

Computer
Univac 1108

497

Program name
STRESS

Abstract
This is a programming system for the analysis of linearly-elastic, statically-loaded, framed structures. Analysis is possible with two- or three-dimensional models. The system consists of a language which describes a problem in terms which are generally familiar to an engineer. No programming experience is necessary to operate the system. Displacements, forces and distortions in members, bending moments and reactions are calculated

References
NBRI (SA) abstract X/BOU-COMP 1

Source
Scientific and Engineering Division, INFONET
CSSL, PO Box 31497
Braamfontein, Transvaal
South Africa
Telephone Johannesburg 724–9301

Availability
Bureau service

Language

Computer
Univac 1108

498

Program name
STRAC

Abstract
This is an interactive program for analysis of all structures which can be considered as straight elements joined at various nodes, for example frames and continuous beams. Stress and moments at each node are calculated

References
Danish Building Research Institute
Abstract 48 11 509

Source
ST-data A/S
Bakkedalen 1
3220 Tisvildeleje
Denmark

Availability

Language
Basic

Computer
Hewlett-Packard
9830
Wang 2200

499

Program name
SAGS

Abstract
This is a comprehensive program for the linear analysis of elastic, statically-loaded beam-type structures. It will analyse plane and space frames and trusses, and plane grids and beams. The program uses a stiffness or displacement method of analysis to determine joint displacements and rotations, support reactions, internal member forces and stresses, and strain energies

References
SDRC Mechanical Design Library

Source
Structural Dynamics Research Corporation
5279 Dragon Way
Cincinnati, Ohio 45227
USA
Telephone (513) 272 1100

Availability
Time sharing. Available in UK

Language
Fortran

Computer

500

Program name
DAGSMIC

Abstract
This program determines the vibrational response of frame structures subjected to foundation shock such as would occur during an earthquake. In the case of equipment mounted to support structures, the shock response spectrum at the mounting location can be determined from analysis or testing of the support structure and supplied as input to DAGSMIC

References
SDRC Mechanical Design Library

Source
Structural Dynamics Research Corporation
5729 Dragon Way
Cincinnati, Ohio 45227
USA
Telephone (513) 272 1100

Availability
Time sharing. Available in UK

Language
Fortran

Computer

501

Program name
SUPERTAB

Abstract
This is a graphics computer program for interactive generation of finite element models and may be used to develop two- and three-dimensional models, using conventional or isoparametric finite elements. Flexible display and editing features are available for checking and modifying the model

References
SDRC Mechanical Design Library

Source
Structural Dynamics Research Corporation
5729 Dragon Way
Cincinnati, Ohio 45227
USA
Telephone (513) 272 1100

Availability
Time sharing. Available in UK

Language
Fortran

Computer

Program name
Calculus suite

Abstract
This program analyses and designs structures by finite elements. Structures may be of linear or non-linear arrangement, with static or dynamic loadings. Where required, the program automatically generates the design or modification of steel and concrete frames and plates. Results may be printed and plotted, and include a full listing of input data

References

Source
UCC, University Computing Company
344–350 Euston Road
London NW1
UK
Telephone 01–387 9661

Availability
Bureau service

Language
Fortran

Computer

503

Program name
STRESS

Abstract
This program is designed for the linear analysis of elastic, statically-loaded frame and truss structures. Simple plane frames, grids or three- dimensional structures can be solved. The output gives a listing of member loads and moments and joint loads, moments and deflections

References

Source
UCC, University Computing Company
344–350 Euston Road
London NW1
UK
Telephone 01–387 9661

Availability
Bureau service

Language

Computer

504

Program name
Frame analysis/2

Abstract
This program is designed for the linear analysis of elastic, skeletal frames with straight members of uniform cross-section. The output gives member end moments, forces, joint deflections and rotations, support reactions, and a full listing of input data

References
Developed by GENESYS Ltd

Source
UCC, University Computing Company
344–350 Euston Road
London NW1
UK
Telephone 01–387 9661

Availability
Bureau service

Language
Fortran
Gentran

Computer

505

Program name
Non-linear plane frame

Abstract
This program analyses skeletal plane frames taking into account factors such as stability, change of geometry, bowing of members, plastic hinges and improperly-fitting components

References

Source
UMIST
Department of Civil and Structural Engineering
PO Box 88, Manchester
UK
Telephone 061–236 3311

Availability

Language
Atlas Autocode

Computer
Any with 64k

506

Program name
Finite element system

Abstract
This program analyses two– and three-dimensional space frames by the linear finite element method. Deflections and stresses in members are calculated and the equilibrium of forces is checked

References

Source
UMIST
Department of Civil and Structural Engineering
PO Box 88, Manchester
UK
Telephone 061–236 3311

Availability

Language
Fortran

Computer
CDC 7600

507

Program name
Non-linear space frame program

Abstract
This program performs analysis of plastic space frames, allowing for changes of the geometry of the frame

References

Source
UMIST
Department of Civil and Structural Engineering
PO Box 88, Manchester
UK
Telephone 061–236 3311

Availability

Language
Algol 60

Computer
CDC 7600

508

Program name
Reinforced concrete frames

Abstract
This program carries out analysis of concrete plane frames under various levels of stress to the point of collapse. It is intended to be used as an overall check on design. Concrete not under tension, variable reinforcement along beams, slender columns, building sway, shear walls and plastic hinges are taken into consideration

References

Source
UMIST
Department of Civil and Structural Engineering
PO Box 88, Manchester
UK
Telephone 061–236 3311

Availability

Language
Atlas Autocode

Computer
ICL 1906A

509

Program name
PLATE

Abstract
This finite element analysis program is one of a suite of analysis programs. It will calculate stresses in frame or plated shell structures. Problems in two– or three-dimensional structures may be dealt with, and variable outputs include deflections, moments, membrane surface stresses, reactions, reinforcing moments and equivalent stresses

References

Source
Computer Consortium Services Ltd
5 Windmill Street
London W1P 1HF
UK
Telephone 01–638 3118

Availability
Bureau service

Language
Fortran

Computer
CDC
IBM
PDP

510

Program name
WAVE

Abstract
Designed to calculate the wave forces on a LEAP frame structure, this is one of a suite of analysis programs. Pre-processing data such as wave height and phase positions are fed in and the resultant output is used as load data for LEAP

References

Source
Computer Consortium Services Ltd
5 Windmill Street
London W1P 1HF
UK
Telephone 01–638 3118

Availability
Bureau service

Language
Fortran

Computer
CDC
IBM
PDP

511

Program name
Offshore structures

Abstract
This system of programs solves problems associated with steel and concrete offshore structures. Wave-loading programs include WAVEGEN, suitable for steel jackets, and NPLWAVE, suitable for concrete platforms. Pre-processors generate geometry, properties of members and loading. Post-processors can be used for combining loading conditions producing actual combined loads, load factors and allowable loads

References
ECLIPSE program library

Source
Electronic Calculus Limited
344 to 350 Euston Road
London NW1 3BJ, UK
Telephone 01–388 7705, Telex 27192

Availability
Purchase, hire, bureau service

Language
Fortran V

Computer
Univac 1106, 1108
CDC 6600, 7600
DEC System 10
IBM
ICL

512

Program name
PSHER

Abstract
This program calculates the margin of safety for a joint in punching shear. This check is in accordance with the publications of the American Petroleum Institute and Det Norske Veritas on the construction of fixed offshore platforms. Output also includes the applied and allowable punching-shear stresses, together with tensions and compressions within joints

References

Source
Faber Computer Operations Limited
Upper Marlborough Road
St Albans
Herts AL1 3UT
Telephone St Albans 61222

Availability
Bureau service

Language

Computer
IBM 1130, System 7

513

Program name
WAVEL/WAVEF

Abstract
These linked programs calculate the force on structures, due to sea waves. WAVEL establishes various parameters of a wave required by WAVEF, so that the latter can then calculate the velocities and acceleration of that wave, and the resultant forces produced on any structure. Forces, velocities and accelerations on a vertical or sloping pile may be output or member forces can be punched onto cards for structural analysis by STRESS

References

Source
Faber Computer Operations Limited
Upper Marlborough Road
St Albans
Herts AL1 3UT
Telephone St Albans 61222

Availability
Bureau service

Language

Computer
IBM 1130, System 7

514

Program name
WFM

Abstract
This program calculates the effect of wave forces on any submerged or partially submerged structure. It can also consider non-structural members such as fenders and conductors. The structure may be subjected to a given sea-wave assumed to be approaching from any given direction. A visual display unit is used to depict the position of the structure in the wave, together with the total forces on the structure at that position

References

Source
Faber Computer Operations Limited
Upper Marlborough Road
St Albans
Herts AL1 3UT
Telephone St Albans 61222

Availability
Bureau service

Language

Computer
IBM 1130, System 7

515

Program name
SEALOAD

Abstract
This sub-system calculates the loadings from waves, current, wind and gravity on off-shore structures. A determinative wave is applied, in steps, to a structure in order to find the wave position resulting in maximum shear or overturning moment. The combined effects of all forces are then considered. These may be varied to analyse different conditions of loading

References
Part of the MARCS system

Source
Scicon Computer Services Limited
Brick Close, Kiln Farm
Milton Keynes MK11 3EJ
UK
Telephone 0908 565656 Telex 825171

Availability
Bureau service. Available in USA

Language

Computer
Univac 1108

516

Program name
MARCS

Abstract
A comprehensive set of computer programs providing complete design and analysis of off-shore structures. (See also AUTOPLAT, SEALOAD, STRAN and PILE/AN). The system generates a detailed, three-dimensional model of a structure, performs an analysis of all pertinent conditions, and evaluates the total structure in terms of allowable stresses. Allowance is made for semi-submersible and jacked structures

References
Developed by Synercom Technology Inc

Source
Scicon Computer Services Limited
Brick Close, Kiln Farm
Milton Keynes MK11 3EJ
UK
Telephone 0908 565656 Telex 826171

Availability
Bureau service. Available in USA

Language

Computer
Univac 1108

517

Program name
AUTOPLAT

Abstract
This sub-system manipulates and generates geometrical, topological and flexural data related to off-shore structures. It uses a computer-driven plotter to generate scale drawings of structures in plan and elevation. A bill of materials is also produced, tabulating the weights and quantities of the different structural shapes which make up the platform

References
Part of the MARCS system

Source
Scicon Computer Services Limited
Brick Close, Kiln Farm
Milton Keynes MK11 3EJ
UK
Telephone 0908 565656 Telex 826171

Availability
Bureau service. Available in USA

Language

Computer
Univac 1108

518

Program name
STRAN

Abstract
This sub-system provides information related to forces operating on an off-shore structure. Using the 'stiffness matrix' method of analysis, it calculates the forces operating within each member or sub-structure of the overall construction. This program interacts with PILE/AN sub-system. It may also be used effectively to analyse large space frames with up to 4000 joints

References
Part of the MARCS system

Source
Scicon Computer Services Limited
Brick Close, Kiln Farm
Milton Keynes MK11 3EJ
UK
Telephone 0908 565656 Telex 826171

Availability
Bureau service. Available in USA

Language

Computer
Univac 1108

519

Program name
PILE/AN

Abstract
This sub-system interrelates with the STRAN sub-system in performing an interactive analysis of off-shore structures. The effects of forces operating on and in the structure are analysed with respect to pile foundations. STRAN and PILE/AN reciprocate data until the complete structural system would be in equilibrium

References
Part of the MARCS system

Source
Scicon Computer Services Limited
Brick Close, Kiln Farm
Milton Keynes MK11 3EJ
UK
Telephone 0908 565656 Telex 826171

Availability
Bureau service. Available in USA

Language

Computer
Univac 1108

520

Program name
NPLWAVE

Abstract
A program for use in the design and analysis of off-shore structures subjected to wave loads in which inertial and diffraction forces are dominant. The system provides, for any number of wave conditions, information relating to pressure distribution over the surface of the structure, total pressure forces and overturning forces, and how these vary

References

Source
Scicon Computer Services Limited
Brick Close, Kiln Farm
Milton Keynes MK11 3EJ
UK
Telephone 0908 565656 Telex 826171

Availability
Bureau service

Language

Computer
Univac 1108

521

Program name
53–T8, RCNARC

Abstract
This program calculates tensions and movement in bearing structures. It is based on the element method. The elements are assumed to be rectangular with eight degrees of freedom per element. Load and apertures are specified inside the rectangular area. The maximum capacity of the program is approximately 20 000 degrees of freedom

References

Source
A/S Regnecentralen
Falkonralle 1
2000 Kobenhavn F
Denmark
Telephone (01) 10 53 66

Availability

Language

Computer

Program name
COGO

Abstract
This program is a co-ordinate geometry system, originally part of the ICES suite, and has been adapted for time-sharing use

References

Source
Atkins Computing Services Limited
Woodcote Grove, Ashley Road
Epsom, Surrey
UK
Telephone Epsom 40421

Availability
Bureau service, time-sharing. Available in Netherlands

Language
Fortran

Computer
Honeywell Sigma 9

523

Program name
Integral structural design system

Abstract
This program calculates the loading on every element of a building. From the overall geometry of the building and the superimposed loading, it uses sub-routines to design automatically each element in the chosen material

References

Source
Camutek
39 Newnham Road
Cambridge B3 9EY
UK
Telephone Cambridge (0223) 9686

Availability
From owner

Language
Basic

Computer
Hewlett-Packard
9830 (2k) or (6k)

524

Program name
Towers and chimneys

Abstract
This program calculates stresses in reinforced concrete towers or chimneys with given foundations. Calculations are carried out to DS411:1973 and DS415:1965

References

Source
CE-data
Lundtoftevej 1G
2800 Lyngby
Denmark

Availability
Bureau service

Language

Computer

525

Program name
EASANAL

Abstract
A program for solving structural engineering problems. It is based on structural and finite-element analysis

References

Source
Computel Limited
Eastern Road
Bracknell, Berkshire
UK
Telephone Bracknell 23031

Availability

Language

Computer

526

Program name
CABLN

Abstract
This program makes a non-linear analysis of cable networks. The program will consider varying degrees of fixity of nodes, prestressing and cable slackness. Output can be via a variety of plotting routines in addition to a terminal or a line-printer. Static analysis only is carried out

References

Source
Department of Architectural Science
The University of Sydney
Sydney
New South Wales 2006
Australia

Availability
Sale, bureau service

Language
Fortran IV

Computer
CDC Cyber 72

527

Program name
1459 Dynamic modal response and time history analysis

Abstract
This program analyses the natural frequencies, modes and responses of structures under dynamic loads, such as earthquakes, over a period of time. Structures can include beams, triangular and quadrilateral plates, and solids in any combination. Joints may have up to six degrees of freedom. Masses may be lumped at joints with up to three dynamic translational degrees of freedom

References
ECLIPSE program library

Source
Electronic Calculus Limited
344 to 350 Euston Road
London NW1 3BJ
UK
Telephone 01–388 7705, Telex 27192

Availability
Purchase, hire, bureau service

Language
Fortran V

Computer
Univac 1106, 1108
CDC 6600, 7600
DEC System 10
IBM
ICL

528

Program name
603–606 Large displacement and stability analysis

Abstract
This iterative program uses the Newton-Ralphson method to evaluate geometrical (large deflection) and non-linear stability effects. It uses S and C stability functions and modifies inertial properties depending on the axial forces in the members. At the start of each iteration, the deformed shape obtained at the end of the previous one is taken as the input and all transformation matrices are modified accordingly

References
ECLIPSE program library

Source
Electronic Calculus Limited
344 to 350 Euston Road
London NW1 3BJ
UK
Telephone 01–388 7705, Telex 27192

Availability
Purchase, hire, bureau service

Language
Fortran V

Computer
Univac 1106, 1108
CDC 6600, 7600
DEC System 10
IBM
ICL

529

Program name
FATIG

Abstract
This program calculates the expected fatigue life of chord to weld, and brace to weld intersections, on a tubular steel structure. Stresses at twelve points around the tube are calculated for peak-and-trough stress reversals of up to ten wave heights. The critical position is selected from a stress range matrix. The relevant expected life and increments of cumulative damage are also output

References

Source
Faber Computer Operations Limited
Upper Marlborough Road
St Albans
Herts AL1 3UT
Telephone St Albans 61222

Availability
Bureau service

Language

Computer
IBM 1130, System 7

530

Program name
S-calculation

Abstract
This suite of programs is for analysis of the structure of houses. It indicates how loads are borne in each part of the structure leading down to the foundations. Reinforced concrete slabs, 'toadstool' ceilings (ie ceilings supported on a rectangular network of columns), columns, cellar walls and foundations are included in the library of standard elements

References
Danish Building Research Institute
Abstract 48 12 203

Source
Geodata A/S
Dagmarhus
HC Andersens Boulevard 7
1553 Kobenhavn V
Denmark

Availability
Bureau service

Language

Computer

531

Program name
Thin lapped constructions

Abstract
This program analyses stress and tension in thin lapped constructions. Elements with either open or closed cross section can be examined. The program uses Bredt and Saint-Venant formulae

References
Danish Building Research Institute
Abstract 48 12 003

Source
Geodata A/S
Dagmarhus
HC Andersens Boulevard 7
1553 Kobenhavn V
Denmark

Availability
Bureau service

Language

Computer

Program name
STRUDL

Abstract
A program for use in analysis and design of structures such as drilling rigs, storage tanks and derricks. Forces and stresses within members may be analysed and a combination of results, such as maximum stresses and force and stress envelopes, produced. Different loading conditions may be considered and analysed. The finite-element method of analysis is used

References

Source
Scicon Computer Services Limited
Brick Close, Kiln Farm
Milton Keynes MK11 3EJ
UK
Telephone 0908 565656 Telex 826171

Availability
Bureau service

Language

Computer
Univac 1108

533

Program name
SDRC Mechanical Design Library

Abstract
This library includes programs for the dynamic testing and analysis of frames, sectional properties, rotating machinery, system simulation data, machine linkage and general and special purpose structures

References

Source
Structural Dynamics Research Corporation
5279 Dragon Way
Cincinnati, Ohio 45227
USA
Telephone (513) 272 1100

Availability
Remote batch, time sharing. Available in UK

Language

Computer
Honeywell 400, 6000
XDS Sigma 9
CDC 6000, 7000 series
Univac 1100
IBM 370

534

Program name
ANSYS

Abstract
This program employs finite-element technology to perform static and dynamic, elastic and plastic structural analysis, as well as fluid-flow and heat-transfer analysis of the performance of mechanical machinery. The matrix displacement method of analysis based upon finite-element idealisations is employed throughout the program. It will solve static non-linear as well as linear structural analysis problems

References
SDRC Mechanical Design Library

Source
Structural Dynamics Research Corporation
5729 Dragon Way
Cincinnati, Ohio 45227
USA
Telephone (513) 227 1100

Availability
Remote batch. Available in UK

Language

Computer

535

Program name
SUPERB

Abstract
This is an isoparametric finite-element program, designed to solve static and dynamic structural problems. It employs advanced isoparametric with conventional elements to enable a wide range of structures to be efficiently represented. Elements with curved boundaries and wide strain variations permit curved regions and areas with high stress concentration to be accurately represented with a minimum number of elements

References
SDRC Mechanical Design Library

Source
Structural Dynamics Research Corporation
5729 Dragon Way
Cincinnati, Ohio 45227
USA
Telephone (513) 272 1100

Availability
Remote batch. Available in UK

Language

Computer

536

Program name
NASTRAN

Abstract
This program contains twelve standard Rigid Format Solutions for the following analyses, 1 static response to concentrated or distributed loads, thermal expansion, and enforced deformation; 2 dynamic response to transient, steady-state and random excitation; 3 determination of real and complex eigenvalues; 4 dynamic and elastic stability analysis; 5 static plasticity analysis; and 6 transient analysis of non-linear dynamic systems

References
SDRC Mechanical Design Library

Source
Structural Dynamics Research Corp
5729 Dragon Way
Cincinnati, Ohio 45227
USA
Telephone (513) 272 1100

Availability
Remote batch. Available in UK. Also available from Maersk Data, Denmark

Language

Computer

537

Program name
VISCOSUPERB

Abstract
This is a finite element program for predicting the large-deflection non-linear behaviour of viscoelastic/structure assemblies including mounts, couplings, bushing, packaging filler and noise-damping treatments

References
SDRC Mechanical Design Library

Source
Structural Dynamics Research Corporation
5729 Dragon Way
Cincinnati, Ohio 45227
USA
Telephone (513) 272 1100

Availability
Time sharing, remote batch. Available in UK

Language
Fortran

Computer
CDC 6400, 6500, 6600

538

Program name
SUPER

Abstract
This program is an interactive pre– and post-processor for the SDRC SUPERB and SUPERB/DYNAMICS programs. It increases efficiency by decreasing the time required to prepare and de-bug SUPERB finite-element models. Free-field data prepared off-line on a paper-tape, or image data on punched cards, may also be input to SUPER to provide flexibility: editing capabilities are also available

References
See also SUPERB

Source
Structural Dynamics Research Corporation
5729 Dragon Way
Cincinnati, Ohio 45227
USA
Telephone (513) 272 1100

Availability
Time sharing. Available in UK

Language

Computer

539

Program name
ABACUS

Abstract
This is a suite of thirteen programs, intended for analysing and giving the best solution to the design of various types of structure. Using interactive graphic techniques, these programs give the most favourable functional performance for simple or complex structures, including schools, hospitals and housing estates

References
Developed by the Architecture Computer Unit, Strathclyde University

Source
UCC, University Computing Company
344–350 Euston Road
London NW1
UK
Telephone 01–387 9661

Availability
Bureau service

Language
Fortran

Computer

Structural elements

540

Program name
Reinforced concrete plates

Abstract
This program calculates the load capacity of a rectangular reinforced-concrete plate with given geometry. Evenly distributed loads are calculated. Calculations are to DS411:1973

References

Source
CE-data
Lundtoftevej 1G
2800 Lyngby
Denmark

Availability
Bureau service

Language

Computer

541

Program name
COMP-CONSTRUCT/1

Abstract
This sub-system enables an engineer to design, analyse, detail and cost a simply supported composite deck, including shear connectors, constructed in accordance with BS CP117:Part 1:1965 and Part 2:1967. The program incorporates a data table of universal beams. Slab design is in accordance with BS CP110:Part 1:1969

References
GENESYS program library

Source
GENESYS Limited
Pennine House, Lemyngton Street
Loughborough, Leicestershire
LE11 1XA, UK
Telephone 0509 39185 Telex 341747

Availability
Bureau service, hire

Language
Gentran

Computer
CDC 6500, 6600, 7600
DEC 10
Honeywell 6000
IBM 360, 370
ICL 1900, System 4
Philips P1400
PRIME 300
Univac 1100

542

Program name
Toadstool ceiling

Abstract
This program analyses tension and loads in ceilings constructed of beams and panels supported by columns arranged in a regular rectangular pattern

References
Danish Building Research Institute
Abstract 48 12 202

Source
Geodata A/S
Dagmarhus
HC Andersens Boulevard 7
1553 Copenhagen V
Denmark

Availability
Bureau service

Language

Computer

543

Program name
COMP-CONSTRUCT/1

Abstract
This program analyses, designs and details a simply-supported floor comprising reinforced concrete slabs resting on universal beams, in accordance with BS CP110:Part 1:1972. Output details the sizes, reinforcement arrangements and bending schedules for slabs, the moments and shears for beams, and a full listing of input data

References
Developed by GENESYS Ltd

Source
UCC, University Computing Company
344–350 Euston Road
London NW1
UK
Telephone 01–387 9661

Availability
Bureau service

Language
Fortran
Gentran

Computer

544

Program name
Single-bay portal-frame design

Abstract
This program designs portal frames. Given the geometry, basic loading and wind pressure, it automatically calculates the pressure coefficients. It also gives the load factors and deflections under various load combinations, the weight and the sizes of the columns, rafters, haunches and ridge gussets

References

Source
Camutek
39 Newnham Road
Cambridge CB3 9EY
UK
Telephone Cambridge (0223) 69686

Availability
From owner

Language
Basic

Computer
Hewlett-Packard
9830 (2k) or (6k)

Program name
TRUSS

Abstract
This program performs a static linear analysis of a three-dimensional truss structure with pin-ended members. Large trusses can be handled. Provision has been made for symmetry about an axis inclined to the global axis, and for repeated members of identical geometry, for use in the analysis of space-frame systems. Data for regular structures can be generated from simplified input

References

Source
CSIRO, Division of Building Research
Graham Road, Highett
Victoria 3190
Australia
Telephone 95 0333

Availability

Language
Fortran

Computer
CDC 6600

546

Program name
TRUSS

Abstract
This program determines maximum tensions in bars and joints of wooden structures of haphazard configuration, built up of rectangular cross-sections. It also calculates the combination of normal and deflected tensions. It distinguishes between bars and joints of different physical characteristics. The analysis is carried out by the rigidity method. Reactions are calculated separately and the result is shown in diagram form

References

Source
Danmarks Ingeniorakademi
Bygningsafdelingen
Bygning 373
2800 Lyngby
Denmark

Availability

Language
Fortran

Computer
IBM 370/165

547

Program name
CABNET

Abstract
This program calculates movement and tension in a stressed-cable construction, for example a suspended roof, influenced by an arbitrary static load and temperature variations. The construction is considered as a system of straight elements. Border beams or curves can be considered as supports

References
Danish Building Research Institute
Abstract 48 11 701

Source
Danmarks tekniske, Hojskole
Afd f Baerende Konstruktioner
Bygning 118
2800 Lyngby
Denmark

Availability
Bureau service

Language
Fortran

Computer
IBM 360, 370

548

Program name
CONGRAD

Abstract
This program calculates movement and tension in a stressed-cable construction, for example a suspended roof, in which the cables are anchored in border beams or to elastic supports. The construction is assumed to be influenced by an external static load and by arbitrary temperature variations

References
Danish Building Research Institute
Abstract 48 11 702

Source
Danmarks tekniske, Hojskole
Afd f Baerende Konstruktioner
Bygning 118
2800 Lyngby
Denmark

Availability
Bureau service

Language
PL/1

Computer
IBM 360, 370

549

Program name
DFL2

Abstract
This program analyses space trusses, and two-dimensional structures, where the effects of deflections cannot be assumed to be small, such as in cable-suspended roofs. The structure is defined by a set of nodes which are joined together by straight, pin-ended members. Members may be prestressed. Loads can be applied at nodes only, but in any direction. Temperature effects within members may also be applied as loadings

References

Source
Faber Computer Operations Limited
Upper Marlborough Road
St Albans
Herts AL1 3UT
Telephone St Albans 61222

Availability
Bureau service

Language

Computer
IBM 1130, System 7

550

Program name
TRUSS

Abstract
This program calculates the support reactions and axial forces in each member of a pin-jointed truss which is statically determinate

References
Mark III software library
User manual 5202·12

Source
Honeywell Information Systems Limited
114 to 118 Southampton Row
London WC1B 5AB
UK
Telephone 01-242 5725

Availability
Bureau service

Language
Basic

Computer
Honeywell 6000 series

551

Program name
A06

Abstract
This program determines forces in a parallel-chorded Warren truss with zig-zag shear members of either the 'deck' or 'through' type. There are no limits to height, span or number of panels. Equal or varying vertical forces can be entered at all node points

References
NBRI (South Africa) abstract
X/BOU-COMP 9

Source
Metricomp Programmes (Pty) Limited
PO Box 4
Johannesburg 2000
South Africa
Telephone Johannesburg 41-8501

Availability
Subscription service

Language

Computer
Hewlett-Packard
9820A

552

Program name
A09

Abstract
This program operates in the same way as A07, but covers double sloping trusses. The truss may have a 'ridge', defined as the node at which diagonals change direction. The rafter may have different slopes and width of panels on either side of the ridge. A maximum of seventy panels can be handled if top and bottom nodes are equally loaded. Maximum number of panels diminishes by two for every node with additional loading

References
NBRI (South Africa) abstract
X/BOU-COMP 9

Source
Metricomp Programmes (Pty) Limited
PO Box 4
Johannesburg 2000
South Africa
Telephone Johannesburg 41-8501

Availability
Subscription service

Language

Computer
Hewlett-Packard
9820A

553

Program name
A07

Abstract
This program determines forces in a truss with a single top chord, which may be sloping or horizontal, and a horizontal bottom chord. Posts should be vertical. Diagonals may slope in two directions on either side of the bottom node. A maximum of 25 panels can be handled, if top and bottom nodes are equally loaded. Maximum number of panels diminishes by two for every node with additional loading. All applied forces must be vertical

References
NBRI (South Africa) abstract
X/BOU-COMP 9

Source
Metricomp Programmes (Pty) Limited
PO Box 4
Johannesburg 2000
South Africa
Telephone Johnnesburg 41-8501

Availability
Subscription service

Language

Computer
Hewlett-Packard
9820A

554

Program name
Timber portal frames

Abstract
A number of programs for producing tables and designs for portal frames formed from uniform solid or ply-web members, or with tapered members

References

Source
TRADA
Chiltern House, Hughenden Valley
High Wycombe, Buckinghamshire
UK
Telephone Naphill 3091

Availability

Language

Computer

Program name
Roof truss design

Abstract
Programs for producing load-span tables for domestic truss and truss-rafter constructions, and for industrial trusses, all jointed by nailed plywood gussets

References

Source
TRADA
Chiltern House, Hughenden Valley
High Wycombe, Buckinghamshire
UK
Telephone Naphill 3091

Availability

Language

Computer

556

Program name
Span chart plotting

Abstract
A number of programs for plotting span load charts in different forms for solid or built-up timber beams and timber portals, and for other materials

References

Source
TRADA
Chiltern House, Hughenden Valley
High Wycombe, Buckinghamshire
UK
Telephone Naphill 3091

Availability

Language

Computer

557

Program name
53–T7

Abstract
This program calculates tensions, movements and reactions in a box-girder or similar construction. It is based on the deflection method and elasticity theory. A single-span connection is assumed between the upper and lower flanges of the girders (Vlasov's method). Rigid cross-supports are permitted

References

Source
A/S Regnecentralen
Falkoneralle 1
2000 Copenhagen F
Denmark
Telephone (01) 10 53 66

Availability

Language

Computer

558

Program name
Simply-supported steel-beam design

Abstract
This program designs steel beams in bending and deflection to BS 449:1969. It chooses beam, column or channel sections from BS 4:Part 1:1972 and BS 4:Part 2:1969

References

Source
Camutek
39 Newnham Road
Cambridge CB3 9EY
UK
Telephone Cambridge (0223) 69686

Availability
From owner

Language
Basic

Computer
Hewlett-Packard
9830 (2k) or (6k)

559

Program name
Single-span beam analysis

Abstract
This program gives the shear forces, bending moments, slope and deflection of a single-span beam. It also includes fixed ends or end moments

References

Source
Camutek
39 Newnham Road
Cambridge CB3 9EY
UK
Telephone Cambridge (0223) 69686

Availability
From owner

Language
Basic

Computer
Hewlett-Packard
9830 (2k) or (6k)

560

Program name
Reinforced concrete beams

Abstract
This program calculates stress and tension in continuous beams of given cross section. Beams can be rectangular or T-shaped in section. Ends of beams can be free, simply supported or fixed

References

Source
CE-data
Lundtoftevej 1G
2800 Lyngby
Denmark

Availability
Bureau service

Language

Computer

561

Program name
CRANE

Abstract
This program makes an analysis of a simply-supported span for a moving load train composed of up to three electric overhead travelling cranes. The program determines maximum horizontal and vertical bending moments for the span; the maximum beam shear; maximum reactions to the supporting structure and also the out-of-balance load to the support; and maximum co-existent reactions to the supporting structure

References
Bradshaw, Buckton and Tonge

Source
Civil and Structural Computing (Northern) Limited
14 Bramley Centre
Leeds LS13 2ET
Telephone 0532 563322

Availability
Bureau service, time-sharing, in-house

Language

Computer
Hewlett Packard 9800 and others

562

Program name
HETENYI

Abstract
A program for the general analysis of a beam on an elastic foundation

References
GEOCOMP

Source
Computel Limited
Eastern Road
Bracknell, Berkshire
UK
Telephone Bracknell 23031

Availability

Language

Computer

563

Program name
BEAMDET/COLDET

Abstract
This program for automatic detailing of concrete beams and columns to BS CP 110:1972 and CP 114:1969 is one of a suite of detailing programs. The program enables engineers to detail beams and columns from nominal input. Outputs are variable, and include drawings, bar charts, schedules, quantities and calculation sheets

References

Source
Computer Consortium Services Ltd
5 Windmill Street
London W1P 1HF
UK
Telephone 01–638 3118

Availability
Bureau service

Language
Fortran

Computer
CDC
IBM

564

Program name
STRUPAK

Abstract
This package is used for sizing beams, columns, and elastic elements of plane and space frames. Loads may be static, dynamic or thermal. Up to 250 elements of different cross– section can be handled

References
Danish Building Research Institute
Abstract 48 11 405

Source
Control Data
Sonder Boulevard 35
1720 Copenhagen V
Denmark

Availability
Interactive

Language

Computer

Program name
GIRDER

Abstract
This program facilitates the design of rolled-steel or castellated girders in accordance with the elastic design requirements of the steel structures code AS 1250–1975. These may be designed to act compositely with a concrete slab or may be non-composite. Design load cases may include concentrated loads, uniformly or triangularly distributed loads, or applied moments: only one design load condition can be applied to each girder

References

Source
CSIRO, Division of Building Research
Graham Road, Highett
Victoria 3190
Australia
Telephone 95 0333

Availability
ACADS

Language
Fortran IV

Computer
CDC 6600, Cyber 74

566

Program name
ABDUL

Abstract
This program analyses and designs reinforced concrete beams to meet BS CP110:Part 1:1972 requirements. Factored load-combinations are automatically generated with bending moment and shear force envelopes produced for each span. Output includes selected sizes and spacing for main and shear reinforcement

References
PSA program library

Source
Directorate of Civil Engineering Services
Property Services Agency
Lunar House, 40 Wellesley Road
Croydon CR9 2EL
UK
Telephone 01–686 3499

Availability

Language
Fortran

Computer

567

Program name
AISC

Abstract
This program calculates the safety margin for the mid-span and ends of any member carrying both direct loading and bending moments. It is in accordance with the handbook of the American Institute of Steel Construction. The interactive ratio of applied axial stress is listed together with the applied bending stress and a signifier for tension or compression. The slenderness ratio is also checked

References

Source
Faber Computer Operations Limited
Upper Marlborough Road
St Albans
Herts AL1 3UT
Telephone St Albans 61222

Availability
Bureau service

Language

Computer
IBM 1130, System 7

568

Program name
GB1

Abstract
This program analyses a ground beam. A beam is considered to be made up of a number of beam elements, and the accuracy of the results depends upon the number of elements considered, a large number of beam elements giving the more exact solution. The program will cover up to eighty separate beam elements and is run at least three times with an increasing number of elements

References

Source
Faber Computer Operations Limited
Upper Marlborough Road
St Albans
Herts AL1 3UT
Telephone St Albans 61222

Availability
Bureau service

Language

Computer
IBM 1130, System 7

569

Program name
UBM/1

Abstract
This sub-system enables a designer to calculate the ultimate bending moment of reinforced and prestressed concrete sections of any shape, which may be subject to both tensile and compressive loads. The section may or may not be restrained to the plane of bending. All calculations are to BS CP110:Part 1:1972

References
GENESYS program library

Source
GENESYS Limited
Pennine House, Lemyngton Street
Loughborough, Leicestershire
LE11 1XA UK
Telephone 0509 39185Telex 341747

Availability
Bureau service, hire

Language
Gentran

Computer
CDC 6500, 6600, 7600
DEC 10
Honeywell 6000
IBM 360, 370
ICL 1900, System 4
Philips P1400
PRIME 300
Univac 1100

570

Program name
Reinforced concrete girders

Abstract
This program gives dimensions of reinforcing wires to be used in concrete girders. Tension for a given cable is also calculated. The program can handle simply-supported and continuous girders

References
Danish Building Research Institute
Abstract 48 12 305

Source
Geodata A/S
Dagmarhus
HC Andersens Boulevard 7
1553 Copenhagen V
Denmark

Availability
Bureau service

Language

Computer

571

Program name
Prestressd beam analysis and design

Abstract
This program designs pretensioned single-span beams, conforming to AC1 318–71 and AASH0 Bridge Specification. Design parameters are input and the program suggests an approximate number of strands. A number is chosen and the program determines the permissible zone of the centroid of the steel. Three harp points (points where reinforcing bars are supported in the formwork before the concrete is poured) may be specified

References
Part number 09830–74260

Source
Hewlett-Packard Limited
King Street Lane, Winnersh
Wokingham, Berks RG11 5AR
UK
Telephone Wokingham 784774

Availability
Purchase

Language
Basic

Computer
HP 9830A with
3808–word memory
11270B matrix ROM
11274B strings
ROM
9865A tape cassette
9866A thermal
printer

572

Program name
Reinforced concrete beam design

Abstract
This program designs reinforced concrete beams in accordance with the ACI 318–71 code. The cross-sectional shape of the beams can be rectangular, T, inverted T, L or inverted L. Given the properties of the material and a description of the loading conditions, the program provides a complete design

References
Part number 09830–74255

Source
Hewlett-Packard Limited
King Street Lane, Winnersh
Wokingham, Berks RG11 5AR
UK
Telephone Wokingham 784774

Availability
Purchase

Language
Basic

Computer
HP 9830A with
3808–word memory
11270B matrix ROM
9866A thermal
printer

573

Program name
Three-dimensional beam analysis

Abstract
This program gives forces, moments and deformations at specified points on straight prismatic beams of constant section loaded with three-dimensional forces or moments which are uniform, concentrated and/or linearly orthogonal. It uses a stiffness method and the results may be plotted if desired. It may also be used as a post-processor for general space-frame analysis where reactions and deformations are already known

References
Part number 09830–74235

Source
Hewlett-Packard Limited
King Street Lane, Winnersh
Wokingham, Berks RG11 5AR
UK
Telephone Wokingham 784774

Availability
Purchase

Language
Basic

Computer
HP 9830A with
3808–word memory
11270B matrix ROM
11274B strings
ROM
9866A thermal
printer

574

Program name
Steel beam columns

Abstract
This program, given the geometry, bracing and loading conditions, selects trial wide-flange sections for columns with biaxial loading and checks their compliance with the 1970 code of the American Institute of Steel Construction. Slenderness ratios KX and KY, and moment amplification modifiers CMX and CMY, may be calculated. The program contains pre-recorded data on bending factors and design properties for all wide-rolled flanges

References
Part number 09830–74240

Source
Hewlett-Packard Limited
King Street Lane, Winnersh
Wokingham, Berks RG11 5AR
UK
Telephone Wokingham 784774

Availability
Purchase

Language
Basic

Computer
HP 9830A with
3808–word memory
11270B matrix ROM
11274B strings
ROM
9866A thermal
printer

575

Program name
Elastically bedded beams

Abstract
This program calculates the values and influence lines of moments, soil pressure and settlement by the stiffness-coefficient method. It can handle up to thirty layers with up to fifteen loads. Loads may be uniform, trapezoidal or point. End and point moments may also be used

References

Source
Hewlett-Packard Limited
King Street Lane, Winnersh
Wokingham, Berks RG11 5AR
UK
Telephone Wokingham 784774

Availability
Purchase

Language
Basic

Computer
HP 9830A with 3808–word memory

576

Program name
BEAMDS

Abstract
This program analyses and designs single-span beams

References
Mark III software library
User manual 5202·24

Source
Honeywell Information Systems Limited
114 to 118 Southampton Row
London WC1B 5AB
UK
Telephone 01–242 5725

Availability
Bureau service

Language
Basic

Computer
Honeywell 6000 series

577

Program name
BETANGLE

Abstract
This program calculates the beta angle of beams for use in STRESS. It is self-documenting

References
Mark III software library
See also STRESS

Source
Honeywell Information Systems Limited
114 to 118 Southampton Row
London WC1B 5AB
UK
Telephone 01–242 5725

Availability
Bureau service

Language
Basic

Computer
Honeywell 6000 series

578

Program name
Thin-walled sections

Abstract
This program analyses thin-walled girders, which may be non-prismatic and may consist of open and/or closed cells. The girder is subjected to tension and bending, and the cross-sectional properties and shear stresses are calculated

References

Source
Laing Computing Services
Elstree Way
Borehamwood
Hertfordshire
WD6 1NF, UK
Telephone 01–207 2000

Availability
Sale, bureau service

Language
Fortran

Computer
IBM 370–50

579

Program name
A08 Beam properties and fixed-end moments

Abstract
This program computes stiffness factors and carry-over factors for a non-prismatic beam. It can handle a maximum of twenty-one different stiffness sections along the beam and it assumes a linear variation of stiffness between these given points. Thereafter it accepts any number of vertical-point and uniformly distributed loads, and calculates the fixed-end moments at each end. It is based on the 'column analogy'

References
NBRI (South Africa) abstract
X/BOU-COMP 5

Source
Metricomp Programmes (Pty) Limited
PO Box 4
Johannesburg
South Africa
Telephone Johannesburg 41–8501

Availability
Subscription service

Language

Computer
Hewlett-Packard 9820

580

Program name
AO3 Beam deflections

Abstract
This program calculates deflections at increments along a beam between any two points measured in one direction from a reference at one support. All forces acting on the beam, such as vertical-point and uniformly distributed loads, must be defined. The beam must begin at a support. Imposed moments are handled by loading the beam with a couple

References
NBRI (South Africa) abstract
X/BOU-COMP 5

Source
Metricomp Programmes (Pty) Limited
PO Box 4
Johannesburg
South Africa
Telephone Johannesburg 41–8501

Availability
Subscription service

Language

Computer
Hewlett-Packard
9820

581

Program name
A02 Simply supported beam with end moments

Abstract
This program calculates reactions, shear forces and bending moments for a simply-supported beam with given end moments. Any combination of vertical-point and uniformly distributed loads can be accepted, but the total number of loads must not exceed twenty-three. Various output options are available, including a tabulation of the full envelope of beam moments and shear forces for pre-selected intervals on the beam

References
AO1 Multispan beam. NBRI (SA) abstract
X/BOU-COMP 5

Source
Metricomp Programmes (Pty) Limited
PO Box 4
Johannesburg
South Africa
Telephone Johannesburg 41–8501

Availability
Subscription service

Language

Computer
Hewlett-Packard
9820

582

Program name
AO5 Encastre beam

Abstract
This program calculates reactions, shear forces, bending moments and fixed-end moments for a beam with either one or both ends built in. Any combination of vertical-point and uniformly distributed loads can be accepted, but the total number of loads must not exceed twenty-three. Various output options are available, including a tabulation of the full envelope of beam moments and shear forces for pre-selected intervals on the beam

References
NBRI (South Africa) abstract
X/BOU-COMP 5

Source
Metricomp Programmes (Pty) Limited
PO Box 4
Johannesburg
South Africa
Telephone Johannesburg 41–8501

Availability
Subscription service

Language

Computer
Hewlett-Packard
9820

583

Program name
FINWL

Abstract
This program analyses cellular structures with thin-walled cross-sections, such as box girders and lift cores, which are subjected to bending and torsion. For each segment along the length of the girder, a description of the cross-section is required, plus details of the applied loading and support conditions. Cross-sectional bending and shear stresses are calculated together with values of twist and distribution of torque

References
SZABO, J, Hoehere Technicke Mechanik
Dritte Auflag, 1960

Source
Ove Arup and Partners
13 Fitzroy Street
London W1
UK
Telephone 01–636 1531

Availability
Bureau service

Language
Fortran

Computer
DEC 10

584

Program name
DP102

Abstract
This program carries out analysis and design of continuous reinforced concrete beams in accordance with CP110. It makes analysis for ultimate limit state and deflection. A 'plotting' ROM can be attached, making the program capable of plotting bending-moment and shear-force envelopes

References
DOC Evaluation Report No 2

Source
Ove Arup Partnership
13 Fitzroy Street
London W1P 6BQ
Telephone 01–636 1531

Availability
Purchase

Language
Basic

Computer
Hewlett-Packard
9830 with ROM

585

Program name
CONBEAM 4 and 5

Abstract
CONBEAM 4 carries out the structural analysis, and CONBEAM 5 the structural design, of continuous beams in accordance with CP110. CONBEAM makes analysis for ultimate limit state and for deflections, which are calculated in accordance with CP114. It does not design shear reinforcement but shear force diagrams are provided in the structural analysis

References
DOC Evaluation Report No 2

Source
Scott Wilson Kirkpatrick & Partners
53 Bedford Square
London WC1B 3DP
Telephone 01–580 0422

Availability
Hire, purchase

Language
Fortran

Computer
Univac 1108

586

Program name
SASA

Abstract
This program determines cross-sectional properties and detailed stress distribution of arbitrary beams. General beam cross-section can be modelled as a collection of plane quadrilateral finite elements. Features include location of the centroid, principal axes and shear centre; area of the cross-section; area moments of inertia about axes parallel to the given axes but with the origin at the centroid; and area moments of inertia about the principal axes

References

Source
Structural Dynamics Research Corporation
5729 Dragon Way
Cincinnati, Ohio 45227
USA
Telephone (513) 272 1100

Availability
Time sharing. Available in UK

Language

Computer

587

Program name
Span tables for timber beams

Abstract
A number of programs for producing span tables, in various forms, for simply-supported uniformly-loaded beams of rectangular section of any timber. Also, programs for laminated, ply-web and stressed-skin constructions and for tabulating the properties of rectangular sections

References

Source
TRADA
Chiltern House, Hughenden Valley
High Wycombe, Buckinghamshire
UK
Telephone Naphill 3091

Availability

Language

Computer

588

Program name
CP110–BEAMS/1

Abstract
This program analyses and designs reinforced concrete beams to BS CP110:Part 1:1972. The program will consider continuous beams or sub-frames with beams. Output gives bending moments, shear force envelopes, moments of resistance, cross-sectional properties, areas of required steel, bar sizes and a full list of input data

References
Developed by GENESYS Ltd

Source
UCC, University Computing Company
344–350 Euston Road
London NW1
UK
Telephone 01–387 9661

Availability
Bureau service

Language
Fortran
Gentran

Computer

589

Program name
RETWAL

Abstract
This program makes a cross-sectional, elastic analysis of retaining walls. The program will consider a maximum of seven reinforcement bands. Output gives the minimum dimensions of each band and associated reinforcement and a full listing of input data

References
Developed by the computer branch of the DoE (Highway Engineering)

Source
UCC, University Computing Company
344–350 Euston Road
London NW1
UK
Telephone 01–387 9661

Availability
Bureau service

Language
Fortran

Computer
Fortran

590

Program name
Beam 110

Abstract
A terminal program for analysis and design of reinforced concrete continuous beams in accordance with CP110. Beams may be up to 12 spans, and rectangular or T-shaped in profile. Column profiles are considered. Output includes details of the bending moment envelope and the shear force envelope, the support reactions and information concerning the shear reinforcement

References
DOC Evaluation Report No 2

Source
W J Crocker and Partners
25 Market Square
Bromley, Kent
Telephone 01–460 9282–7

Availability
Bureau service from Atkins Computing Services Ltd

Language
Fortran

Computer
Sigma

591

Program name
DS411

Abstract
This program carries out the calculations for reinforced concrete beams and columns required for DS411: 1973. Carrying capacity and deflection are calculated, and bending schedules produced

References
Danish Building Research Institute
Abstract 48 12 301

Source
Viggo Michaelsen A/S
Radgivende ingeniorfirma
Sondre alle 43
4600 Koge
Denmark

Availability

Language

Computer

592

Program name
FSLAB

Abstract
The program produces flat-slab reinforcement details (within the definitions of BS CP114:1969), bar schedules and steel quantities. Slabs may be solid or of waffle type. Input data is specified using DRAW which produces basic slab information. Additional data such as 'continuity' conditions, and bar curtailments and projections are added to the information derived from DRAW. A conventionally-styled and referenced drawing is produced by plotter

References

Source
Building Computer Services Limited
Bush House
72 Prince Street
Bristol BS1 4HU
Telephone 0272 290651

Availability
Bureau service, hire

Language

Computer

593

Program name
SLADE

Abstract
The program analyses and designs continuous one-way spanning slabs which must be of prismatic section throughout, but which may differ in thickness, for different spans. Input data should include support type and width, span type and length, slab thickness, loading, and depth to steel. Outputs (in tabular form) give moments and steel requirements for maximum moments, support reactions, warnings and failure indicators

References

Source
Building Computer Services Limited
Bush House
72 Prince Street
Bristol BS1 4HU
Telephone 0272 290651

Availability
Bureau service, hire

Language

Computer

594

Program name
SAFE

Abstract
The program carries out a finite element analysis of slabs (including waffles) or more complex constructions. It will deal with slabs containing randomly-distributed holes of any shape, including areas of different thicknesses which allow for drops and heads around columns. The form of input is such that the user defines his problem in simple terms by a 'shorthand'. Outputs give deflections, forces, moments and shears in tabular form

References

Source
Building Computer Services Limited
Bush House
72 Prince Street
Bristol BS1 4HU
Telephone 0272 290651

Availability
Bureau service, hire

Language

Computer

Program name
FRIDAY

Abstract
This post-processing program is used with LEAP and is one of a suite of analysis programs. The program sums, edits and re-formulates LEAP calculations of member stresses and deflections in bridge decking

References

Source
Computer Consortium Services Ltd
5 Windmill Street
London W1P 1HF
UK
Telephone 01–638 3118

Availability
Bureau service

Language
Fortran

Computer
CDC
IBM
PDP

596

Program name
LEAPWA

Abstract
This analysis of slab reinforcement in bridge decking is one of a suite of analysis programs. The program will calculate reinforcement moments by a grillage analogy, using Wood & Armer equations. Outputs include the effect of torsion within the slab, and top and bottom moments in the direction of the major and minor reinforcement

References

Source
Computer Consortium Services Ltd
5 Windmill Street
London W1P 1HF
UK
Telephone 01–638 3118

Availability
Bureau service

Language
Fortran

Computer
CDC
IBM
PDP

597

Program name
FLAT-SLAB/1

Abstract
This sub-system enables an engineer to design and detail a reinforced concrete building, including bar schedules, which incorporates flat slabs in accordance with BS CP110:Part 1:1972. There is no limit to the number of elements to be considered. The size of structure to be analysed is limited only by the size and type of computer used

References
GENESYS program library

Source
GENESYS Limited
Pennine House, Lemyngton Street
Loughborough, Leicestershire
LE11 1XA, UK
Telephone 0509 39185 Telex 341747

Availability
Bureau service, hire

Language
Gentran

Computer
CDC 6500, 6600, 7600
DEC 10
Honeywell 6000
IBM 360, 370
ICL 1900, System 4
Philips P1400
PRIME 300
Univac 1100

598

Program name
Unreinforced concrete raft flooring

Abstract
This program calculates the bearing capacity of unreinforced concrete rafts on earth. It calculates carrying capacity for both distributed and point loads

References
Danish Building Research Institute
Abstract 48 13 40

Source
Geodata A/S
Dagmarhus
HC Andersens Boulevard 7
1553 Copenhagen V
Denmark

Availability
Bureau service

Language

Computer

599

Program name
Flat slab

Abstract
This program analyses and designs flat slabs, with or without dropped panels, and ribbed slabs. The program deals with up to twelve spans, and can accept cantilever ends. Results are in accordance with BS CP114:1969

References

Source
Laing Computing Services
Elstree Way
Borehamwood
Hertfordshire
WD6 1NF, UK
Telephone 01–207 2000

Availability
Sale, bureau service

Language
Fortran

Computer
IBM 370–50

600

Program name
CIRCTANK/1

Abstract
This sub-system enables an engineer to analyse a circular tank wall with fixed, free or partially-fixed ends. Provision can be made for prestressing hoops

References
GENESYS program library

Source
GENESYS Limited
Pennine House, Lemyngton Street
Loughborough, Leicestershire
LE11 1XA UK
Telephone 0509 39185Telex 341747

Availability
Bureau service, hire

Language
Gentran

Computer
CDC 6500, 6600, 7600
DEC 10
Honeywell 6000
IBM 360, 370
ICL 1900, System 4
Philips P1400
PRIME 300
Univac 1100

601

Program name
SHEARWALL/1

Abstract
This sub-system enables an engineer to analyse shear stress in wall structures, by means of an idealised elastic stiffness frame, a method described by MacLeod. Structures comprising several interconnected walls may be analysed. The size of the problem to be handled is limited only by the size and type of computer used

References
GENESYS program library

Source
GENESYS Limited
Pennine House, Lemyngton Street
Loughborough, Leicestershire
LE11 1XA UK
Telephone 0509 39185Telex 341747

Availability
Bureau service, hire

Language
Gentran

Computer
CDC 6500, 6600, 7600
DEC 10
Honeywell 6000
IBM 360, 370
ICL 1900, System 4
Philips P1400
PRIME 300
Univac 1100

602

Program name
Shear walls

Abstract
This program calculates moments, shear forces, stresses and wind forces for walls of up to thirty storeys and twenty-five panel walls in each direction. Walls may be of brickwork and/or concrete. It also checks compliance with the appropriate code of practice

References

Source
Hewlett-Packard Limited
King Street Lane, Winnersh
Wokingham, Berks RG11 5AR
UK
Telephone Wokingham 784774

Availability
Purchase

Language
Basic

Computer
HP 9830A with 3808–word memory

603

Program name
SHEWALLS

Abstract
This program calculates forces and distortion in walls of multi-storey buildings of tubular form. It assumes that walls are alike on all floors, although vertical joints and doors can be taken into consideration

References
Danish Building Research Institute
Abstract 48 11 303

Source
SBI
Postbox 119
2970 Horsholm
Denmark

Availability
Bureau service (CE-data or CDC Data Center)

Language

Computer

604

Program name
CIRCTANK/1

Abstract
This program analyses reinforced concrete circular tank walls of varying thickness and degrees of rigidity. It will consider both uncracked and cracked tanks. Output gives bar sizes and spacing for hooping and vertical steel, and an estimate of concrete and formwork costs. Results also include a full listing of input data

References
Developed by GENESYS Ltd

Source
UCC, University Computing Company
344–350 Euston Road
London NW1
UK
Telephone 01–387 9661

Availability
Bureau service

Language
Fortran
Gentran

Computer

Program name
SHEAR-WALL/1

Abstract
This program makes a frame analysis of shear walls using the elastic stiffness method. Structures comprising several interconnected shear walls can be analysed. Output gives deformation at nodes, axial shear forces, bending moments acting on each member, and a full listing of input data

References
Developed by GENESYS Ltd

Source
UCC, University Computing Company
344–350 Euston Road
London NW1
UK
Telephone 01–387 9661

Availability
Bureau service

Language
Fortran
Gentran

Computer

606

Program name
53–T12

Abstract
This program calculates tensions, reactions and deflections in the columns of a plane structural frame. It is based on the deformation method. Consideration is taken of the effect on the columns by setting-up conditions of equilibrium for the deformed frame structure

References

Source
A/S Regnecentralen
Falkoneralle 1
2000 Kobenhavn F
Denmark
Telephone (01) 10 53 66

Availability

Language

Computer

607

Program name
Symmetrically-reinforced-concrete columns

Abstract
This program designs reinforced-concrete columns to BS CP 110:1972

References

Source
Camutek
39 Newnham Road
Cambridge CB3 9EY
UK
Telephone Cambridge (0223) 69686

Availability
From owner

Language
Basic

Computer
Hewlett-Packard
9830 (2k) or (6k)

608

Program name
Steel-column design

Abstract
This program designs steel columns to BS 449:1969

References

Source
Camutek
39 Newnham Road
Cambridge CB3 9EY
UK
Telephone Cambridge (0223) 69686

Availability
From owner

Language
Basic

Computer
Hewlett-Packard
9830 (2k) or (6k)

609

Program name
Reinforced columns

Abstract
This program calculates tension in an eccentrically loaded column of given strength. The column is assumed to be simply supported at both ends

References

Source
CE-data
Lundtoftevej 1G
2800 Lyngby
Denmark

Availability
Bureau service

Language

Computer

610

Program name
BECOL

Abstract
This program carries out the elastic design of members in steel to BS449 when subjected to combinations of axial loading and bi-axial bending. It is therefore suitable for the design of either beam or column elements of a structure. The program can be run in an interactive mode, allowing the engineer to make pertinent decisions, or automatically, when it will select the most efficient section based on minimum weight

References
Bradshaw, Buckton and Tonge

Source
Civil and Structural Computing (Northern) Limited
14 Bramley Centre
Leeds LS13 2ET
Telephone 0532 563322

Availability
Bureau service, time-sharing, in-house

Language

Computer
Hewlett Packard 9800 and others

611

Program name
PLATE

Abstract
This program makes an analysis of a column baseplate, the plan dimensions and bolt configurations of which have been input by the engineer. Up to six loadings may be applied and each load can consist of a column in axial tension or compression, a major axis moment and a horizontal shear

References
Bradshaw, Buckton and Tonge

Availability
Bureau service, time-sharing, in-house

Source
Civil and Structural Computing (Northern) Limited
14 Bramley Centre
Leeds LS13 2ET
Telephone 0532 563322

Language

Computer
Hewlett Packard 9800 and others

612

Program name
COLUMN

Abstract
This program facilitates the design of steel compression members in accordance with the elastic design requirements of the steel structures code AS 1250–1975. There are seven design categories: universal, box, tube, angle, channel, plated-I and plated-box. Members designed using symmetrical sections can be subjected to uni-axial or bi-axial bending. Non-symmetrical sections can be subjected to pure compression only

References

Source
CSIRO, Division of Building Research
Graham Road, Highett
Victoria 3190
Australia
Telephone 95 0333

Availability
ACADS

Language
Fortran

Computer
CDC 6600, Cyber 74

613

Program name
COLUMN

Abstract
This program computes the allowable working stress for columns with or without eccentric loads and linear elastic or non-linear elastic-plastic materials. Results are valid for all slenderness ratios up to 300. Linear, non-eccentrically loaded columns are solved by a combined parabolic-Euler formula. Eccentric loads are solved by the secant formula. Non-linear columns with no eccentricity are solved by the Engresser equation

References
CALL library

Source
Data Center Services
IBM World Trade Corporation
821 United Nations Plaza
New York 10017
USA

Availability
Also available from IBM offices throughout the world

Language
Basic

Computer
IBM 360

614

Program name
BIAX

Abstract
This program analyses the combined axial loading and bi-axial bending of a column section. A solution is achieved by the successive alteration of sectional concrete so that tension would be prevented until the concrete boundary moved imperceptibly. Maximum concrete and steel stresses are listed, together with the maximum tensile steel stresses, the centroid in a cracked section, the equation of the neutral axis and a plot of the cracked section

References

Source
Faber Computer Operations Limited
Upper Marlborough Road
St Albans
Herts AL1 3UT
Telephone St Albans 61222

Availability
Bureau service

Language

Computer
IBM 1130, System 7

Program name
BASE

Abstract
The program analyses the pressure distribution below column bases subjected to both axial loading and bi-axial bending. Moments of inertia, product of inertia, centroid and area of the new base section are calculated, and the imposed moments are modified. Any number of bases can be analysed consecutively in one run. Outputs include base to ground pressures at each corner, the locus of the zero pressure line and the position of the centroid

References

Source
Faber Computer Operations Limited
Upper Marlborough Road
St Albans
Herts AL1 3UT
Telephone St Albans 61222

Availability
Bureau service

Language

Computer
IBM 1130, System 7

616

Program name
Reinforced concrete column design

Abstract
This program gives the preliminary design and final check of circular-spiral or rectangular- tied columns to the ACI 318–71 code. It is particularly suited to situations involving biaxial bending and to columns where length effects may influence the design. Column-interaction diagrams are available

References
Part number 09830–74250

Source
Hewlett-Packard Limited
King Street Lane, Winnersh
Wokingham, Berks RG11 5AR
UK
Telephone Wokingham 784774

Availability
Purchase

Language
Basic

Computer
HP 9830A with
3808–word memory
11270B matrix ROM
9866A thermal
printer

617

Program name
COLDES

Abstract
This program, which is maintained by the DoE, is for the design or analysis of reinforced concrete columns. These may be circular, rectangular or elliptical in shape and may be subjected to any combination of axial loading and biaxial bending. The design is based on minimum cost criteria, but will not exceed the permissible stresses or violate the code requirements. The user specifies costs of materials, shuttering, bar sizes and strengths

References
CALL, IBM United Kingdom Limited

Source
Highway Engineering Computer Branch
Department of the Environment
St Christopher House
Southwark Street
London SE1 UK
Telephone (01) 928 7999

Availability
Also available from IBM offices

Language

Computer

618

Program name
RCSECT

Abstract
This program analyses the stresses in a reinforced concrete member of any section

References

Source
Atkins Computing Services Limited
Woodcote Grove, Ashley Road
Epsom, Surrey
UK
Telephone Epsom 40421

Availability
Bureau service, time-sharing. Available in Netherlands

Language
Basic

Computer
Honeywell Sigma 9

619

Program name
ASAS

Abstract
This program is for general stress analysis of finite elements of all forms of structure under varying load conditions, including thermal and dynamic. Associated programs give graphic displays of the structure, indicating displacement etc

References

Source
Atkins Computing Services Limited
Woodcote Grove, Ashley Road
Epsom, Surrey
UK
Telephone Epsom 40421

Availability
Bureau service, time-sharing. Available in Netherlands

Language
Fortran IV

Computer
Honeywell Sigma 9

Program name
Reinforced-concrete design

Abstract
This program designs reinforced-concrete sections in bending or shear. It checks for deflection to BS CP 110:1972

References

Source
Camutek
39 Newnham Road
Cambridge CB3 9EY
UK
Telephone Cambridge (0223) 69686

Availability
From owner

Language
Basic

Computer
Hewlett-Packard
9830 (2k) or (6k)

621

Program name
Cross-section

Abstract
This program calculates stress and tension through a cross-section of reinforced or unreinforced structural members

References

Source
CE-data
Lundtoftevej 1G
2800 Lyngby
Denmark

Availability
Bureau service

Language

Computer

622

Program name
BARSHED

Abstract
This program prepares general concrete detailing to BS 4466:1969. It is one of a suite of detailing programs. It reduces the cost and increases the accuracy of information by producing all written and checking parts of traditional detailing. Outputs are variable and include bar-checking reports, weight summaries for bill of quantities and bar-fixing instruction lists for drawing

References

Source
Computer Consortium Services Ltd
5 Windmill Street
London W1P 1HF
UK
Telephone 01–638 3118

Availability
Bureau service

Language
Fortran

Computer
CDC
IBM
PDP

623

Program name
SECSTRESS

Abstract
A program for the calculation of stresses in sections, caused by direct loads and moments. Circular areas of reinforcement may be specified. The program requires the co-ordinates of the peripheral points, and details of the position and size of circular reinforcement, the modular ratio, and the loads and moments to be applied

References

Source
CRC Engineering Services
83 Clerkenwell Road
London
EC1R 5HP
Telephone 01–242 0747

Availability

Language

Computer

624

Program name
SECPROP

Abstract
A program for the calculation of essential properties of cross-sections. The input data describes the shape of the section by listing the co-ordinates of the peripheral points. This method allows for irregular shapes, including hollow sections

References

Source
CRC Engineering Services
83 Clerkenwell Road
London
EC1R 5HP
Telephone 01–242 0747

Availability

Language

Computer

Program name
BUCKL

Abstract
This program calculates the critical tensions in curved structural members. Stability fails if the sections are twisted. The linear-elastic stability method is used. The program uses an iterative solution

References

Source
Danmarks Ingeniorakademi
Bygningsafdelingen
Bygning 373
2800 Lyngby
Denmark

Availability

Language
Fortran

Computer
IBM 370/165

626

Program name
MIX

Abstract
This program designs concrete mixes by the method specified in BRE publication, Design of normal concrete mixes. Default value of parameters to BS 5328:1976 and BS CP110:Part 1:1972 are used for speed and simplicity. It may be used for trial mix design or to control closely proportions of materials when mix strengths are known

References
PSA program library

Source
Directorate of Civil Engineering Services
Property Services Agency
Lunar House, 40 Wellesley Road
Croydon CR9 2EL
UK
Telephone 01–686 3499

Availability

Language
Fortran

Computer

627

Program name
CHIM

Abstract
This program will design reinforced concrete chimneys to the extent of calculating shell thicknesses and required steel areas, in accordance with the ACI Code 505–54. It covers lined and unlined chimneys, with or without insulation between shell and lining, and can analyse and specify flue openings, as well as calculating the fundamental period of vibration. Dimensions, design moments, concrete and steel stresses are listed in the output

References

Source
Faber Computer Operations Limited
Upper Marlborough Road
St Albans
Herts AL1 3UT
Telephone St Albans 61222

Availability
Bureau service

Language

Computer
IBM 1130, System 7

628

Program name
ECHO

Abstract
This program calculates the natural frequency of a chimney or a similar structure, defined in SI or Imperial units. The program uses the Holzer method, which assumes the chimney to be a weightless cantilever with concentrated masses at discrete points along its length

References

Source
Faber Computer Operations Limited
Upper Marlborough Road
St Albans
Herts AL1 3UT
Telephone St Albans 61222

Availability
Bureau service

Language

Computer
IBM 1130, System 7

629

Program name
STEP

Abstract
This program calculates the moment diagram for the core of a spiral staircase subjected to any combination of step loadings. It is calculated about two axes at right angles and, for every step, the magnitude and direction of the resultant moment is found. For each step position the maximum and minimum values of moments about the two chosen axes are given. Finally, the reaction at the top of the core of the staircase is output

References

Source
Faber Computer Operations Limited
Upper Marlborough Road
St Albans
Herts AL1 3UT
Telephone St Albans 61222

Availability
Bureau service

Language

Computer
IBM 1130, System 7

630

Program name
Cross-section

Abstract
This program calculates constants for cross-sections of structural elements, as well as tension for given moments and normal stress. Calculations are based on elasticity theory

References
Danish Building Research Institute
Abstract 48 12 002

Source
Geodata A/S
Dagmarhus
HC Andersens Boulevard 7
1553 Copenhagen V
Denmark

Availability
Bureau service

Language

Computer

631

Program name
Ring-frame analysis

Abstract
This program analyses ring frames under coplanar loading. Gable frames, circular and parabolic arches and many single-span arches can be analysed. The use of flexural energy is necessary and the effects of shear and axial energies may be added. Almost any possible support-constraint condition may be specified. The frame may have a variable cross-section. Moments, shears, axial loads and deformations are computed and may be plotted

References
Part number 09830–74230

Source
Hewlett-Packard Limited
King Street Lane, Winnersh
Wokingham, Berks RG11 5AR
UK
Telephone Wokingham 784774

Availability
Purchase

Language
Basic

Computer
HP 9830A with 3808–word memory
11270B matrix ROM
11274B strings ROM
9866A thermal printer

632

Program name
FINGEN and FINITE

Abstract
These programs perform stress analysis for finite elements

References
Mark III software library
User manual 5202·16

Source
Honeywell Information Systems Limited
114 to 118 Southampton Row
London WC1B 5AB
UK
Telephone 01–242 5725

Availability
Bureau service

Language
Basic

Computer
Honeywell 6000 series

633

Program name
AISC

Abstract
This random-access master file contains data for programming designs in hot rolled steel, such as beams, piles, columns and sections. It contains accessible, indexed files which include GEX series, which is ordered by ascending weight per length and, within identical weights, by moment of inertia; GEA series, which is ordered by shape; and the COLMN series, which is ordered by shape with properties grouped in ascending order and weight

References
Mark III software library
User manual 5202·25

Source
Honeywell Information Systems Limited
114 to 118 Southampton Row
London WC1B 5AB
UK
Telephone 01–242 5725

Availability
Bureau service

Language
Basic

Computer
Honeywell 6000 series

634

Program name
Reinforcement quantities from bending schedules

Abstract
This program sizes quantities of reinforcement for structural members. The following input data is punched directly from the schedules: type of steel, bar size, number of bars, length, shape code. Output consists of a table of weights for links, straight lengths and other types for every bar size and type of steel, with sub-totals of length and weight, and finally a grand total

References

Source
Laing Computing Services
Elstree Way
Borehamwood
Hertfordshire
WD6 1NF, UK

Availability
Sale, bureau service

Language
Fortran

Computer
IBM 370–50

Program name
GLADYS

Abstract
A computer system which performs various calculations for structural engineering design. The system comprises a master program and sub-systems covering the following topics: design of irregular concrete columns; design of concrete pad-footings; design of pile-caps; analysis and design of beams; or calculation of elastic section properties of irregular sections. Reinforced concrete design and analysis is carried out to BS CP110

References
DOC Bulletin, March 1976

Source
Ove Arup and Partners
13 Fitzroy Street
London W1
UK
Telephone 01–636 1531

Availability
Contact owner

Language

Computer
DEC 10

636

Program name
SPIN

Abstract
This program calculates the critical speeds of rotating shafts and the natural frequencies in bending of multi-span beams of arbitrary cross-sections. The program also calculates the dynamic response due to off-resonant, sinusoidally applied forces, as well as determining deflections, bending moments, shear forces and stresses created by static forces. It uses a distributed or lumped mass method for dynamic analysis

References
SDRC Mechanical Design Library

Source
Structural Dynamics Research Corporation
5729 Dragon Way
Cincinnati, Ohio 45227
USA
Telephone (513) 272 1100

Availability
Time-sharing. Available in UK

Language

Computer

637

Program name
DECIDE 30

Abstract
This package is used for designing structural concrete elements to BS CP110:Part 1:1972. The programs may be used individually or as a series, one handing data on to the next within the machine. They include programs for designing the beams, slabs and columns within a structure. The design is taken from initial structural analysis to the provision of bars and shear reinforcement. Manuals are provided for designer and checking authority

References
BS CP110 The structural use of concrete

Source
Taylor and Beeby
7 Woodlands Drive
Beaconsfield Bucks
UK

Availability
Contact owner

Language
Basic

Computer
Hewlett-Packard 9830

638

Program name
Laminated arch design

Abstract
A program for the design of glue-laminated portal arches

References

Source
TRADA
Chiltern House, Hughenden Valley
High Wycombe, Buckinghamshire
UK
Telephone Naphill 3091

Availability

Language

Computer

639

Program name
UBM/1

Abstract
This program calculates the ultimate bending moment of reinforced and prestressed concrete sections of any shape in accordance with BS CP110:Part 1:1972. Output gives depth of neutral axis, ultimate bending moment, stresses in concrete and steel, and a full listing of input data

References
Developed by GENESYS Ltd

Source
UCC, University Computing Company
344–350 Euston Road
London NW1
UK
Telephone 01–387 9661

Availability
Bureau service

Language
Fortran
Gentran

Computer

640

Program name
COLDES

Abstract
Using the linear elastic design theory, this program analyses and designs reinforced concrete sections subjected to bi-axial bending and axial loading. Output plots crack widths, gives steel and concrete stresses, cost of materials and formwork, and includes a full listing of input data

References
Developed by the computer branch of the DoE (Highway Engineering)

Source
UCC, University Computing Company
344–350 Euston Road
London NW1
UK
Telephone 01–387 9661

Availability
Bureau service

Language
Fortran

Computer

641

Program name
PREBEM

Abstract
This program is used to design prestressed and pre-tensioned single spans of constant inertia. Output gives stresses, strand arrangements, shear steel and end block requirements, and a full listing of input data

References
Developed by the Midland Road Construction Unit

Source
UCC, University Computing Company
344–350 Euston Road
London NW1
UK
Telephone 01–387 9661

Availability
Bureau service

Language
Fortran

Computer

642

Program name
Sub-frame/1

Abstract
This program analyses sub-frames in accordance with BS CP114:1969 or BS CP110:Part 1:1972. (Partial safety factors of 1·4 and 1·6 are automatically applied). Output gives printed or plotted bending moment and shear force envelopes plus a full listing of input data

References
Developed by GENESYS Ltd

Source
UCC, University Computing Company
344–350 Euston Road
London NW1
UK
Telephone 01–387 9661

Availability
Bureau service

Language
Fortran
Gentran

Computer

643

Program name
UMIST structural steelwork system

Abstract
This program details end-plate connections in structural steel frames consisting of beams and columns. Calculations are carried out to BS 449:1969. When automatic detailing fails, bolt clashes and excessive stresses are noted. Correction is interactive

References

Source
UMIST
Department of Civil and Structural Engineering
PO Box 88, Manchester
UK
Telephone 061 236 3311

Availability
Contact NRDC

Language
Fortran

Computer
CDC 7600, Cyber 72

644

Program name
Abcons computer system

Abstract
The program carries out a complete elastic analysis and provides the necessary calculations, fixing instructions and schedules for an in-situ reinforced concrete building. It can deal with solid and hollow tile floors, spanning one or two ways; beams and columns. Quantities of materials for shuttering, concrete and reinforcement are given for each element and summarised for the whole structure. The design is in accordance with BS CP114

References
ABC4

Sources
Associated British Consultants (Computers) Limited
100 College Road
Harrow, Middlesex
HA1 1EW UK
Telephone 01–863 8555

Availability
Bureau service

Language
Fortran IV

Computer
ICL 1900
Univac 1108

Pipework, ductwork and sound control

Pipework
Ductwork
Sound control

645

Program name
TRIFLEX

Abstract
This program is for the design and analysis of pipework systems. Analysis is based on the static or dynamic effects of temperature, pressure, weight of the system, external loads and the position of anchors and supports

References

Source
AAA Technology and Specialties
3130 Southwest Freeway
Houston, Texas
USA
Telephone 713 524 8111

Availability
Batch

Language

Computer

646

Program name
MO28

Abstract
This program is for sizing components for steam pipe networks. A recursive method is used, which allows for initial and terminal pressures to be specified

References

Source
Albert Kahn Associates
New Center Building
Detroit, Michigan 48202
USA
Telephone 313 871 8500

Availability

Language
Fortran IV

Computer
IBM 1130

647

Program name
MA36

Abstract
This program is used for the analysis of flow in pipework systems, to check a design for possible interference

References

Source
Albert Kahn Associates
New Center Building
Detroit, Michigan 48202
USA
Telephone 313 871 8500

Availability

Language
Fortran IV

Computer
IBM 1130

648

Program name
MC27

Abstract
This program is for sizing components for pipe networks where flow is recirculated. Hydraulics of the system are balanced automatically. Cost estimates are also produced

References

Source
Albert Kahn Associates
New Center Building
Detroit, Michigan 48202
USA
Telephone 313 871 8500

Availability

Language
Fortran IV

Computer
IBM 1130

649

Program name
MO54

Abstract
This program is used for the analysis of flow in grid piping systems

References

Source
Albert Kahn Associates
New Center Building
Detroit, Michigan 48202
USA
Telephone 313 871 8500

Availability

Language
Fortran IV

Computer
IBM 1130

650

Program name
NO1P

Abstract
This program will provide basic information for design of pipework from specifications and design criteria, and material and labour costs. Flow, size of pipe, pressure drop and heat loss or gain are calculated for each section. For special systems, pump capacity, sizing of the required expansion tanks and balancing valves will also be indicated. An overall cost estimate is also produced

References

Source
APEC Executive Office
Grant-Deneau Tower, Suite M–15
Dayton, Ohio 45402
USA
Telephone 513 228 2602

Availability

Language
Fortran IV

Computer
IBM 360, 1130
CDC Cyber
GE Mark III

651

Program name
PSA 5

Abstract
This Whessoe pipe-stress program is available with interactive aids for data-checking and results interrogation

References

Source
Atkins Computing Services Limited
Woodcote Grove, Ashley Road
Epsom, Surrey
UK
Telephone Epsom 40421

Availability
Bureau service, time-sharing. Available in Netherlands

Language
Fortran

Computer
Honeywell Sigma 9

652

Program name
PANP

Abstract
This CIRIA program is for the analysis of large-scale pipe networks including pressure-reducing valves and pumps

References

Source
Atkins Computing Services Limited
Woodcote Grove, Ashley Road
Epsom, Surrey
UK
Telephone Epsom 40421

Availability
Bureau service, time-sharing. Available in Netherlands

Language
Fortran

Computer
Honeywell Sigma 9

653

Program name
Autoflex

Abstract
This program performs stress analysis in pressure-pipe systems. Up to four combinations of load, resulting from internal pressure, weight of components and thermal effects, can be considered. Options allow a user to specify metric rather than Imperial units and to take account of the expansion effects of internal pressure

References

Source
Auton Computing Corporation
Engineering Services Division
10 Columbus Circle
New York, NY 10019
USA

Availability
Time-sharing

Language

Computer

654

Program name
PUMPHD

Abstract
This program sizes components and estimates the pump head required for a water-pipe system. The user may select pre-sized pipe sections and override limitations of velocity and drop in pressure

References

Source
Ayres and Hayakawa
1180 South Beverly Drive
Los Angeles, California 90036
USA
Telephone 213 879 4477

Availability
Purchase, batch

Language
Fortran IV

Computer

655

Program name
PS1

Abstract
This program calculates the sizes of steel pipes (from six inches to ten feet in diameter) for carrying water at given flow rates. The flow rate (lb/h or gal/min) together with the desired water velocity (ft/sec) is input. A pipe size is selected which will give a velocity just below that required. The pipe diameter, pressure loss and velocity are also output. The same information is supplied for pipes one size larger, and two sizes smaller

References

Source
Building Service Designs
322 Carshalton Road
Carshalton, Surrey
UK
Telephone 01–661 1416

Availability
Bureau service, time-sharing

Language
Basic

Computer
Honeywell Sigma 7, Sigma 9

656

Program name
MULPIP

Abstract
This program calculates heat losses and gains of underground pipes buried together. Heat transfer to and from each pipe is calculated, taking into account temperature, thermal insulation, depth, ground temperature and thermal properties of the soil

References
Underground Heat and Chilled Water Distribution Systems, NBS Building Science Series, Number 66

Source
Center for Building Technology, IAT
National Bureau of Standards
Washington, DC 20234
USA

Availability

Language

Computer

657

Program name
Closed-circuit pipe sizing

Abstract
A program for the calculation of Btu/hour distribution and minimum pipe sizes for a given circuit layout

References
Program made available by ICL

Source
Computel Limited
Eastern Road
Bracknell, Berkshire
UK
Telephone Bracknell 23031

Availability

Language

Computer

658

Program name
Fluid-distribution network-analysis Mark 3

Abstract
A program to calculate, from data on network supply and demand, the flows and pressures in gas and water distribution networks

References
Program made available by ICL

Source
Computel Limited
Eastern Road
Bracknell, Berkshire
UK
Telephone Bracknell 23031

Availability

Language

Computer

659

Program name
Pipe stressing

Abstract
A program for the evaluation of forces, moments and stresses at any point in a piping system made up of straight pipes, circular arcs and rigid sections. See also FLAPS

References
Program made available by ICL

Source
Computel Limited
Eastern Road
Bracknell, Berkshire
UK
Telephone Bracknell 23031

Availability

Language

Computer

Program name
FLAPS

Abstract
FLAPS (Flexibility Analysis of Pipe Systems) is for the analysis of large pipe systems and covers factors such as expansion, wind loading and rigid or free joints

References
Program made available by Dataskil

Source
Computel Limited
Eastern Road
Bracknell, Berkshire
UK
Telephone Bracknell 23031

Availability

Language

Computer

661

Program name
MEC 21

Abstract
This program is for analysis of the flexibility of multiple-branch and closed-loop pipework systems subject to thermal, uniform and concentrated loads. It is suitable for analysis of cryogenic piping systems

References

Source
COSMIC
University of Georgia
Athens, Georgia 30602
USA
Telephone 404 542 3265

Availability
Purchase

Language
Fortran

Computer
CDC 6600
Univac 1108

662

Program name
PIPLQ

Abstract
This program sizes components for pipe networks with a steady incompressible flow. Analysis of flow is in one dimension only. Temperature and viscosity of the fluid carried may be considered as variable

References

Source
COSMIC
University of Georgia
Athens, Georgia 30602
USA
Telephone 404 542 3265

Availability
Purchase

Language
Fortran IV

Computer
CDC 6600

663

Program name
ONEPIPE C/ONEPIPE 4

Abstract
These programs will size one-pipe systems to achieve correct temperature and pressure balance. ONEPIPE C covers pipe/radiator arrangements across purely horizontal planes, while ONEPIPE 4 covers all other types of one-pipe system. The output is identical for both versions and gives, for each section of a system, a list of dimensions and materials, pressures, fluid flows, velocities, heat emissions and the total heat requirement

References

Source
CSTC
41 Rue du Lombard
1000 Brussels
Belgium
Telephone 02–511 06 83

Availability
Bureau service

Language
Fortran IV

Computer

664

Program name
TWOPIPE

Abstract
This program sizes two-pipe systems to achieve correct temperature and pressure balance in any type of building. A circuit diagram of the system is drawn and divided into sections, each section being considered separately by the program. For each section, a list is given of dimensions and materials, pressures, fluid flows, velocities, heat emissions and the total heat requirement

References

Source
CSTC
41 Rue du Lombard
1000 Brussels
Belgium
Telephone 02–511 06 83

Availability
Bureau service

Language
Fortran IV

Computer

665

Program name
PIPES

Abstract
This program produces the most economical design for two-pipe hot-water systems. It gives a detailed list of piping and fittings required for the installation. The program operates with metric or Imperial units

References

Source
Dewco Programming and Computer Services
20 Park Street
Bristol BS1 5JA
UK
Telephone 0272 23352

Availability
Bureau service, remote batch, purchase

Language
Fortran

Computer
Honeywell 6000

666

Program name
PIPEFRC

Abstract
This program calculates pipe friction for turbulent flow (Reynolds' number greater than 4000). Relative roughness (surface roughness/diameter) and Reynolds' number are input. The Colebrook (Moody diagram) equation is solved for the turbulent pipe-flow friction factors by an iterative scheme. Friction factors are computed to an accuracy of 0·01 per cent

References
CALL library

Source
Data Center Services
IBM World Trade Corporation
821 United Nations Plaza
New York 10017
USA

Availability
Also available from IBM offices throughout the world

Language
Basic

Computer
IBM 360

667

Program name
PIPEFLO

Abstract
This program solves three types of pipe-flow problem, head loss, flow rate and pipe diameter. It includes friction for both the laminar and turbulent situations, but will not provide a solution for the transition problem. Pipe length, kinematic viscosity and surface roughness are input for all three problems. In addition, the input must include two out of three of the following quantities, flow rate, pipe diameter and head loss

References
CALL library

Source
Data Center Services
IBM World Trade Corporation
821 United Nations Plaza
New York 10017
USA

Availability
Also available from IBM offices throughout the world

Language
Basic

Computer
IBM 360

668

Program name
PASS

Abstract
This program analyses the flow of fluid through a pipework system. Pipe sizes, pressure, temperature, and size of expansion tank and pump required are calculated. Several types of fluid may be examined, and the pipework and insulation may be of one of several materials

References

Source
Daverman Associates Incorporated
200 Monroe Avenue NW
Grand Rapids, Michigan 49502
USA
Telephone 616 451 3525

Availability
Time-sharing

Language

Computer
CDC Cyber

669

Program name
PIPE

Abstract
This program constructs a pipe sizing chart, consisting of fluid flow and friction loss axes, plus lines of constant velocity and diameter. Input parameters may be altered until a satisfactory chart is produced which can then be printed on the plotter. A table of fluid flows for pipe diameters and friction losses may be calculated. The data base uses Colebrook-White's equation for turbulent flow and Poisenille's formula for lamina flow

References

Source
Faber Computer Operations Limited
Upper Marlborough Road
St Albans
Herts UK
Telephone St Albans 61222

Availability
Bureau service

Language

Computer
IBM 1130, System 7

Program name
TPSS 2

Abstract
Given the room heat loads, this program will size two-pipe systems and determine the correct temperature and pressure balance. The program will accept only pure two-pipe systems, where the return pipe exactly follows the flow pipe. For other systems the linked program, CLOP, should be used. The output gives for each section a listing of dimensions, pressures, fluid flows, velocities, heat emissions and the total heat requirement

References

Source
Faber Computer Operations Limited
Upper Marlborough Road
St Albans
Hertfordshire, UK
Telephone St Albans 61222

Availability
Bureau service

Language

Computer
IBM 1130, System 7

671

Program name
MESH

Abstract
Given flows or relative pressures at inflow/outflow points, this program distributes flows to achieve pressure balance in closed, open-ended or combined pipe networks. For each pipe section the generated output lists lengths, diameters, calculated flows, friction per metre run and pressure drops. The program uses the Colebrooke-White equation for turbulent flow and Poisenille's formula for lamina flow

References

Source
Faber Computer Operations Limited
Upper Marlborough Road
St Albans
Hertfordshire, UK
Telephone St Albans 61222

Availability
Bureau service

Language

Computer
IBM 1130, System 7

672

Program name
LPHW-PIPES/1

Abstract
This sub-system enables an engineer to calculate the pipe sizes for any two-pipe heating system. Design may be for minimum cost or specific water velocities

References
GENESYS program library

Source
GENESYS Limited
Pennine House, Lemyngton Street
Loughborough, Leicestershire
LE11 1XA, UK
Telephone 0509 39185 Telex 341747

Availability
Bureau service, hire

Language
Gentran

Computer
CDC 6500, 6600, 7600
DEC 10
Honeywell 6000
IBM 360, 370
ICL 1900, System 4
Philips 1400
PRIME 300
Univac 1100

673

Program name
MNINE

Abstract
This program is for use in the design of open piping systems. Sizes of components are output together with velocity and head loss in each length of pipe and through fittings. Existing systems can be analysed. Total flow and pressure drop in the system are calculated. The program is operational for piping carrying water, natural gas, steam and oils

References

Source
Giffels Associates Incorporated
Marquette Building
243 W Congress
Detroit, Michigan 48226
USA
Telephone 313 961 2084

Availability
Purchase negotiable

Language
Fortran V

Computer
Univac 1108

674

Program name
MTOSIX

Abstract
This program is for analysis of pipework. Velocity and head loss in each length of pipe and also loss through fittings are calculated. Existing systems can be analysed. The program is for use with closed piping systems

References

Source
Giffels Associates Incorporated
Marquette Building
243 W Congress
Detroit, Michigan 48226
USA
Telephone 313 961 2084

Availability
Purchase negotiable

Language
Fortran V

Computer
Univac 1108

675

Program name
UPIPE

Abstract
This program calculates heat losses from underground pipes in accordance with the IHVE Guide (Section C3)

References

Source
Haden Young Limited
7 Tavistock Square
London WC1
UK
Telephone 01–387 1288

Availability
By arrangement with DOC members

Language

Computer
ICL 1902T

676

Program name
CONFLO

Abstract
This program is for sizing one-pipe circuits for hot-water radiators. It aids the design of heating loops by the method used by Haden Young

References

Source
Haden Young Limited
7 Tavistock Square
London WC1
UK
Telephone 01–387 1288

Availability
By arrangement with DOC members

Language

Computer
ICL 1902T

677

Program name
PIPDAT

Abstract
This program calculates the relationship between pipe size, flow rate and drop in pressure for particular piping and fluids carried, using the method described in the IHVE guide (Section C4)

References

Source
Haden Young Limited
7 Tavistock Square
London WC1
UK
Telephone 01–387 1288

Availability
By arrangement with DOC members

Language

Computer
ICL 1902T

678

Program name
X3A4

Abstract
This program aids the detailed stress analysis of three-dimensional pipework systems

References
Developed by ICL

Source
Haden Young Limited
7 Tavistock Square
London WC1
UK
Telephone 01–387 1288

Availability
By arrangement with DOC members

Language

Computer
ICL 1902T

679

Program name
CD 20

Abstract
This program calculates the minimum pipe thickness required for pipework with a given temperature and pressure to BS 3601:1974

References

Source
Haden Young Limited
7 Tavistock Square
London WC1
UK
Telephone 01–387 1288

Availability
By arrangment with DOC members

Language

Computer
ICL 1902T

Program name
PIPE

Abstract
This program calculates the pump head for a direct-return or a reverse-return piping system. Friction loss is calculated using Darcy's equation. A bill of quantities may be produced and an expansion tank selected

References

Source
Hankins and Anderson Incorporated
2117 North Hamilton Street
PO Box 6872, Richmond
Virginia 23230
USA
Telephone 804 353 1221

Availability

Language
Fortran IV

Computer

681

Program name
Pipe dimensions (central-heating systems)

Abstract
This program gives dimensions for a two-pipe central-heating system with given radiator performance. Division of quantity of water, pressure loss, pump performance, resistance to regulation for adjustment of valves, total quantity of water and total length of piping in each size are also calculated. A maximum of 1000 radiators per system can be handled

References
Danish Building Research Institute
Abstract 48 15 002

Source
Henning, Hansen & Erik Carlsen
Jens E Frolund
HC Orstedsvej 4
1879 Copenhagen V
Denmark

Availability
Bureau service from CE-data

Language

Computer

682

Program name
Pipe-network balancing

Abstract
This program calculates how to balance the flow in a pipe network. The procedure requires a rough estimate of the heads of each node. There are no limitations to the topological characteristics of the network. It may consist of closed loops, pipe connections without loops or combinations of the two

References
Part number 09830–75001

Source
Hewlett-Packard Limited
King Street Lane, Winnersh
Wokingham, Berks RG11 5AR
UK
Telephone Wokingham 784774

Availability
Purchase

Language
Basic

Computer
HP 9830A with 3808–word memory 9866A thermal printer

683

Program name
NETWKS

Abstract
This program calculates the flow and head loss in each pipe of a water-distribution system. It uses the Hardy-Cross method

References
Mark III software library
User manual 5202·03

Source
Honeywell Information Systems Limited
114 to 118 Southampton Row
London WC1B 5AB
UK
Telephone 01–242 5725

Availability
Bureau service

Language
Basic

Computer
Honeywell 6000 series

684

Program name
RAPID

Abstract
This system comprises a suite of programs, built up as a set of sub-systems, which can be used as a drawing-office aid to analyse and produce large piping components, and to plot isometric drawings for fabrication and erection. It can be used on all projects with a large quantity of service piping, to national and international standards

References

Source
Humphreys and Glasgow Limited
22 Carlisle Place
London SW1P 1JA
UK
Telephone 01–828 1234

Availability
Bureau service, purchase

Language
Fortran

Computer
Any machine with 32K core

Program name
PIPEX

Abstract
This program calculates stresses in linear steel or copper piping systems using the general method for square corner systems outlined in the Kellogg Handbook. The program handles single-end multi-plane pipe systems with no intermediate restraints or branches. The program is interactive

References

Source
Inatome and Associates
10140 West Nine Mile Road
Oak Park, Michigan 48237
USA
Telephone 313 542 4862

Availability
Time-sharing

Language

Computer

686

Program name
Pipe stress (R01019)

Abstract
The program calculates the loads and stresses in a pipework system, including the effects of temperature changes, internal pressure, forces and moments due to fluid flow and specified deformations. The pipe system can be plotted

References

Source
Industridata AB
Fack
Solna, Sweden
171 20
Telephone 08 98 03 50

Availability
Contact owner

Language
Fortran

Computer
Honeywell 6000

687

Program name
Velocity calculation (R02004)

Abstract
The program performs a steady-state calculation for meshed pipe networks. Flow and pressure in each branch and node of the network are calculated. The program can be used for incompressible gases and fluids

References

Source
Industridata AB
Fack
Solna, Sweden
171 20
Telephone 08 98 03 50

Availability
Contact owner

Language
Fortran

Computer
Honeywell 6000

688

Program name
HYDEDP

Abstract
This program aids the design of sprinkler and main fire-protection systems. Pipe sizes are calculated and the necessary hydraulic calculations carried out. Simple 'tree' systems, complex looped main underground systems and a variety of other designs, with loops or grids, can be handled

References

Source
M&M Protection Consultants
PO Box 105008
Atlanta, Georgia 30348
USA
Telephone 404 231 1770

Availability
Bureau service, interactive

Language

Computer

689

Program name
TRYKSTOD

Abstract
This program deals with pressure-shock in water pipes. It covers pumped systems with a reservoir where the pressure-shock is damped after the control valve. Pipes can be made up of an arbitrary number of lengths with different diameters and surface roughness. The program is based on the Bergerons method. The pressure-loss in the pipe is calculated by Colebrook's formula

References
Danish Building Research Institute
Abstract 48 15 003

Source
Nielsen & Rauschenberger
Radgivende Ingeniorer A/S
Lundtoftevej 7
2800 Lyngby
Denmark

Availability

Language

Computer

Program name
Network optimise

Abstract
This program creates plans for networks of water supply pipes. The most economic system, that is, a system in which pipe dimensions are the smallest which will give the required supply, is designed. Mass, current and pressure of water in the various parts of the system are calculated

References
Danish Building Research Institute
Abstract 45 15 001

Source
Nielsen & Rauschenberger
Radgivende Ingeniorer A/S
Lundtoftevej 7
2800 Lyngby
Denmark

Availability

Language
Fortran

Computer

691

Program name
Heating pipe resistance, simple

Abstract
This is a program for calculating the internal resistance of pipework for symmetrical two-pipe heating or cooling systems. The program has been modified for application in houses, flats and offices where most pipework branches are the same and only radiator outputs differ

References
Simplified version of 'two-pipe' program

Source
Ontwerp-en Adviesbureau
Dijkgraafstraat 12, Postbus 73
Krimpen ad Ijssel
Netherlands
Telephone Ijssel (01807) 14839

Availability
Bureau service, purchase

Language
Fortran
Also Basic version

Computer
CDC 6500
Basic version for Data General Nova 1220

692

Program name
Heating pipe resistance, two-pipe

Abstract
This program calculates the internal resistance of pipework for any symmetrical two-pipe heating or cooling system. The program calculates the overall pressure for each branch pipe and each radiator in the system. Details are given in the output of total length of pipe, insulation and number of appliances, and all totals are priced

References

Source
Ontwerp-en Adviesbureau
Dijkgraafstraat 12, Postbus 73
Krimpen ad Ijssel
Netherlands
Telephone Ijssel (01807) 14839

Availability
Bureau service, purchase

Language
Fortran
Also Basic version

Computer
CDC 6500
Basic version for Data General Nova 1220

693

Program name
Pipe resistance, Tiggelmann

Abstract
This program calculates the internal resistance of any pipework system, with any given pipe dimensions, according to the Tiggelmann system

References

Source
Ontwerp-en Adviesbureau
Dijkgraafstraat 12, Postbus 73
Krimpen ad Ijssel
Netherlands
Telephone Ijssel (01807) 14839

Availability
Bureau service, purchase

Language
Fortran
Also Basic version

Computer
CDC 6500
Basic version for Data General Nova 1220

694

Program name
Water pipe resistance

Abstract
This program calculates the internal resistance of pipework for hot- and cold-water supply in domestic premises, and sizes the pipes for a given flow of water. Output prints and prices the total length of pipes, including insulation if required, and the number of valves, check-valves and water meters

References

Source
Ontwerp-en Adviesbureau
Dijkgraafstraat 12, Postbus 73
Krimpen ad Ijssel
Netherlands
Telephone Ijssel (01807) 14839

Availability
Bureau service, purchase

Language
Fortran
Also Basic version

Computer
CDC 6500
Basic version for Data General Nova 1220

695

Program name
PIPE 1

Abstract
Given certain details of heating/cooling units, their connections and the flow and return mains, this program will calculate the pipe sizes required and the maximum pressure loss through the network. Output gives total emissions, mass flows, excess pressures, maximum pressure loss, diameter and length of each pipe run, and water volumes. The program uses the IHVE 1970 method to solve the problem

References

Source
Ove Arup and Partners
13 Fitzroy Street
London W1
UK
Telephone 01–636 1531

Availability
Bureau service

Language
Fortran

Computer
DEC 10

696

Program name
Isolation

Abstract
Estimation of the optimum for relationship of isolation to thickness of pipes

References

Source
Technies Rekencentrum Polybit bv
Postbus 305, Archipelstraat 96
Nijmegen
Netherlands
Telephone Nijmegen 228382

Availability
Bureau service, remote batch, time sharing, purchase

Language
Fortran

Computer
CDC 6600

697

Program name
LPHW-PIPES/1

Abstract
This program sizes two-pipe heating systems. Design can be based on either minimum cost or water velocity. For each pipe, the output gives a listing of heat loss, temperatures and pressures, flow velocity and a record of the input data

References
Developed by GENESYS Ltd

Source
UCC, University Computing Company
344–350 Euston Road
London NW1
UK
Telephone 01–387 9661

Availability
Bureau service

Language
Fortran
Gentran

Computer

698

Program name
SPAN

Abstract
This program is used to analyse the flexibility of multiple branch, closed-loop pipe systems, taking into account thermal expansion, weight effects, pressure effects, imposed movements and loads and various types of constraint. Stresses at each point, deflections, anchor loads and constraint forces can be calculated

References

Source
UCC, University Computing Company
344–350 Euston Road
London NW1
UK
Telephone 01–387 9661

Availability
Bureau service

Language

Computer

699

Program name
LK003

Abstract
The purpose of this program is to size ducts in high-velocity systems. It creates designs for both circular and rectangular ducts, to achieve the smallest total pressure difference between units in a supply or exhaust system and economy in the amount of metal used. The results include dimensions, air flow and velocity, and fall in total pressure for each section. A parts list of components for the ducting is also included

References

Source
AB Svenska Flaktfabriken
Fack
S–104 60 Stockholm
Sweden
Telephone 08–23 83 20 Telex 10430

Availability
By arrangement. Available in UK from SF Air Treatment Limited

Language
Fortran

Computer
CDC 6600

Program name
HVDUCT

Abstract
This program aids the design of a high-velocity ducted air system by analysis of the duct network. Six types of fitting are used to define the system

References

Source
ACTS Computing Corporation
29200 Southfield Road
Southfield, Michigan 48076
USA
Telephone 313 557 6800

Availability

Language

Computer

701

Program name
DUCT

Abstract
This program calculates ductwork sizes by one of three methods (constant friction, constant velocity or static regain). The program selects the ducting recommended by SMACNA for each section of the system, based on the pressure at that section. Costs are estimated. Comparisons can be made between uninsulated and insulated systems and existing or pre-sized ductwork analysed

References

Source
APEC Executive Office
Grant-Deneau Tower, Suite M–15
Dayton, Ohio 45402
USA
Telephone 513 228 2602

Availability

Language
Fortran IV

Computer
IBM 360, 1130
CDC Cyber

702

Program name
SUPERDUCT

Abstract
This is an improved version of DUCT. The program calculates ductwork sizes by one of three methods (constant friction, constant velocity or static regain). The longest run of ducting to maintain a required pressure is calculated, and also the gauge of metal to be used, based on methods of ASHRAE and SMACNA. Pre-sized ductwork can be analysed

References

Source
APEC Executive Office
Grant-Deneau Tower, Suite M–15
Dayton, Ohio 45402
USA
Telephone 513 228 2602

Availability

Language
Fortran IV

Computer
IBM 360
CDC Cyber

703

Program name
DADDS

Abstract
This program is for sizing ductwork. Pressures, temperatures and quantities of material are calculated for each design. One of two methods can be used for calculating sizes (equal friction or static regain). As an option, the program can re-calculate air quantities and duct sizes to compensate for heat gains of the ducting, and can analyse the system for noise

References

Source
Daverman Associates Incorporated
200 Monroe Avenue NW
Grand Rapids, Michigan 49502
USA
Telephone 616 451 3525

Availability
Time-sharing

Language

Computer
CDC Cyber

704

Program name
DUCT

Abstract
This program sizes ventilating or extraction duct systems to determine pressure losses and velocities. Facilities are available to achieve balanced air-flows and to determine the effects of damping. The program operates for standard ducting as approved by the HVCA

References

Source
Dewco Programming and Computer Services
20 Park Street
Bristol BS1 5JA
UK
Telephone 0272 23352

Availability
Bureau service, remote batch, purchase

Language
Fortran

Computer
Honeywell 6000

705

Program name
DUNE

Abstract
This program sizes open-ended air duct networks, and will calculate pressure losses and air temperatures if required. It will consider both supply and extract systems, housed in any combination of round, rectangular or flat-oval ductwork. Materials and surrounding air temperatures may be variable. Section properties are given, followed by a listing of fan static pressure and total air flow for both design and standard air conditions

References

Source
Faber Computer Operations Limited
Upper Marlborough Road
St Albans
Hertfordshire, UK
Telephone St Albans 61222

Availability
Bureau service

Language

Computer
IBM 1130, System 7

706

Program name
DUCT 3

Abstract
This program constructs an air-duct sizing chart for any air temperature between 0°C and 300°C, and any duct material. The chart consists of air-flow and friction-loss axes with lines of constant velocity and diameter. Input parameters may be altered until a satisfactory chart is produced which can then be printed on the plotter. The data base of the program uses Colebrook-White's equation for turbulent flow

References

Source
Faber Computer Operations Limited
Upper Marlborough Road
St Albans
Hertfordshire, UK
Telephone St Albans 61222

Availability
Bureau service

Language

Computer
IBM 1130, System 7

707

Program name
M–28

Abstract
This program calculates heat losses through uninsulated ducts or ducts with either insulation or an enclosed air space and insulation

References

Source
Giffels Associates Incorporated
Marquette Building
243 W Congress
Detroit, Michigan 48226
USA
Telephone 313 961 2084

Availability
Purchase negotiable

Language
Fortran V

Computer
Univac 1108

708

Program name
MSEVEN

Abstract
This program sizes ductwork systems by either the static-regain or constant-friction methods. It performs the same calculations as MTWO, but also calculates the amount of damping required and power of fans to be used. Fan selection is an optional output

References

Source
Giffels Associates Incorporated
Marquette Building
243 W Congress
Detroit, Michigan 48226
USA
Telephone 313 961 2084

Availability
Purchase negotiable

Language
Fortran V

Computer
Univac 1108

709

Program name
Air duct calculation

Abstract
This program calculates changes in air velocity in ventilation ductwork due to friction and dynamic loss or regain. Suitable for supply or exhaust systems with ductwork of round or square section. Roughness factors may be introduced for various materials. Output gives total air volume and external resistance, as well as, for round ducts, overall length, and for square ducts, total area of sheet metal for any given thickness

References

Source
Ontwerp-en Adviesbureau
Dijkgraafstraat 12, Postbus 73
Krimpen ad Ijssel
Netherlands
Telephone Ijssel (01807) 14839

Availability
Bureau service, purchase

Language
Fortran
Also Basic version

Computer
CDC 6500
Basic version for
Data General Nova
1220

Program name
DUCT 1

Abstract
This program sizes low-velocity, low-pressure supply and extract air duct systems. The systems are analysed by sections, each section being defined by dimensions, materials, fittings and, where relevant, air flow rates, velocities and required pressures. For each section, the output gives the air velocity, total pressure drop, size, surface area and weight. For the whole network, it gives the totals for surface area, weight, air flow and pressure drop

References

Source
Ove Arup and Partners
13 Fitzroy Street
London W1
UK
Telephone 01–636 1531

Availability
Bureau service

Language
Fortran

Computer
DEC 10

711

Program name
Air duct system

Abstract
This program aids design of air-duct systems for air-conditioning installations with high- and low-velocity, round and rectangular ducts, for inlet and extraction. Pressure losses for duct systems may also be calculated

References

Source
Technies Rekencentrum Polybit bv
Postbus 305, Archipelstraat 96
Nijmegen
Netherlands
Telephone Nijmegen 228382

Availability
Bureau service, remote batch, purchase

Language
Fortran

Computer
CDC 6600

712

Program name
Air slit

Abstract
Dimensioning of a duct with air slit for a uniform air flow

References

Source
Technies Rekencentrum Polybit bv
Postbus 305, Archipelstraat 96
Nijmegen
Netherlands
Telephone Nijmegen 228382

Availability
Bureau service, remote batch, time sharing, purchase

Language
Fortran

Computer
CDC 6600

713

Program name
VariTrane duct program

Abstract
This program is used at the design stage to make the best use of, and balance, variable air-volume ductwork using VariTrane boxes of the shut-off type. It uses static regain to minimise pressure variations in the system and reduce static pressure through the fittings. Output includes a report showing predicted static pressure along the trunk system, selected boxes with predicted room noise levels and a complete bill of materials.

References

Source
The Trane Company
La Crosse
Wisconsin 54601
USA
Telephone 608 782 8000 Telex 29–3415

Availability
Bureau service

Language
Fortran

Computer
IBM 370

714

Program name
ACOU

Abstract
A program designed to calculate sound levels in rooms or complete structures

References

Source
CSTC
41 Rue du Lombard
1000 Brussels
Belgium
Telephone 02–511 06 83

Availability
Bureau service

Language
Fortran IV

Computer

715

Program name
Acoustical analysis (ACOUS4)

Abstract
This program computes the total sound absorption of all surfaces in a room and derives the reverberation time at three frequencies. Two types of data are used: the first is a table giving the 'names' and absorption coefficients of each surface material, and the second, the 'names' of the surfaces in each room and their relevant dimensions

References

Source
Cusdin Burden and Howitt
Greencoat House, 5th Floor
Francis Street, London
SW1P 1DB, UK
Telephone 01–828 4051/7

Availability
Bureau service, time-sharing

Language
Basic

Computer
Honeywell GE635
CDC 6600

716

Program name
MEIGHT

Abstract
This program calculates the natural sound attenuation of ductwork systems and determines the effectiveness of duct lining in reducing noise over seven octave bands

References

Source
Giffels Associates Incorporated
Marquette Building
243 W Congress
Detroit, Michigan 48226
USA
Telephone 313 961 2084

Availability
Purchase negotiable

Language
Fortran V

Computer
Univac 1108

717

Program name
Acoustic program

Abstract
This program calculates internal noise levels (octave or 1/3 octave spectra) and subjective levels (dBA and NRC) that result from given external noise spectra, or using figures for typical aircraft or road traffic noise stored in the program. Using window and room sizes, and the absorption of room surfaces, the program evaluates the effect of any glazing design

References

Source
Pilkington Brothers Limited
Prescot Road
St Helens, Merseyside
WA10 3TT UK
Telephone St Helens 28882

Availability

Language

Computer

Heating, ventilating and air-conditioning

718

Program name
Heat load and radiator selection

Abstract
This program calculates the heat losses of a building, based upon the method described in DIN 4701:1959. If required, the dimensions of suitable radiators for each space in the building can also be calculated

References

Source
Ontwerp-en Adviesbureau
Dijkgraafstraat 12, Postbus 73
Krimpen ad Ijssel
Netherlands
Telephone Ijssel (01807) 14839

Availability
Bureau service, purchase

Language
Fortran
Also Basic version

Computer
CDC 6500
Basic version for Data General Nova 1220

719

Program name
VOK

Abstract
This program calculates air and surface temperatures within a building. Heating and cooling loads are also calculated. External air temperatures, delayed heat transmission (through roof and walls), solar heat gains through glazing, and ventilation systems are all taken into account

References

Source
AB Bahco Ventilation
Box 27078
102 51 Stockholm
Sweden

Availability

Language

Computer

720

Program name
VENTAC

Abstract
This program calculates temperatures or heating and cooling requirements in zones throughout a building. Information for the selection of heating and cooling equipment is produced. Energy consumption over each hour, month and year is also calculated. Compound room structures may be taken into account

References

Source
AB Svenska Flaktfabriken
Fack
S–104 60 Stockholm
Sweden
Telephone 468 238320

Availability

Language
Fortran IV

Computer
Requires 170K octal storage

721

Program name
LK012

Abstract
This program calculates the heating and cooling requirements for a building with up to twelve zones, for each hour over a period of twelve months. Calculations are based on normal meteorological conditions and provide the basis for a subsequent analysis of an air-conditioning system, or of energy consumption. It is especially suited to office buildings, hotels and hospitals

References

Source
AB Svenska Flaktfabriken
Fack
S–104 60 Stockholm
Sweden
Telephone 08–23 83 20 Telex 10430

Availability
By arrangement. Available in UK from SF Air Treatment Limited

Language
Fortran

Computer
CDC 6600

722

Program name
HCC

Abstract
This program calculates heating and cooling loads in rooms, using ASHRAE methods. Conventional analysis of transmitted heat loss is carried out. Cooling load calculations are made on an hourly basis for the selected design day. Heat gains through glazing are separated as solar and transmitted effects, taking into account the glazing material and shading devices

References

Source
APEC Executive Office
Grant-Deneau Tower, Suite M–15
Dayton, Ohio 45402
USA
Telephone 513 228 2602

Availability

Language
Fortran IV

Computer
CDC Cyber
GE Mark III
IBM 360, 1130

Program name
ATKOOL

Abstract
This is a suite of programs to evaluate cooling and heating loads in buildings. Comprehensive interactive facilities are provided, including investigating temperature swings, shadow effects and effect of plant size

References

Source
Atkins Computing Services Limited
Woodcote Grove, Ashley Road
Epsom, Surrey
UK
Telephone Epsom 40421

Availability
Bureau service, time-sharing. Available in Netherlands

Language
Fortran

Computer
Honeywell Sigma 9

724

Program name
CAMEL

Abstract
This program calculates the hourly cooling load in a building, taking account of storage effects. Peak heating loads are calculated, but excluding storage effects and also psychrometric conditions. The program is based on the Carrier method. It takes into consideration shading from window overhangs and reveals but does not include shading from adjacent buildings. The program is suitable for use in any southern latitude between 0° and 50° south

References
Handbook of Air Conditioning System Design, Carrier International Corporation

Source
Australian Department of Construction
695 Burke Road
Camberwell, Victoria 3124
Australia
Telephone 0382 8041

Availability

Language
Fortran V

Computer
Univac 1108

725

Program name
FCCAL

Abstract
This program calculates cooling load factors owing to solar radiation and thermal conduction through glazing, using the method described in the ASHRAE handbook. Depths of shadows cast by a unit length of overhang or side projection are also calculated. Latitude and orientation of the building are taken into consideration. Solar heat gains through tilted windows and skylights can also be considered

References

Source
Ayres and Hayakawa
1180 South Beverly Drive
Los Angeles, California 90036
USA
Telephone 213 879 4477

Availability
Purchase, batch

Language

Computer

726

Program name
Air systems analysis

Abstract
This program calculates the heating and cooling requirements of a building, and computes requirements for interior and exterior zones. It determines the air quantities to be handled by supply and return fans for systems operating with variable, inducted variable or constant air volume. Required reheating capacity is also calculated. It will not consider internal or external latent air-loads, external sensible air-loads or refrigeration block loads

References

Source
Barber-Colman Company
Air Distribution Products Division
1300 Rock Street, Rockford
Illinois 61101
USA

Availability
Free of charge through field offices in USA

Language

Computer

727

Program name
THERM

Abstract
This program simulates the thermal behaviour of buildings. It predicts loads, temperatures and humidities at hourly intervals over a specified period. Heating/cooling loads and seasonal consumption can be obtained. It can be used at the design stage, at the plant design stage or at the plant management stage. It contains the weather data of major British cities for the last twenty years

References
SYSTEM

Source
British Gas Corporation
Watson House, Peterborough Road
London SW6 3HN
UK
Telephone 01-736 1212 Telex 919082

Availability
Bureau service

Language
Fortran

Computer
Univac 1106

728

Program name
HG2

Abstract
This program calculates heat gains through external glazing, in shade, throughout a design day. External air temperature, diffuse radiation incident on the glass, shading coefficient, thermal transmittance, internal air temperature and window area are input. The heat gains in Btu/h, per square foot of glass or per window, are produced as an hourly value for each of the twenty-four hours

References

Source
Building Service Designs
332 Carshalton Road
Carshalton, Surrey
UK
Telephone 01–661 1416

Availability
Bureau service, time-sharing

Language
Basic

Computer
Honeywell Sigma 7, Sigma 9

729

Program name
HG5

Abstract
This program calculates the sol-air temperatures for a design day from total direct and diffuse solar intensities. In addition, diurnal variation, maximum temperature and surface absorption coefficient are input, together with correction factors for height above sea level, sky clarity and ground reflectance. Sol-air temperatures for eight wall orientations and for a horizontal surface are produced in degrees Fahrenheit and Celsius

References

Source
Building Service Designs
332 Carshalton Road
Carshalton, Surrey
UK
Telephone 01–661 1416

Availability
Bureau service, time-sharing

Language
Basic

Computer
Honeywell Sigma 7, Sigma 9

730

Program name
HG7

Abstract
This is an optional addition to program HG5. It produces print-out of air temperatures calculated by that program. These are calculated for each of the twenty-four hours and are expressed in degrees Fahrenheit and Celsius. No additional input data is required other than that used by HG5

References

Source
Building Service Designs
332 Carshalton Road
Carshalton, Surrey
UK
Telephone 01–661 1416

Availability
Bureau service, time-sharing

Language
Basic

Computer
Honeywell Sigma 7, Sigma 9

731

Program name
BS1

Abstract
This program calculates heat gains and losses in rooms, and the air-flow rates required from air-conditioning plant in order to maintain specific temperatures in summer and winter. The program will also create a preliminary lighting design. Calculations for each room may be summarised in one line or printed out in greater detail. Heat gain and loss calculations are based on the IHVE Guide (1970)

References

Source
Building Service Designs
332 Carshalton Road
Carshalton, Surrey
UK
Telephone 01–661 1416

Availability
Bureau service, time-sharing, remote batch

Language
Basic

Computer
Honeywell Sigma 7, Sigma 9

732

Program name
HG3

Abstract
This program calculates heat gains through horizontal roofs from sol-air temperatures. In addition to the sol-air temperatures, internal air temperature, decrement factor, time-lag and U-value of the wall structure are input. Heat gains in Btu/h are produced as hourly values for each hour throughout a design day

References

Source
Building Service Designs
332 Carshalton Road
Carshalton, Surrey
UK
Telephone 01–661 1416

Availability
Bureau service, time-sharing

Language
Basic

Computer
Honeywell Sigma 7, Sigma 9

Program name
HG4

Abstract
This program calculates heat gains through external walls from sol-air temperatures. These values must be supplied, over twenty-four hours, for each elevation and a wall in shade. Additional inputs are internal air temperature, decrement factor, time-lag and U-value of the wall structure. Heat gains through walls in shade and for each elevation are produced as hourly values in Btu/h/ft². Sol-air temperatures may be derived from program HG5

References

Source
Building Service Designs
332 Carshalton Road
Carshalton, Surrey
UK
Telephone 01–661 1416

Availability
Bureau service, time-sharing

Language
Basic

Computer
Honeywell Sigma 7, Sigma 9

734

Program name
CIHDP (Cadsden International Heating Design Package)

Abstract
This package, based on the CIBS (IHVE) guide, is in two sections. The first section calculates heat losses for each room in a building, using dimensional and other data provided by the user. The second section designs a hot-water heating system to specified constraints, meeting the losses calculated in the first section. The system can be one-pipe, two-pipe or hybrid

References

Source
Cadsden International Management Services
Cadsden House, Princes Risborough
Aylesbury, Bucks HP17 0NB
UK
Telephone 08444 3020

Availability
Purchase, hire, bureau service

Language
Basic

Computer
Wang 2200

735

Program name
Temperature zones

Abstract
This program calculates temperatures on a cross-section through a building, given the temperature at certain points or heat supplied and patterns of convection

References

Source
CE-data
Lundtoftevej 1G
2800 Lyngby
Denmark

Availability
Bureau service

Language

Computer

736

Program name
NBSLD

Abstract
This program calculates the hourly heating and/or cooling load in a building. The thermal-response factor is used to calculate transient heat conduction through walls and roofs. The program includes a sub-routine which can calculate the temperature of rooms with little or no air-conditioning or natural ventilation

References
Algorithms for Building Heat Transfer Sub-routines, ASHRAE Bulletin, 1975

Source
Center for Building Technology, IAT
National Bureau of Standards
Washington, DC 20234
USA

Availability
Purchase

Language

Computer

737

Program name
THERMAL

Abstract
This program calculates heating and cooling loads in a room, in an air-conditioned area or throughout a whole building. Weather, solar radiation, building materials, ventilation, internal heat gains and geographical location are all taken into account. The program uses the procedures outlined in the ASHRAE Handbook of Fundamentals, 1967

References

Source
Compu-Serve Network Incorporated
5000 Arlington Center Boulevard
Columbus, Ohio 43220
USA
Telephone 614 457 8600

Availability
Time-sharing

Language

Computer

738

Program name
TEMPER

Abstract
This program calculates the sensible and latent air-conditioning loads (heating and cooling) within a building at a specific air temperature and humidity. Alternatively, the indoor air conditions for a specified cooling effect can be calculated

References
Journal of the Australian Institute, Air Conditioning and Heating, December 1973, Volume 27, Number 12

Source
CSIRO, PO Box 26, Highett
Victoria 3190
Australia
Telephone Highett 95 0333

Availability

Language
Fortran

Computer
Cyber 74–76
ICL 1100
Univac 1108

739

Program name
BRIS

Abstract
This program calculates indoor temperatures and cooling loads in buildings. It uses Fourier heat equations (solved numerically), and Stephan-Boltzmann's Law to calculate long-wave radiant interchange. Short-wave radiation transmitted through windows is distributed by reflectance of surfaces. Calculations are made over a period specified by the user

References
Report 9, Royal Institute of Technology, Sweden

Source
Datasystem AB
Stocksund
Stockholm
Sweden

Availability

Language
Algol and Assembler
Fortran version available

Computer
TRASK 2

740

Program name
BLESS

Abstract
This program calculates cooling loads for each hour during summer months, and heating loads during the winter. Calculations are based on the method described in the Carrier handbook. The program is interactive. Input errors may be corrected as they occur and values changed to allow repeated re-processing

References

Source
Daverman Associates Incorporated
200 Monroe Avenue NW
Grand Rapids, Michigan 49502
USA
Telephone 616 451 3525

Availability
Time-sharing

Language

Computer
CDC Cyber

741

Program name
AIRCON

Abstract
This program calculates cooling and heating loads for an air-conditioning system, throughout a building. The time at which peak load occurs, the quantities of air required and supply temperatures are also calculated. The program uses data from The Carrier Load-Estimating Guide

References

Source
Deere & Company
John Deere Road
Moline
Illinois 61265
USA

Availability

Language
Fortran IV

Computer
IBM 360

742

Program name
CLOADS

Abstract
This program calculates the sensible and latent heat gains and the mass of air required for cooling each room by summation of the heat gains through walls, windows, ceiling and floor and from infiltration; occupancy; lighting and electrical equipment. It calculates these for all rooms to give the total sensible and latent gains and the total mass of air for cooling. The program also calculates the sensible to total heat ratio and the total cooling load

References
The Chartered Institution of Building Services

Source
Department of the Environment
(Property Services Agency)
Rm 1126, Lunar House, 40 Wellesley Road
Croydon CR9 2EL, UK

Availability

Language
Fortran II

Computer
Honeywell GZ65

Program name
HTLOSS

Abstract
This program calculates total heat loss and heat loss per unit volume for individual rectangular rooms and complete buildings heated by either radiant panels or conventional radiators

References
PSA program library

Source
Directorate of Mechanical and Electrical Engineering Services
Property Services Agency
Lunar House, 40 Wellesley Road
Croydon CR9 2EL, UK
Telephone 01–686 3499

Availability

Language
Fortran

Computer
Honeywell MK III

744

Program name
GAINS

Abstract
This program determines cooling loads for a whole building and zones within it. It calculates both sensible and latent component gains and thermal balance temperature. It operates in metric or Imperial units with simulated weather conditions for any climate over a typical month. Shadowing effects of other buildings can be considered

References

Source
Dewco Programming and Computer Services
20 Park Street
Bristol BS1 5JA
UK
Telephone 0272 23352

Availability
Bureau service, remote batch, purchase

Language
Fortran

Computer
Honeywell 6000

745

Program name
Absorption and transmission of thermal radiation

Abstract
This program calculates the absorption and transmission of thermal radiation by windows made of common glass. Single– and double-glazing can be taken into account. Polynominal coefficients for average absorption, transmission and reflection are also given

References

Source
Division of Building Research
National Research Council
Ottawa K1A 0R6
Canada

Availability
Purchase

Language
Fortran IV

Computer
IBM 360

746

Program name
Radiant energy interchange

Abstract
This suite of three programs is for calculation of the interchange of energy between the surfaces that enclose a room. Up to fifty such surfaces can be considered

References

Source
Division of Building Research
National Research Council
Ottawa K1A 0R6
Canada

Availability
Purchase

Language
Fortran IV

Computer
IBM 360

747

Program name
Z-transfer functions

Abstract
This program calculates Z-transfer functions for transient heat conduction through walls and roofs

References

Source
Division of Building Research
National Research Council
Ottawa K1A 0R6
Canada

Availability
Purchase

Language
Fortran IV

Computer
IBM 360

748

Program name
ENDSOP

Abstract
This is a suite of programs based on the design methods of the IHVE guide (Section A). It calculates heat gains from solar radiation, taking into account location, building structure, radiation transmission through glass and blinds and gains through opaque walls and roofs, as well as casual gains from lighting

References

Source
DJ Hardy
16 Howard Road
London NW2
UK

Availability

Language
Basic
Algol

Computer
Hewlett Packard
2000F
DEC System 10

749

Program name
HEAT

Abstract
This program is for the calculation of indoor temperatures and heating or cooling loads in buildings. Heat balance in outer walls is calculated using the response factor method. A number of different types of window can be defined for use with the program. Heat balance is calculated at half-hour periods over twenty-four hours, or at hourly intervals over four days

References

Source
Ekono
Kasarmikatu 46–48
PO Box 27
00131 Helsinki 13
Finland

Availability
Bureau service

Language
Fortran

Computer
DEC 10

750

Program name
MACP–201

Abstract
This program estimates the energy consumption and building demands for heating, cooling, lighting and base loads. Although primarily for evaluating energy requirements of smaller buildings, it can be used on larger buildings under certain conditions. It determines monthly and annual energy consumption, and the demands of alternative energy sources. It utilises the time-temperature duration method during occupied and unoccupied time periods

References

Source
Envirodyne Energy Services
421 E Cerritos Ave
Anaheim
California 92805
USA

Availability

Language

Computer

751

Program name
FUME

Abstract
This program is used to analyse and adjust the room pressures and air movement between rooms in a building, so that in the event of a fire, smoke and toxic gases can be more easily controlled. The program creates a three-dimensional air-flow model for the building and solves the non-linear sets of equations, taking into account specified external temperature conditions and wind speed/direction

References

Source
Faber Computer Operations Limited
Upper Marlborough Road
St Albans
Herts UK
Telephone St Albans 61222

Availability
Bureau service

Language

Computer
IBM 1130, System 7

752

Program name
LOSS

Abstract
This program calculates the heat losses from a building, room by room. Losses are calculated from air change or conduction through room elements. The heat loss via each element is calculated, the total for each room found and a running total of room losses gives the eventual heat loss from the zone. A feature of the program is that duplicate rooms can be specified without duplicating the input data

References

Source
Faber Computer Operations Limited
Upper Marlborough Road
St Albans
Herts UK
Telephone St Albans 61222

Availability
Bureau service

Language

Computer
IBM 1130, System 7

Program name
COLD

Abstract
This program makes an air-conditioning load calculation on a building for each hour of a typical day in every month. Gains caused by solar radiation through various elements are calculated. Calculations may be performed for any number of types of room, and totals are computed according to the number of rooms of each type. There is also the facility for predicting the variation of internal temperature if there were no air-conditioning

References

Source
Faber Computer Operations Limited
Upper Marlborough Road
St Albans
Herts UK
Telephone St Albans 61222

Availability
Bureau service

Language

Computer
IBM 1130, System 7

754

Program name
AFLO

Abstract
This program calculates the air movement through a building. It creates a three-dimensional air-flow model for the building and solves the non-linear equations, taking into account specified external temperature conditions and wind speed/direction. Temperatures, pressures and details of flow through all air-flow paths in the building are given, to enable the determination of suitable infiltration and natural ventilation rates

References

Source
Faber Computer Operations Limited
Upper Marlborough Road
St Albans
Herts UK
Telephone St Albans 61222

Availability
Bureau service

Language

Computer
IBM 1130, System 7

755

Program name
HYGRO

Abstract
This program calculates and plots psychrometric charts for any altitude and atmospheric pressure, in either Imperial or SI units. The chart boundaries are fixed by specifying the limiting values of dry bulb temperatures, moisture content, enthalpy and volume. The chart is plotted on the data plotter and includes annotations

References

Source
Faber Computer Operations Limited
Upper Marlborough Road
St Albans
Herts UK
Telephone St Albans 61222

Availability
Bureau service

Language

Computer
IBM 1130, System 7

756

Program name
Post office program

Abstract
This program calculates the energy requirements for heating and cooling post office buildings. The thermal-response factor is used to calculate hourly loads. The energy required by an air-conditioning system is then calculated. Annual economic analyses may also be produced

References

Source
GARD
7449 North Natchez Avenue
Niles, Illinois 60648
USA
Telephone 312 647 9000

Availability

Language
Fortran

Computer
CDC 3600, 6400, 6600
IBM 360
Univac 1108

757

Program name
Design temperatures

Abstract
This program allows the modification of applied data to suit air or environmental temperature calculations, and the selection of proposed external dry-bulb temperature at any given time of year

References
Aries system of programs

Source
Genair (Data Processing) Limited
Lower Tovil Mill, Tovil
Maidstone, Kent
UK
Telephone Maidstone 54783,4,5

Availability
Purchase, bureau service

Language

Computer
Hewlett-Packard
HP9830A

758

Program name
Thermal transmittance factors

Abstract
This program makes possible the determination of U-value for a composite structural material, from the input of either resistances or thicknesses and conductivities. Inside and outside surface resistances may be derived from aspect, emissivity and exposure data used in the calculation

References
Aries system of programs

Source
Genair (Data Processing) Limited
Lower Tovil Mill, Tovil
Maidstone, Kent
UK
Telephone Maidstone 54783,4,5

Availability
Purchase, bureau service

Language

Computer
Hewlett-Packard
HP9830A

759

Program name
Solar intensities

Abstract
This program calculates mean, fluctuating, direct and indirect solar intensities for any specified orientation and angle of slope for an external facade. The calculation is based upon the relationship between direct normal intensity and solar altitude proposed by P Moon, and between background sky and diffuse radiation by AG Loudon. The values taken are adjusted to include ground level radiation (reflected) and the height above sea level

References
Aries system of programs

Source
Genair (Data Processing) Limited
Lower Tovil Mill, Tovil
Maidstone, Kent
UK
Telephone Maidstone 54783,4,5

Availability
Purchase, bureau service

Language

Computer
Hewlett-Packard
HP9830A

760

Program name
Glazing cooling load

Abstract
This program calculates solar cooling load through glazing, using BRS admittance method, for twenty-six glazing variations and two weights of building structure, to give either air or environmental temperature maintenance. It determines gains or losses through glazing by conduction

References
Aries system of programs

Source
Genair (Data Processing) Limited
Lower Tovil Mill, Tovil
Maidstone, Kent
UK
Telephone Maidstone 54783,4,5

Availability
Purchase, bureau service

Language

Computer
Hewlett-Packard
HP9830A

761

Program name
Aries

Abstract
This system performs cooling load calculations for air-conditioning designs. It includes facilities for the determination of sun position and solar intensities, thermal transmission coefficients and temperature and pressure gradients. It can produce cooling-load calculations for ten individual zones, or for one zone for ten periods, providing up to 1200 results in one operation. Results, in watts, are printed in tabular form

References
Designed in accordance with CIBS(IHVE) and BSRIA

Source
Genair (Data Processing) Limited
Lower Tovil Mill, Tovil
Maidstone, Kent
UK
Telephone Maidstone 54783,4,5

Availability
Purchase, bureau service

Language

Computer
Hewlett-Packard
HP9830A

762

Program name
Steady cooling load

Abstract
This program calculates cooling loads due to internal structural gains and conduction gains through thin structures

References
Aries system of programs

Source
Genair (Data Processing) Limited
Lower Tovil Mill, Tovil
Maidstone, Kent
UK
Telephone Maidstone 54783,4,5

Availability
Purchase, bureau service

Language

Computer
Hewlett-Packard
HP9830A

763

Program name
Periodic cooling load

Abstract
This program applies solar intensities to calculate solar cooling load through opaque building components, using external surface resistance, U-value, absorption coefficient and emissivity. Allowances are made in the calculation for decrement factor. Time scale is modified for those components subjected to time lags

References
Aries system of programs

Source
Genair (Data Processing) Limited
Lower Tovil Mill, Tovil
Maidstone, Kent
UK
Telephone Maidstone 54783,4,5

Availability
Purchase, bureau service

Language

Computer
Hewlett-Packard
HP9830A

764

Program name
Internal gains load

Abstract
This program calculates internal gains from two categories of occupants, three categories of electrical and lighting loads, and two additional categories with known latent and sensible component values

References
Aries system of programs

Source
Genair (Data Processing) Limited
Lower Tovil Mill, Tovil
Maidstone, Kent
UK
Telephone Maidstone 54783,4,5

Availability
Purchase, bureau service

Language

Computer
Hewlett-Packard
HP9830A

765

Program name
Ventilation cooling load

Abstract
This program produces gain to zone resulting from up to three forms of ventilation ie infiltration from outside, infiltration from an adjoining space, and mechanical ventilation using air-change rate. Infiltration from outside is considered to be at the temperature of the outside air

References
Aries system of programs

Source
Genair (Data Processing) Limited
Lower Tovil Mill, Tovil
Maidstone, Kent
UK
Telephone Maidstone 54783,4,5,

Availability
Purchase, bureau service

Language

Computer
Hewlett-Packard
HP9830A

766

Program name
Temperature and pressure gradients

Abstract
For a structure having a U-value determined by the thermal transmittance program, this program calculates component surface temperatures from given inside and outside temperatures. Vapour-pressure gradients are compared with saturation vapour pressures, from given inside and outside wet-bulb temperatures, and component diffusion resistance factors

References
Aries system of programs

Source
Genair (Data Processing) Ltd
Lower Tovil Mill, Tovil
Maidstone, Kent
UK
Telephone Maidstone 54783,4,5

Availability
Purchase, bureau service

Language

Computer
Hewlett-Packard
HP9830A

767

Program name
MTEN

Abstract
This program calculates heat losses and maximum instantaneous heat gains for each space in a building and for the building itself. The same values are calculated for each fan system (multi-zone and zone-reheat types). Required air quantities and the resulting air change, per hour, is estimated. Data for selecting chilled-water coils is also produced

References

Source
Giffels Associates Incorporated
Marquette Building
243 W Congress
Detroit, Michigan 48226
USA
Telephone 313 961 2084

Availability
Purchase negotiable

Language
Fortran IV

Computer
Univac 1108

768

Program name
M–27

Abstract
This program calculates heat requirements in a building over monthly and annual periods, based on degree-days, production hours, temperature inside the building and internal heat gains

References

Source
Giffels Associates Incorporated
Marquette Building
243 W Congress
Detroit, Michigan 48226
USA
Telephone 313 961 2084

Availability
Purchase negotiable

Language
Fortran V

Computer
Univac 1108

769

Program name
CD 11

Abstract
This program makes estimates of cooling loads for rooms or buildings using the Carrier method. The program assesses the effect of building structure, radiation transmission through glass and blinds, gains through walls and roofs, and casual gains, as well as the effects of location and climate

References

Source
Haden Young Limited
7 Tavistock Square
London WC1
UK
Telephone 01–387 1288

Availability
By arrangement with DOC members

Language
Fortran IV

Computer
ICL 1902T

770

Program name
CD 24

Abstract
This program calculates the thermal energy flowing into and out of a building through its envelope

References

Source
Haden Young Limited
7 Tavistock Square
London WC1
UK
Telephone 01–387 1288

Availability
By arrangement with DOC members

Language
Fortran

Computer
ICL 1902T

771

Program name
BUFLA

Abstract
This program calculates the maximum heat gain to an air-conditioned building produced by weather conditions. The time of its occurrence is also calculated

References

Source
Haden Young Limited
7 Tavistock Square
London WC1
UK
Telephone 01–387 1288

Availability
By arrangement with DOC members

Language
Fortran

Computer
ICl 1902T

772

Program name
HLHG

Abstract
This program calculates heating and cooling loads for each room of a building, including internal and external loads. Solar heat gain and equivalent pressure differences are calculated by the Carrier method, including effect of wall mass on thermal storage, but conversion to ASHRAE methods is under development

References

Source
Hankins and Anderson Incorporated
2117 North Hamilton Street
PO Box 6872, Richmond
Virginia 23230
USA
Telephone 804 353 1221

Availability

Language
Fortran IV

Computer

Program name
COOL

Abstract
This program calculates heat gains and cooling loads for a series of rooms in a building, over each hour of a given day, using the method of the IHVE guide (section A). The program includes information for shading produced by adjacent buildings, or the building itself, and accounts for the various specified areas and types of exposed glazing and walls, and the time lag for different types of structure.

References

Source
Heating Ventilating Computed Sizing
33 Catherine Place
London SW1E 6DY
UK
Telephone (01) 828 3921

Availability
Purchase, time-sharing

Language
Basic

Computer
Honeywell MK III

774

Program name
SUMTEMP

Abstract
This program calculates heat gains and cooling loads for a series of rooms in a building, over each hour of a given day, using the method of the IHVE guide (section A). This facility forms part of a more comprehensive 'room environment' program where the maximum internal environmental temperature, throughout the summer, is calculated for a given set of information on exposed materials and internal gains

References

Source
Heating Ventilating Computed Sizing
33 Catherine Place
London SW1E 6DY
UK
Telephone (01) 828 3921

Availability
Purchase, time-sharing

Language
Basic

Computer
Honeywell MK III

775

Program name
Heating, ventilating and air conditioning

Abstract
This package computes the heating and cooling loads of a building, either one room at a time or for the whole building. In either case, the peak load is determined from a file of specified days and times. The package also includes programs for the sizing of ducts, gas pipes and water pipes

References
Part number 09830–74500

Source
Hewlett-Packard Limited
King Street Lane, Winnersh
Wokingham, Berks RG11 5AR
UK
Telephone Wokingham 784774

Availability
Purchase

Language
Basic

Computer
HP 9830A
with3808–word memory
9866A thermal printer

776

Program name
PSYCH

Abstract
This program is for psychrometric analysis of moist air. A table of psychrometric properties is produced, together with an analysis of cooling loads, including dew-point of apparatus and by-pass factor calculations, and a complete analysis of the air-conditioning cooling cycle

References

Source
Inatome and Associates
10140 West Nine Mile Road
Oak Park, Michigan 48237
USA
Telephone 313 542 4862

Availability
Time-sharing

Language

Computer

777

Program name
ACLD2

Abstract
This program calculates the maximum heating and cooling loads for each room in a building and for the building itself, based upon design data. The required amount of air to be supplied to each area, and energy required for re-heating it, if necessary, are also calculated

References

Source
Inatome and Associates
10140 West Nine Mile Road
Oak Park, Michigan 48237
USA
Telephone 313 542 4862

Availability
Time-sharing

Language
Fortran IV

Computer
GE 630
PDP 10

778

Program name
QDOT1, QDOT2

Abstract
QDOT1 evaluates the costs of using the TRU–70 heat pipe, manufactured by the Q-DOT Corporation, over a period of use. Immediate savings on costs of equipment are subtracted from initial costs to give a net cost. The annual savings from reduction of expenses for utilities are divided into the net cost to give the period over which initial costs may be justified. QDOT2 evaluates initial and continuing cost savings over a given amortisation period

References

Source
Inatome and Associates
10140 West Nine Mile Road
Oak Park, Michigan 48237
USA
Telephone 313 542 4862

Availability
Time-sharing

Language

Computer

779

Program name
ALEXANDER (R02016)

Abstract
The program carries out heat-transfer analysis. Steady-state and transient problems can be solved, including effects of conduction, convection and radiation. Temperature field and heat flow are calculated. The temperature field can be plotted. Material characteristics, geometry, heat sources and time conditions are given. The input data can be generated in a pre-processor

References
Can be interfaced with R01041 LUCAS

Source
Industridata AB
Fack
Solna, Sweden
171 20
Telephone 08 98 03 50

Availability
Contact owner

Language
Fortran IV

Computer
Honeywell H6080

780

Program name
TEMPO (R02001)

Abstract
A program to calculate the non-steady-state heat transfer through a multilayer wall

References

Source
Industridata AB
Fack
Solna, Sweden
171 20
Telephone 08 98 03 50

Availability
Contact owner

Language
Fortran

Computer
Honeywell 6000

781

Program name
SOLIND

Abstract
This program calculates solar radiation incident on facades, roofs and through windows with one or more layer of glazing. Diffuse and reflected radiation on a surface with a given inclination and orientation is given as a set of hourly values for a certain date. Radiation absorbed by the glazing, and heat gains in rooms, are also calculated

References

Source
Laboratoriet for Varmeisolering
Danmarks tekniske, Hojskole
Bygning 118
2800 Lyngby
Denmark

Availability
Time-sharing

Language

Computer

782

Program name
BA4

Abstract
This program calculates indoor air and surface temperatures, together with heating and cooling loads in a room or building over a period of one year. Screening from sunlight and light sources within the building are taken into consideration

References

Source
Laboratoriet for Varmeisolering
Danmarks tekniske, Hojskole
Bygning 118
2800 Lyngby
Denmark

Availability
Bureau service

Language
Fortran

Computer
IBM 370

Program name
Temperature history and heat balance

Abstract
This program is part of a suite which can calculate the temperatures and/or the heating and cooling loads in a building. The program can take into account such factors as solar radiation, external temperatures, thermal storage, any number of rooms or zones, window sizes, U-values of roofs and walls. The main program may be used alone, or fed by subsidiary programs which evaluate solar radiation and radiation exchange

References

Source
Lanchester Polytechnic
Priory Street
Coventry CV 5FB
UK
Telephone Coventry 28337

Availability

Language
Algol

Computer
ICL 1900 series

784

Program name
LAMSAC Application code 32064952240A

Abstract
This program calculates summertime temperatures in buildings based on IHVE requirements for rooms. It is part of a suite for building services and is interactive

References
LAMSAC

Source
Architect's Department, Leicestershire County Council
County Hall, Glenfield
Leicester LE3 8RA
Telephone Leicester 871313

Availability

Language
APL

Computer
Univac 1106; 23K core; 1 disc drive

785

Program name
LAMSAC Application code 32063126070A

Abstract
This program calculates heat loss in buildings. Slow peripheral units used are a card reader and line printer

References
LAMSAC

Source
Architect's Department, Mid-Glamorgan County Council
County Hall,
Cardiff CF1 3NE
Telephone Cardiff 28033

Availability

Language
Fortran

Computer
ICL 1904S; 5K core

786

Program name
LAMSAC Application code 32065126170A

Abstract
This program calculates heat losses. Slow peripheral units used are a card reader and line printer

References
LAMSAC

Source
Architect's Department, Cardiff City Council
City Hall
Cardiff, S Glamorgan CF1 3ND
Telephone Cardiff 31033

Availability

Language
ICL extended Fortran

Computer
ICL 1904S; 9K core

787

Program name
Heat loads

Abstract
This program determines the heating and air-conditioning requirements of a building. In determining the heat gains and losses for each room or air-conditioned area within a building, the following factors are considered: weather, solar radiation, building materials, mechanical equipment, ventilation, internal heat gains, building orientation and geographical location

References

Source
McDonnell Douglas Automation Company
PO Box 516, St Louis
Missouri 63166
USA

Availability
Time-sharing

Language

Computer

788

Program name
HCE8REC

Abstract
This program takes output from the four basic MEDSI programs to determine the need for cooling in one zone, coincident with heating in other zones, from a heat pump with an internal source. Heat in Btu recovered and lost are printed

References
MEDSI library

Source
Mechanical Engineering Data Services Inc
30 Kimler Drive, Maryland Heights
Missouri 63043
USA
Telephone (314) 434 2340

Availability
Time-sharing

Language

Computer

789

Program name
STAST

Abstract
This program solves numerically the differential equation of two-dimensional stationary heat flow. Structures of any shape may be analysed. The structure may be made up of different materials with different properties combined in orthogonally anisotropic patterns, and may also have internal sources of heat. The structure to be analysed may be modelled by a combination of triangular (three nodes) and square (four nodes) elements

References

Source
Norwegian Building Research Institute
POB 322 Blindern
Oslo 3
Norway
Telephone 46 98 80

Availability
Purchase, bureau service

Language
Fortran IV

Computer
Univac 1100

790

Program name
Cooling load

Abstract
This program calculates the total cooling load imposed by a building due to internal and external influences, eg solar radiation, building occupants, light fittings and machines. The program will take into account daily temperature range, latitude, building orientation and the storage effect of various materials. The program is especially useful for discovering the effects of screening or shading

References

Source
Ontwerp-on Adviesbureau
Dijkraafstraat 12, Postbus 73
Krimpen ad Ijssel
Netherlands
Telephone Ijssel (01807) 14839

Availability
Bureau service, purchase

Language
Fortran
Also Basic version

Computer
CDC 6500
Basic version for Data General Nova 1220

791

Program name
HVAC 2

Abstract
This program calculates the equivalent temperature differences through walls at any latitude and altitude, in deg C. The program will consider walls of any colour, uninsulated or insulated (internally or externally). Details of position, climate, room dimensions and temperatures are entered and the output gives tabulations for one or more months. Values are given for total incident solar radiation, sol-air temperatures, solar altitudes and azimuths

References

Source
Ove Arup and Partners
13 Fitzroy Street
London W1
UK
Telephone 01–636 1531

Availability
Bureau service

Language
Fortran

Computer
DEC 10

792

Program name
HVAC 4

Abstract
This program calculates the heat losses from rooms and complete buildings using either radiant or convective heating systems. A detailed description is entered, room by room, which may run to ninety-nine separate room types and up to 999 incidences of each room type. Heat losses from individual rooms are calculated and combined to give the total heat losses from the section or building. The program uses the IHVE 1970 method

References

Source
Ove Arup and Partners
13 Fitzroy Street
London W1
UK
Telephone 01–636 1531

Availability
Bureau service

Language
Fortran

Computer
DEC 10

Program name
HVAC 1

Abstract
This program calculates basic tables of information for total incident radiation, sol-air temperature, glazing heat gains for buildings or rooms, in any given latitude and climate. Relevant information such as U-values of opaque walls, windows and blinds and window areas are considered. The program can also calculate heat gains and losses using the method of the IHVE Guide (1970)

References

Source
Ove Arup and Partners
13 Fitzroy Street
London W1
UK
Telephone 01–636 1531

Availability

Language
Fortran IV

Computer
IBM 1130
CDC 6400

794

Program name
HL1

Abstract
This program calculates the R factor for various types of wall. Temperature throughout a section of the wall is also calculated

References

Source
PCTS
Box 5841
Coralville
Iowa 52241
USA

Availability
Purchase

Language

Computer
Hewlett-Packard
9815, 9825, 9831
Texas Instruments
SR52

795

Program name
SP3

Abstract
This program calculates average hourly temperatures over a specified day

References

Source
PCTS
Box 5841
Coralville
Iowa 52241
USA

Availability
Purchase

Language

Computer
Hewlett-Packard
9815, 9825, 9831
Texas Instruments
SR52

796

Program name
SP2

Abstract
This program calculates the length of a day at a given time of year. Incident solar radiation on an inclined surface is calculated from horizontal solar radiation. Data concerning climate is available for 100 locations throughout the USA

References

Source
PCTS
Box 5841
Coralville
Iowa 52241
USA

Availability
Purchase

Language

Computer
Hewlett-Packard
9815, 9825, 9831
Texas Instruments
SR52

797

Program name
SP4

Abstract
This program calculates the solar heat gains through different types of glass, at any time of day in any month. Any orientation of building can be considered. Input can be obtained from SP2

References

Source
PCTS
Box 5841
Coralville
Iowa 52241
USA

Availability
Purchase

Language

Computer
Hewlett-Packard
9815, 9825, 9831
Texas Instruments
SR52

798

Program name
ANT5

Abstract
This interactive program calculates the thermal performance of buildings with air-conditioning. Outputs include, for a given space, air-conditioning loads during a day in a specified month and annual energy consumption. Any design may be modified until an acceptable thermal performance is achieved in terms of energy consumption and air-conditioning requirements

References

Source
Pilkington Brothers Limited
Prescot Road
St Helens Merseyside
WA10 3TT UK
Telephone St Helens 28882

Availability
Bureau service, hire

Language
Fortran

Computer

799

Program name
Multiple glazing program

Abstract
This program calculates the transmission characteristics of various combinations of glass and blinds when subject to solar radiation. The window is defined by the reflection, absorption and transmission values of each of the glass and blind surfaces, and the degree of exposure by the heat-transfer coefficients

References

Source
Pilkington Brothers Limited
Prescot Road
St Helens Merseyside
WA10 3TT UK
Telephone St Helens 28882

Availability

Language

Computer

800

Program name
Air-conditioning program

Abstract
This program calculates total heat gains or losses for an air-conditioned building, thereby gauging the effect of a large number of successive days of radiation. It will take into account solar radiation gains and conduction gains and losses through the windows, as well as fabric, internal and ventilation gains (latent and sensible). Line-printed outputs give hourly and peak cooling loads for each mode of heat gain in each zone, or the whole, of the building

References

Source
Pilkington Brothers Limited
Prescot Road
St Helens Merseyside
WA10 3TT UK
Telephone St Helens 28882

Availability
Bureau service

Language
Fortran

Computer

801

Program name
ANTI

Abstract
This interactive program calculates the thermal performance of buildings without air-conditioning. Outputs include room temperatures for a given day in a specified month and annual energy consumption for a given space. Any design may be modified until an acceptable thermal performance is achieved in terms of energy consumption and susceptibility to summer overheating

References

Source
Pilkington Brothers Limited
Prescot Road
St Helens Merseyside
WA10 3TT UK
Telephone St Helens 28882

Availability
Bureau service, hire

Language
Fortran

Computer

802

Program name
HYPER

Abstract
This program compares various alternative arrangements of fenestration and materials for glazing in terms of the energy consumption of a building. It is intended to be used at the initial design stage of a building and is not sufficiently detailed to be used as a basis for selection of equipment

References

Source
PPG Industries
1 Gateway Center
Pittsburgh, Pennsylvania 15222
USA
Telephone 412 434 2818

Availability

Language

Computer

Program name
Design point requirements

Abstract
This program groups various zones into areas to be served by a given air-handling unit, to find totals of air supplied and coil requirements

References
Meriwether analysis series

Source
Ross F Meriwether and Associates
Northwood Executive Building
1600 Northeast Loop 410
San Antonio, Texas
Telephone 512–824 5302

Availability
Bureau service, purchase

Language

Computer
Univac 1108

804

Program name
Zone thermal loads

Abstract
This program calculates heating and cooling loads on a zone-by-zone basis, using twenty-four hours of weather and solar data per month

References
Meriwether analysis series

Source
Ross F Meriwether and Associates
Northwood Executive Building
1600 Northeast Loop 410
San Antonio, Texas
Telephone 512–824 5302

Availability
Bureau service, purchase

Language

Computer
Univac 1108

805

Program name
Solcool

Abstract
This program for the calculation of solar heat gains in a building is based on the 1970 IHVE guide (section A). Environmental or air design temperatures can be specified. Local shading of windows, latitude, height above sea-level, atmospheric conditions, thermal storage, double glazing, U-values of roofs and opaque walls are taken into account. 12- or 24-hour operation of plant can be selected

References

Source
Rosser & Russell Ltd
Queen Caroline Street
London W6 9RG
UK
Telephone 01–748 4161

Availability
Bureau service

Language

Computer
Philips P350

806

Program name
MET 7

Abstract
This program is for the calculation of the cooling load of a building by use of a mathematical model which simulates the physical processes of heat transfer. A large range of factors can be taken into account, including solar gain through windows and blinds, conduction and internal heat gains, and sensible and latent ventilation gains

References

Source
Southbank Polytechnic
Borough Road
London SE1
UK
Telephone 01–928 8989

Availability
Bureau service

Language
Fortran

Computer
ICL 1905E

807

Program name
ARGAIN

Abstract
This program provides the total cooling load due to solar gain, required for a building. It accounts for heat transmission through windows and blinds, thermal storage of the building, its location and climate, overall U-values of opaque walls and roofs, thermal lag and casual gains such as from lighting equipment. It will allow for intermittent plant operation

References

Source
System Share Limited
Pitton Drive
Edinburgh EH5 2XT
UK

Availability
Bureau service

Language
Fortran

Computer
Honeywell G430

808

Program name
Cooling load

Abstract
This program calculates inner temperatures or cooling loads of a building, and also design information for air-conditioning systems. The amount of energy required annually for heating and cooling is also calculated

References

Source
Technies Rekencentrum Polybit bv
Postbus 305 Archipelstraat 96
Nijmegen
Netherlands
Telephone Nijmegen 228382

Availability
Bureau service, remote batch, purchase

Language
Fortran

Computer
CDC 6600

809

Program name
Solar radiation

Abstract
This program calculates the direct and diffuse solar radiation for all periods of the year for every degree of latitude

References

Source
Technies Rekencentrum Polybit bv
Postbus 305, Archipelstraat 96
Nijmegen
Netherlands
Telephone Nijmegen 228382

Availability
Bureau service, remote batch, purchase

Language
Fortran

Computer
CDC 6600

810

Program name
Radiant temperatures

Abstract
This program calculates the mean radiant temperature for any point in a room

References

Source
Technies Rekencentrum Polybit bv
Postbus 305, Archipelstraat 96
Nijmegen
Netherlands
Telephone Nijmegen 228382

Availability
Bureau service, remote batch, time sharing, purchase

Language
Fortran

Computer
CDC 6600

811

Program name
Thermal comfort

Abstract
This program estimates a suitable radiant or air temperature for thermal comfort in a room

References

Source
Technies Rekencentrum Polybit bv
Postbus 305, Archipelstraat 96
Nijmegen
Netherlands
Telephone Nijmegen 228382

Availability
Bureau service, remote batch, time sharing, purchase

Language
Fortran

Computer
CDC 6600

812

Program name
Composite wall

Abstract
This program calculates variable heat flow through homogeneous and composite walls and roofs/ceilings

References

Source
Technies Rekencentrum Polybit bv
Postbus 305, Archipelstraat 96
Nijmegen
Netherlands
Telephone Nijmegen 228382

Availability
Bureau service, remote batch, time sharing, purchase

Language
Fortran

Computer
CDC 6600

Program name
NBSLD

Abstract
This program calculates complete heating and cooling loads in a building. Results are calculated either by design temperature or by degree-days

References

Source
University of Arizona, College of Architecture
Tempe
Arizona
USA

Availability
Remote batch

Language

Computer
CDC 6400

814

Program name
Building energy study

Abstract
This program analyses the internal/external environment of a building so that the heating and cooling requirements can be calculated. This may be used as a basis for comparing the suitability of different energy sources. Mechanical systems can be compared and evaluated, control systems analysed and the operation of a building simulated over a one-year period

References

Source
Westinghouse Electric Corporation
2040 Ardmore Boulevard, Pittsburgh
Pennsylvania 15221
USA

Availability
Bureau service

Language
Fortran

Computer
IBM 370

815

Program name
Building load study

Abstract
This program provides information on the heating and cooling of buildings, for use in designing mechanical systems. Heat gains and losses are assessed from heat-transfer analysis of outside temperature, solar radiation, wind, building materials, amount of glazing, wall harmonics, thermal time-lag, ventilation and infiltration, internal heat gains, shading, building orientation and location

References

Source
Westinghouse Electric Corporation
2040 Ardmore Boulevard, Pittsburgh
Pennsylvania 15221
USA

Availability
Bureau service

Language
Fortran

Computer
IBM 370

816

Program name
DEPI

Abstract
This program calculates the heat losses from a building, room by room. Buildings may be simple or complex. Losses are calculated from air change or conduction through room elements. The heat loss via each element is calculated, the total for each room found, and a running total of room losses gives the eventual heat loss from the zone. With each heat loss from a room, it is also possible to list correction factors

References

Source
41 Rue du Lombard
1000 Brussels
Belgium
Telephone 02–511 06 03

Availability
Bureau service

Language
Fortran IV

Computer

817

Program name
LK022

Abstract
This program simulates the run of a two-pipe inducted air-conditioning system. In doing so, it establishes the dimensions of most of the components and carries out an analysis of energy consumption. The program can be used to calculate the capacities of the components in a specific installation, or to compare different systems

References
Uses data resulting from LK012

Source
AB Svenska Flaktfabriken
Fack
S–104 60 Stockholm
Sweden
Telephone 08–23 83 20 Telex 10430

Availability
By arrangement. Available in UK from SF Air Treatment Limited

Language
Fortran

Computer
CDC 6600

818

Program name
LK042

Abstract
This program simulates the run of a four-pipe inducted air-conditioning system. In doing so, it calculates the dimensions of most of the components and carries out an analysis of energy consumption. The program can be used to calculate the capacities of the components in a specific installation, or to compare different systems

References

Source
AB Svenska Flaktfabriken
Fack
S–104 60 Stockholm
Sweden
Telephone 08–23 83 20 Telex 10430

Availability
By arrangement. Available in UK from SF Air Treatment Limited

Language
Fortran

Computer
CDC 6600

819

Program name
LK044

Abstract
This program simulates the operation of an air-conditioning system in which air volumes are variable, and in which it must be possible to re-heat the air locally at minimum air flow, if there is a heat deficit in the zone. By examining a large number of operational cases, it is possible to determine the capacities of components incorporated in the installation

References
Uses data resulting from LK012

Source
AB Svenska Flaktfabriken
Fack
S–104 60 Stockholm
Sweden
Telephone 08–23 83 20 Telex 10430

Availability
By arrangement. Available in UK from SF Air Treatment Limited

Language
Fortran

Computer
CDC 6600

820

Program name
LK043

Abstract
This program simulates the operation of a re-heating system, ie a system by which the centrally cooled air supply is re-heated locally to meet the prevailing cooling or heating requirements. By examining a large number of operational cases, it is possible to determine the necessary capacities of components incorporated in the installation

References
Uses data resulting from LK012

Source
AB Svenska Flaktfabriken
Fack
S–104 60 Stockholm
Sweden
Telephone 08–23 83 20 Telex 10430

Availability
By arrangement. Available in UK from SF Air Treatment Limited

Language
Fortran

Computer
CDC 6600

821

Program name
MO32

Abstract
This program compares costs of buying and running comparable centrifugal and absorption refrigeration systems. Cooling towers as well as pumps are selected from a data base containing details of those available

References

Source
Albert Kahn Associates
New Center Building
Detroit, Michigan 48202
USA
Telephone 313 871 8500

Availability

Language
Fortran IV

Computer
IBM 1130

822

Program name
E CUBE 75

Abstract
This is a series of programs for evaluating a zone or a building energy system derived from three basic programs, energy requirements, equipment selection and energy consumption, and economic comparison. These estimate the hourly energy requirements of a commercial or industrial operation, finding the resulting energy which would be consumed by each piece of equipment and comparing the economic attraction of various systems

References

Source
American Gas Association
1515 Wilson Boulevard
Arlington
Virginia 22209
USA

Availability
Time-sharing from Control Data Corporation, or remote batch

Language

Computer

Program name
Air-diffuser selection

Abstract
This is a mini-deck program which is used with the output from HCC to make the best selection of a diffuser for each room in a building

References

Source
APEC Executive Office
Grant-Deneau Tower, Suite M–15
Dayton, Ohio 45402
USA
Telephone 513 228 2602

Availability

Language
Fortran

Computer
IBM 1130

824

Program name
SYSTEM

Abstract
This program simulates the thermal performance of central heating systems using water. It predicts the water temperatures throughout the system every few seconds. A heat balance is provided at regular intervals, comprising heat input, heat emissions, boiler-surface losses, flue losses, heat stored and amount of hot water drawn off. This enables efficiencies, fuel consumption and recovery times to be computed

References
THERM

Source
British Gas Corporation
Watson House, Peterborough Road
London SW6 3HN
UK
Telephone 01–736 1212 Telex 919082

Availability
Bureau service

Language
Fortran

Computer
Univac 1106

825

Program name
Equipment selection

Abstract
This program selects air-conditioning equipment of the following types: heating, cooling and DX coils, centrifugal and hermetic-absorption chillers, and induction units. Performance characteristics are calculated for selected equipment

References

Source
Carrier Machinery and Systems
Carrier Parkway
Syracuse, NY 13201
USA

Availability
Available free

Language

Computer

826

Program name
AIRDUCT 2

Abstract
This program will analyse and design an air-conditioning system which is defined in terms of rectangular or circular components. The program is capable of calculating the dimensions of duct covers, and can locate and modify areas where there is a pressure drop or other weakness in the defined network. Results are in tabular form, and, for each section, the air flow and air speed is given together with the total pressure loss

References

Source
CSTC
41 Rue du Lombard
1000 Brussels
Belgium
Telephone 02–511 06 83

Availability
Bureau service

Language
Fortran IV

Computer

827

Program name
MONO

Abstract
This suite of programs is used for comparing different one-pipe central heating systems. The programs provide details of dimensions, flow rates, pump capacities and radiator sizes

References

Source
CSTC
41 Rue du Lombard
1000 Brussels
Belgium
Telephone 02–511 06 83

Availability
Bureau service

Language
Fortran
Basic

Computer
Honeywell GE

828

Program name
DUCTAN

Abstract
This program is used in the design or analysis of supply or exhaust air-conditioning systems. Air-flow characteristics are calculated for all types of ductwork on the basis of pressure, so that effects of both static and velocity pressures are considered. Air outlets are specified for given performance or the performance of given outlets is calculated

References

Source
Deere & Company
John Deere Road
Moline
Illinois 61265
USA

Availability

Language
Fortran IV

Computer
IBM 360

829

Program name
ZONEST

Abstract
This program is used in the design or analysis of new or existing air-conditioning systems. Heating and cooling loads, and the time at which maximum loads occur, are calculated. Performance of a system can be compared with design requirements. Supply air is distributed based on a percentage of sensible cooling load

References

Source
Deere & Company
John Deere Road
Moline
Illinois 61265
USA

Availability

Language
Fortran IV

Computer
IBM 360

830

Program name
MACP–101

Abstract
This is a two-part program. Part I calculates energy requirements: it considers hour-by-hour, programmed building usage and occupancy, and heat losses and gains, solar exposures, structural conditions, and variable electrical and thermal load demands throughout the year. Part II deals with equipment selection and energy consumption. It compares up to nine commonly-used HVAC systems and evaluates the performance of each system

References

Source
Envirodyne Energy Services
421 E Cerritos Ave
Anaheim
California 92805
USA

Availability

Language

Computer

831

Program name
MACP–202

Abstract
This is an advanced version of the MACP–201 program. It permits a more detailed evaluation of constant-volume systems with and without reheat and variable-volume systems. With other modifications, the capacity to simulate water-to-air heat-recovery systems has been added

References

Source
Envirodyne Energy Services
421 E Cerritos Ave
Anaheim
California 92805
USA

Availability

Language

Computer

832

Program name
CLOP

Abstract
This program sizes any form of closed-circuit heating or chill-water network, given the room heating loads. Following the input of general design criteria and physical properties of each section (with an option for choosing from pre-programmed pipe materials and properties), the resultant output gives for each section a listing of dimensions, pressures, fluid flows, velocities, heat emissions (where appropriate), and the total heat requirement

References

Source
Faber Computer Operations Limited
Upper Marlborough Road
St Albans
Herts UK
Telephone St Albans 61222

Availability
Bureau service

Language

Computer
IBM 1130, System 7

Program name
RH

Abstract
This program selects reheat coils for variable-volume and induction-reheat boxes. It calculates the size of reheat coil, water flow and pressure drop for a given size of box, and also the heating load

References

Source
Hankins and Anderson Incorporated
2117 North Hamilton Street
PO Box 6872, Richmond
Virginia 23230
USA
Telephone 804 353 1221

Availability

Language
Fortran IV and APL

Computer

834

Program name
AIRDCS

Abstract
This program designs and analyses air-distribution networks of constant volume. These can be of low or high velocity and with round and/or rectangular segments. The effect, on pressure in the network, of distribution of ducts of various sizes, with different types of fitting, can be examined

References
Mark III software library
User manual 5203·01

Source
Honeywell Information Systems Limited
114 to 118 Southampton Row
London WC1B 5AB
UK
Telephone 01–242 5725

Availability
Bureau service

Language
Basic

Computer
Honeywell 6000 series

835

Program name
DUCTS

Abstract
This program calculates the horsepower of fans and the static pressure required to operate a ducted air-conditioning system. It also determines the static and total pressures at any point so that the system may be balanced when installed. Supply and return ductwork may be handled separately or simultaneously

References

Source
Inatome and Associates
10140 West Nine Mile Road
Oak Park, Michigan 48237
USA
Telephone 313 542 4862

Availability
Time-sharing

Language

Computer

836

Program name
CONDX

Abstract
This program matches air-cooled condensing units with direct-expansion freon cooling coils. The design for each is selected at the point where their respective capacity curves intersect. These curves are generated by assuming suction temperature and ambient temperature are constant

References

Source
Inatome and Associates
10140 West Nine Mile Road
Oak Park, Michigan 48237
USA
Telephone 313 542 4862

Availability
Time-sharing

Language

Computer

837

Program name
DXCOIL

Abstract
This program is for sizing direct-expansion cooling coils. Calculations are based on the by-pass factor method as developed by Dr W Carrier. Trane coils are selected, although the program can easily be adapted to select other coils

References

Source
Inatome and Associates
10140 West Nine Mile Road
Oak Park, Michigan 48237
USA
Telephone 313 542 4862

Availability
Time-sharing

Language

Computer

838

Program name
CWCOIL

Abstract
This program is for sizing chilled-water coils. Calculations are based on the by-pass factor method as developed by Dr W Carrier. Trane coils are selected, although the program can easily be adapted to select other coils

References

Source
Inatome and Associates
10140 West Nine Mile Road
Oak Park, Michigan 48237
USA
Telephone 313 542 4862

Availability
Time-sharing

Language

Computer

839

Program name
STCOIL

Abstract
This program is for sizing steam coils. Calculations are based on the by-pass factor method as developed by Dr W Carrier. Trane coils are selected, although the program can easily be adapted to select other coils

References

Source
Inatome and Associates
10140 West Nine Mile Road
Oak Park, Michigan 48237
USA
Telephone 313 542 4862

Availability
Time-sharing

Language

Computer

840

Program name
HWCOIL

Abstract
This program is for sizing hot-water heating coils. Calculations are based on the by-pass factor method as developed by Dr W Carrier. Trane coils are selected, although the program can easily be adapted to select other coils

References

Source
Inatome and Associates
10140 West Nine Mile Road
Oak Park, Michigan 48237
USA
Telephone 313 542 4862

Availability
Time-sharing

Language

Computer

841

Program name
BEST

Abstract
The program calculates pressure, air flow and damp-throttling for air-conditioning systems

References

Source
Industridata AB
Fack
Solna, Sweden
171 20
Telephone 08 98 03 50

Availability
Contact owner

Language
Fortran IV

Computer
Honeywell H6080

842

Program name
District heating (R22003)

Abstract
The program can carry out steady-state calculations for meshed pipe networks in district heating systems. Flow and pressure in each branch and node of the network are calculated

References

Source
Industridata AB
Fack
Solna, Sweden
171 20
Telephone 08 98 03 50

Availability
Contact owner

Language
Fortran

Computer
Honeywell 6000

Program name
HCE1RH, HCE2HCO, HCE3MZ, HCE4VV

Abstract
These programs model four environmental control systems, reheat, heat/cool/off, multi-zone or double-duct, and variable volume. All give heating and cooling requirements in Btu and ton-hours for night, day and evening periods of each month, as well as monthly and annual totals. Special features, for example, variable lighting, occupant activity and ventilation, are included

References
MEDSI library

Source
Mechanical Engineering Data Services Inc
30 Kimler Drive, Maryland Heights
Missouri 63043
USA
Telephone (314) 434 2340

Availability
Time-sharing

Language

Computer

844

Program name
TOTEN

Abstract
This program takes output from the four basic MEDSI programs and models a total energy plant. Requirements for electricity, engine heat to be salvaged and supplementary heat input are calculated

References
MEDSI library

Source
Mechanical Engineering Data Services Inc
30 Kimler Drive, Maryland Heights
Missouri 63043
USA
Telephone (314) 434 2340

Availability
Time-sharing

Language

Computer

845

Program name
RADZON

Abstract
This interactive program calculates air radiation temperatures in winter for a room with one external wall and a given pattern of windows and radiators. By modifying the input and therefore the design, the effects of altering various parameters can be assessed. Output values are shown on a grid. As part of the service, an environmental engineer runs the program with the client until a suitable size and position of radiator is determined

References

Source
Pilkington Brothers Limited
Prescot Road
St Helens Merseyside
WA10 3TT UK
Telephone St Helens 28882

Availability
Bureau service, hire

Language
Fortran

Computer

846

Program name
TEMPFO4

Abstract
This program calculates indoor temperatures in buildings. The quality of the indoor climate and energy consumption of the heating and air-conditioning systems can also be examined. Calculations are carried out on an hourly basis over a period of one year. Sun-screening and artificial lighting within the building are taken into account

References
Danish Building Research Institute
Abstract 48 14 001

Source
SBI
Postbox 119
2970 Horsholm
Denmark

Availability
Bureau service

Language

Computer

847

Program name
Transmission and radiator choice

Abstract
This program estimates the heat losses in a central heating system. Suitable radiators, of one of several makes, are selected for use in the system

References

Source
Technies Rekencentrum Polybit bv
Postbus 305, Archipelstraat 96
Nijmegen
Netherlands
Telephone Nijmegen 228382

Availability
Bureau service, remote batch, time sharing, purchase

Language
Fortran

Computer
CDC 6600

848

Program name
Coil selection

Abstract
This program is used to select heating and cooling coils, or to evaluate the performance of a selected coil. The tube may contain steam, hot water, cold water or refrigerant

References

Source
The Singer Company
602 Sunnyvale Drive
Wilmington, North Carolina 28401
USA

Availability
Time-sharing

Language
Fortran IV

Computer

849

Program name
Optimised equipment selection

Abstract
This program selects equipment to meet specified duty conditions. It currently provides choice of heating, cooling and refrigerant coils, fans and air-handling units. Output data on coils includes type, flow rate and pressure drop information. Output data on fans includes efficiency and sound power information by octave band for each fan selected. Output data on air-handling units includes two selections for each set of conditions

References

Source
The Trane Company
La Crosse
Wisconsin 54601
USA
Telephone (608) 782 8000 Telex 29–3415

Availability
Free service

Language
Fortran

Computer
IBM 370

850

Program name
TRACE (Trane Air Conditioning Economics)

Abstract
This program analyses the energy requirements and economic viability of various heating, ventilation and air-conditioning systems. Output includes data for design of the system, monthly energy usage, utility bills, operating costs and depreciation for up to four alternative designs. An appendix contains peak heat gains and losses, profiles of loads on the system in operation and the usage by month of each piece of equipment

References

Source
The Trane Company
La Crosse
Wisconsin 54601
USA
Telephone (608) 782 8000 Telex 29–3415

Availability
Bureau service, time-sharing

Language
Fortran with assembler I/0
Edit program in PL/1

Computer
IBM 370

851

Program name
Re-heat coil

Abstract
This program uses standard details concerning terminal boxes, of the type found in catalogues, to calculate the necessary flow of water and the required drop in pressure of terminal re-heat coils

References

Source
WTA Computer Services
2357 59th Street
St Louis, Missouri 63110
USA
Telephone 314 644 1400

Availability

Language

Computer

852

Program name
MA33

Abstract
This program calculates the annual cost of energy used in a building. The program uses specific sub-routines for seven different cities. These contain details of climate and of local charges for building services. Terminal re-heat or dual-duct systems may be examined

References

Source
Albert Kahn Associates
New Center Building
Detroit, Michigan 48202
USA
Telephone 313 871 8500

Availability

Language
Fortran IV

Computer
IBM 1130

Program name
Energy analysis

Abstract
This program calculates the energy used annually to heat and cool a building. Systems which can be considered are of the following types: conventional dual-duct or single– zone, solar-assisted heat pump or one operating from recovered internal heat, and complete solar heating and cooling systems

References

Source
Bridgers and Paxton Incorporated
213 Truman Street NE
Albuquerque, New Mexico 87108
USA
Telephone 505 265 8577

Availability

Language
Fortran

Computer
Univac 1130

854

Program name
FMS (Cheshire)

Abstract
This program compares the calculated theoretical usage of hot-water heating with the actual consumption, records the consumption of gas and electricity and calculates the energy usage per m². For an individual building, it stores building and plant information, calculates monthly theoretical heat consumption, taking into account hourly external temperatures, building situation, plant efficiency, usage, type of controls and mains losses.

References

Source
Cheshire County Council, DepartmentXf Architecture
Goldsmith House, Hamilton Place
Chester CH1 1SE
UK
Telephone Chester 602883

Availability
Under consideration

Language
PL1 in OS

Computer
IBM 370–145

855

Program name
RECUP

Abstract
This program calculates the maximum annual energy consumption and cost of running a heating and ventilating system, within a simple or complex structure. Given specific data on the natural heat losses and gains, the program calculates the optimum thermal and ventilating performance of the building, and then the projected costs of a system. Results are printed

References

Source
CSTC
41 Rue du Lombard
1000 Brussels
Belgium
Telephone 02–511 06 83

Availability
Bureau service

Language
Basic

Computer
PDP 10–11

856

Program name
Infiltration

Abstract
This program is for calculation of air-infiltration in buildings caused by winds, the operation of the air-handling system and the stack effect

References

Source
Division of Building Research
National Research Council
Ottawa K1A 0R6
Canada

Availability
Purchase

Language
Fortran IV

Computer
IBM 360

857

Program name
RUNO 1620

Abstract
This program calculates the energy used annually to heat and cool a building. It expresses this in terms of fuel and compares the relative cost of different fuels. The program is intended for use during the initial design of a building

References

Source
Duke Power Company
422 South Church Street
Charlotte, North Carolina 28242
USA
Telephone 704 373 4304

Availability
Remote batch

Language

Computer

858

Program name
AXCESS

Abstract
This program allows the designer to compare energy requirements of various electrical and mechanical systems in buildings. Energy usage and demand may be compared for each system, using any combination of available energy sources and enabling potential cost savings to be determined readily. Known data is input. The program will then utilise built-in reset values for certain missing data

References

Source
Edison Electric Institute
90 Park Avenue
New York 10016
USA

Availability
Purchase, or through local utilities in USA

Language
Fortran IV

Computer
Developed on IBM 365, but may be run on any computer with 256K core

---

859

Program name
ENPRO

Abstract
This program calculates energy loads on a building during an average year, the energy required to deal with these loads, and energy demands of miscellaneous equipment. The building is analysed by zones. Climatic and geographical details of the location are used, along with cooling load and heat loss calculations, to generate the total energy demand. Daily, monthly and annual values may be listed for any type or combination of heating systems

References

Source
Faber Computer Operations Limited
Upper Marlborough Road
St Albans
Herts UK
Telephone St Albans 61222

Availability
Bureau service

Language

Computer
IBM 1130, System 7

860

Program name
SCOUT

Abstract
This program is an extended version of NECAP for determining the energy consumption of a building and for analysis of running costs

References

Source
GARD
7449 North Natchez Avenue
Niles, Illinois 60648
USA
Telephone 312 647 9000

Availability

Language
Fortran IV

Computer
CDC 6400, 6600
IBM 360, 370
Univac 1108,
Spectra 70–46

861

Program name
CD 07

Abstract
This program estimates the annual electricity consumption of a building with perimeter induction air-conditioning. It then compares this with the electricity consumption of a comparable building without air-conditioning

References

Source
Haden Young Limited
7 Tavistock Square
London WC1
UK
Telephone 01–387 1288

Availability
By arrangement with DOC members

Language
Fortran

Computer
ICL 1902T

862

Program name
BUILDSIM

Abstract
This program is for the analysis of energy consumption in a building over various periods of time. Building materials, heat storage, characteristics of the mechanical systems, and controls are all taken into consideration

References

Source
Honeywell Incorporated
1500 W Dundee Road
Arlington Heights, Illinois 60004
USA
Telephone 312 394 4000

Availability

Language
Fortran IV

Computer

Program name
INSUL

Abstract
This program calculates comparative costs in use for a given roof or wall assembly with different thicknesses of insulation. The best thickness for insulation is calculated, together with the incremental and cumulative savings on heat requirements over each area of 10 000 square feet of surface. Reduction in refrigeration loads is also calculated if air-conditioning is taken into consideration

References

Source
Inatome and Associates
10140 West Nine Mile Road
Oak Park, Michigan 48237
USA
Telephone 313 542 4862

Availability
Time-sharing

Language

Computer

864

Program name
LAMSAC Application code 32125111130A

Abstract
This program makes an analysis of fuel consumption in council property. Slow peripheral units used are a card reader and two line printers. The program was first used in 1975

References
LAMSAC

Source
Architect's Department, Bolton
Metropolitan Borough Council
Town Hall
Bolton BL1 1RU
Telephone Bolton 22311

Availability

Language
Cobol

Computer
ICL 1903T
16K core
1 disc drive

865

Program name
MACE (McDonnell Annual Consumption of Energy)

Abstract
This program calculates the annual, monthly, weekly, daily and hourly cost of heating and cooling buildings. It allows the designer to select the best fuel, or combination of fuels, for this purpose. Output gives values for each building complex, thermal generating system, thermal distribution system and zone (controlled space)

References

Source
McDonnell Douglas Automation Company
PO Box 516, St Louis
Missouri 63166
USA

Availability
Time-sharing

Language

Computer

866

Program name
HCENERG

Abstract
This program takes output from one of the four MEDSI programs, and one input coding sheet, and calculates energy usage in sub-systems and the whole building. Results are tabulated by month, with annual totals, for: fuel input in Btu for heating and ventilating, water heating and heat-powered refrigeration, kwh for illumination, air and fluid handling, appliances, electric-driven refrigeration, domestic water-heating and space-heating

References
MEDSI library

Source
Mechanical Engineering Data Services Inc
30 Kimler Drive, Maryland Heights
Missouri 63043
USA
Telephone (314) 434 2340

Availability
Time-sharing

Language

Computer

867

Program name
MEDSI library

Abstract
These programs model energy usage in buildings. Input consists of two simple coding forms and answers to questions at a teletype. An engineer preparing an energy conservation plan can first modify inputs until the programs accurately simulate energy usage in an existing building. Then he can examine the effects of proposed changes. Weather files exist for many locations throughout the United States

References
Developed by McClure and Associates

Source
Mechanical Engineering Data Services Inc
30 Kimler Drive, Maryland Heights
Missouri 63043
USA
Telephone (314) 434 2340

Availability
Time-sharing

Language

Computer

868

Program name
NECAP

Abstract
This program is for the analysis of energy consumption in a building. Economic comparisons are also produced. Simplified output is available

References

Source
NASA, Construction Engineering Branch
Mail Stop 227
Langley Research Center
Hampton, Virginia
USA

Availability
Bureau service through COSMIC

Language
Fortran IV

Computer
CDC 6400, 6600

869

Program name
VARMETAB

Abstract
This program is used to calculate heat losses from buildings. Basic data concerning the elements of a building and facts about each room are input. The heat loss in each individual room is calculated with regard to the building in which it is contained. A building with up to 500 rooms can be handled. The program is interactive: all variables can be modified and the run repeated without repeating all input data

References
Danish Building Research Institute
Abstract 48 14 004

Source
Nielsen & Rauschenberger
Radgivende ingeniorer A/S
Lundtoftevej 7
2800 Lyngby
Denmark

Availability
Time-sharing

Language

Computer

870

Program name
ENCORE (Energy consumption of residential buildings)

Abstract
This program calculates the energy consumption of residential buildings. These may be of any shape, type, and have any arrangement of interior divisions. Real weather data is used (magnetic tape from weather bureau) and combined with internal heat gains and thermostat settings. The program uses the 'Z-transfer' or 'weighting factor' method, as described in the ASHRAE Handbook

References

Source
Norwegian Building Research Institute
POB 322 Blindern
Oslo 3
Norway
Telephone 46 98 80

Availability
Purchase, bureau service

Language
Fortran IV

Computer
Univac 1100
IBM 360, 370
Xerox Sigma 3
DEC 11
Mini-computer with 32k core, and possibility of program overlay

---

871

Program name
Energy requirements estimate

Abstract
This program calculates thermal and electrical loads for a building on an hourly basis. The operation of the air-distribution system is simulated in meeting these loads

References
Meriwether analysis series

Source
Ross F Meriwether and Associates
Northwood Executive Building
1600 Northeast Loop 410
San Antonio, Texas
Telephone 512–824 5302

Availability
Bureau service, purchase

Language

Computer
Univac 1108

872

Program name
Energy-systems and analysis series

Abstract
This is a series of seventeen programs for hour-by-hour calculation of the annual energy consumption of various types of air-handling system and mechanical plant. Local utility rate schedules are applied to consumption. These costs are combined with other owning and operating costs for year-by-year cash-flow projections

References

Source
Ross F Meriwether and Associates
Northwood Executive Building
1600 Northeast Loop 410
San Antonio, Texas
Telephone 512–824 5302

Availability
Bureau service, purchase

Language

Computer
Univac 1108

Program name
Equipment Energy Consumption/B

Abstract
This program simulates the operation of various pieces of an air-distribution system, to find monthly and annual energy consumption

References
Meriwether analysis series

Source
Ross F Meriwether and Associates
Northwood Executive Building
1600 Northeast Loop 410
San Antonio, Texas
Telephone 512–824 5302

Availability
Bureau service, purchase

Language

Computer
Univac 1108

874

Program name
Total energy

Abstract
This system aids the design of electricity-generating plant in which heat released is to be utilised to the maximum extent. Demands for electric energy and for heat are co-ordinated, and an energy balance is calculated for every hour of the year, together with the power required to produce this

References

Source
Technies Rekencentrum Polybit bv
Postbus 305, Archipelstraat 96
Nijmegen
Netherlands
Telephone Nijmegen 228382

Availability
Bureau service, remote batch, purchase

Language
Fortran

Computer
CDC 6600

875

Program name
BEEP

Abstract
This program is designed to estimate energy demands in buildings, and to provide comparisons of energy consumption and cost for various heating systems and fuel. U values are calculated from information concerning the structure. Heat losses and gains per zone, and for the building as a whole, are estimated against inside and outside design temperatures. A monthly heating and cooling analysis is produced for a typical year

References

Source
The Electricity Council
30 Millbank
London SW1P 4RD
UK
Telephone 01–834 2333

Availability
From area Electricity Boards in the UK. For suitable projects, the service is free

Language
Fortran-based

Computer
IBM 370

876

Program name
HACE

Abstract
This program is used to calculate the energy consumption of buildings. The thermal-response factor is used to calculate hourly loads

References

Source
WTA Computer Services
2357 59th Street
St Louis, Missouri 63110
USA
Telephone 314 644 1400

Availability

Language
Fortran IV

Computer
IBM 360, 370

877

Program name
SUN

Abstract
This program estimates the performance of solar-energy systems, using a mathematical model of a highly idealised building heated by solar energy

References

Source
Berkeley Solar Group
1815 Francisco Street
Berkeley, California 94703
USA

Availability

Language
Fortran IV

Computer
CDC 6400

Program name
SIMSHAC

Abstract
This program is used for the analysis of systems used to heat and cool buildings by solar energy

References

Source
Mechanical Engineering Department
Colorado State University
Fort Collins, Colorado 80523
USA

Availability

Language

Computer
CDC 6000, Cyber
IBM 370

879

Program name
LAMSAC Application code 32066126020A

Abstract
This program calculates heat energy obtained from solar radiation at varying roof angles. Slow peripheral units used are a tape reader and line printer. The program has been in use since 1976

References
LAMSAC

Source
Architect's Department, Dyfed County Council
Lime Grove House, Lime Grove Avenue
Carmarthen, Dyfed
Telephone 0267 4276

Availability

Language
Fortran

Computer
ICL 1904S
8K core

880

Program name
SP6

Abstract
This program calculates the useful heat provided by a solar collector. The temperature of the collector fluid at the outlet, the flow-rate of the fluid and the performance of the collector at any hour of the day, are also calculated

References

Source
PCTS
Box 5841
Coralville
Iowa 52241
USA

Availability
Purchase

Language

Computer
Hewlett-Packard
9815, 9825, 9831
Texas Instruments
SR52

881

Program name
SP5

Abstract
This program calculates heat loss through the cover of solar collectors owing to the effects of conduction, convection and radiation

References

Source
PCTS
Box 5841
Coralville
Iowa 52241
USA

Availability
Purchase

Language

Computer
Hewlett-Packard
9815, 9825, 9831
Texas Instruments
SR52

882

Program name
Sol Cost

Abstract
This program is used for costing and sizing single-zone solar-energy systems. It also calculates heat loads and computes the optimum area of the collector, angle of tilt, sizes of pipes and storage requirements, based on a life-cycle cost analysis. Data banks provide the user with all the information needed to make detailed cost analyses. The user can operate the program with no computer knowledge

References
Martin-Marietta Aerospace Corporation

Source
Solar Heating and Cooling Information Center
PO Box 1607, Rockville
Maryland 20850
USA
Telephone 800 523–2929

Availability
Contact owner

Language
Fortran IV

Computer
CDC
IBM
Univac

Program name
SHACSAC–1

Abstract
This program is for the analysis of solar heating and cooling systems. Costs of buying and running such a system are calculated

References

Source
The Charles Stark Draper Laboratory
75 Cambridge Parkway
Cambridge, Massachusetts 02142
USA

Availability

Language
Fortran IV

Computer
IBM 360

884

Program name
FCHART

Abstract
This program is used for designing solar-heating systems which use either liquid or air as the heat-transfer medium. It treats the area of the collector as the main variable, but also takes into account the capacity of the storage unit. It determines the fraction of monthly and annual loads to be carried by solar energy. An interactive version of this program may be used to give the thermal and economic performance of the collector

References

Source
University of Wisconsin Solar Energy Laboratory
1303 Engineering Research Building
1500 Johnson Drive
Madison, Wisconsin 53706
USA

Availability
Purchase

Language
Fortran II

Computer

885

Program name
TRNSYS (Transient system simulation)

Abstract
This program is used to simulate the operation of various solar-energy systems. Models for components such as collectors, controls, storage tanks, heat exchangers, furnaces, building loads and integrators can be selected. When detailed loads are not required, a 'degree– day' or 'degree-hour' model is used. For a more exact determination, 'wall', 'roof' and 'room' transfer functions can be assembled to model almost any structure

References
A method of simulation of solar processes. Solar Energy, Vol 17, pp 29–37

Source
University of Wisconsin Solar Energy Laboratory
1303 Engineering Research Building
1500 Johnson Drive
Madison, Wisconsin 53706, USA

Availability

Language
Fortran

Computer

886

Program name
LK015

Abstract
This program calculates the temperatures in rooms with varying amounts of air-conditioning. It can be used at an early stage of design to determine the effect on indoor temperatures of the shape of the building, outdoor temperatures and other factors (eg blinds, size of windows, lighting)

References

Source
AB Svenska Flaktfabriken
Fack
S–104 60 Stockholm
Sweden
Telephone 08–23 83 20 Telex 10430

Availability
By arrangement. Available in UK from SF Air Treatment Limited

Language
Fortran

Computer
CDC 6600

887

Program name
SHAD

Abstract
This interactive program is designed to display shadows cast by buildings or other objects onto the ground. It uses a storage screen and a cursor or graphics tablet for input. The location, time of year and time of day are at the discretion of the user. Input can also be from a file produced by another program

References

Source
Department of Architectural Science
The University of Sydney
Sydney
New South Wales 2006
Australia

Availability
Sale, bureau service

Language
Fortran IV

Computer
CDC Cyber 72

888

Program name
COE

Abstract
This program is used to compare the relative efficiency of various combinations of glazing and shading devices, taking into account the amount and cost of air-conditioning required in each case

References

Source
Koolshade Corporation
PO Box 210
Solana Beach, California 92075
USA

Availability

Language
Basic

Computer
Hewlett-Packard
200F

889

Program name
Obstructional shading

Abstract
This program calculates, for each hour of the day that the sun is above the horizon, the shadows due to obstructions falling onto a facade. The effects of shading on the cooling load by other parts of the building, or by adjacent buildings, may thus be determined. The program can be used in conjunction with the air-conditioning program

References

Source
Pilkington Brothers Limited
Prescot Road
St Helens Merseyside
WA10 3TT UK
Telephone St Helens 28882

Availability

Language
Fortran

Computer

890

Program name
EXHAUST

Abstract
This program is used in the design of industrial dust-collection and exhaust-air systems. A mathematical model of the system is balanced by adjusting factors such as air volumes and size of the ducts, while maintaining minimum velocities of air flow

References

Source
Deere & Company
John Deere Road
Moline
Illinois 61265
USA

Availability

Language
Fortran IV

Computer
IBM 360

891

Program name
MTWO

Abstract
This program is for use in design of dust collection systems. Sizes for components of the system are calculated, and the whole system balanced. Velocity and head loss for each length of duct, loss through fittings and the static pressure of the system are calculated. Design is such that no damping is required

References

Source
Giffels Associates Incorporated
Marquette Building
243 W Congress
Detroit, Michigan 48226
USA
Telephone 313 961 2084

Availability
Purchase negotiable

Language
Algol

Computer
Univac 1108

892

Program name
EXHAU

Abstract
This program calculates capacity and capabilities of an industrial exhaust duct system. Flow velocity, accumulated air quantity, losses in pressure and the static pressure required at the exhaust fan are calculated

References
Heating, piping and air conditioning, September 1968

Source
Inatome and Associates
10140 West Nine Mile Road
Oak Park, Michigan 48237
USA
Telephone 313 542 4862

Availability
Time-sharing

Language

Computer

Program name
New ARC environmental package

Abstract
This is a set of interrelated programs for measuring the environmental performance of a building. The data files are based on climatic statistics for Southern England and measure performance in terms of daylight, artificial lighting, heat balance and environmental temperatures. The program covers building location, climate, structure, radiation transmission through glass and blinds as well as gains through opaque walls and roofs

References

Source
ARC Limited
51 Jesus Lane
Cambridge CB5 8BA
UK
Telephone 0223 65015

Availability
Bureau service

Language
Fortran IV

Computer
Atlas II
IBM 370

894

Program name
RESPTK

Abstract
This program calculates response factors for various heat-conduction systems. It utilises the superposition principle, such that the overall thermal response in a building at one time is the sum of many preceding responses

References
Thermal Response Factors for Multi-layer Structures of Various Heat-Conduction Systems, ASHRAE Transactions, Volume 5, 1969

Source
Center for Building Technology, IAT
National Bureau of Standards
Washington, DC 20234, USA

Availability

Language

Computer

895

Program name
PSYCHR

Abstract
This program generates, in tabular form, values determining the thermodynamic properties of partially saturated and dry air. Exact statistical mechanics calculations are used as developed by Goff and Gratch

References
Algorithms for Psychrometric Calculations, NBS Building Science Series, 1970

Source
Center for Building Technology, IAT
National Bureau of Standards
Washington, DC 20234
USA

Availability
Purchase

Language

Computer

896

Program name
CONDNS

Abstract
This program calculates temperatures on the surfaces and at joints of walls. Vapour pressures are also calculated. It also predicts whether or not condensation will occur on the surface or within the wall

References
PSA program library

Source
Directorate of Mechanical and Electrical Engineering Services
Property Services Agency
Lunar House, 40 Wellesley Road
Croydon CR9 2EL, UK
Telephone 01–686 3499

Availability

Language
Fortran

Computer
Honeywell MK III

897

Program name
Smoke shafts

Abstract
This suite of programs calculates the required sizes of smoke shafts and vents

References

Source
Division of Building Research
National Research Council
Ottawa K1A 0R6
Canada

Availability
Purchase

Language
Fortran IV

Computer
IBM 360

898

Program name
Air movement

Abstract
This program calculates air flows and differentials in pressure resulting from the operation of the air-handling system and the stack effect in multi-storey buildings

References

Source
Division of Building Research
National Research Council
Ottawa K1A 0R6
Canada

Availability
Purchase

Language
Fortran IV

Computer
IBM 360

899

Program name
Sun position

Abstract
This program allows the user to determine accurately the position of the sun relative to North and the horizon for any point on the face of the earth and at any given instant in time. Details of location and time must be entered for each calculation, but the data is called for in a form which allows up to 120 results from one input

References
Aries system of programs

Source
Genair (Data Processing) Limited
Lower Tovil Mill, Tovil
Maidstone, Kent
UK
Telephone Maidstone 54783,4,5

Availability
Purchase, bureau service

Language

Computer
Hewlett-Packard
HP9830A

900

Program name
HL2

Abstract
This program calculates the transmission of vapour through walls of various types

References

Source
PCTS
Box 5841
Coralville
Iowa 52241
USA

Availability
Purchase

Language

Computer
Hewlett-Packard
9815, 9825, 9831
Texas Instruments
SR52

Building services

Lighting
Electrical services
Other

901

Program name
NATLIT

Abstract
This conversational program computes the Daylight Factors in a rectangular room at user-specified points, or at points on a user-specified grid. The program is based on the CIE Standard Overcast Sky approach, incorporating an exact analytical solution of the daylight factor integral for rectangular windows. The BRE split-flux method is used for the calculation of the reflected component

References
DOC

Source
ABACUS Services, Department of Architecture and Building Science
University of Strathclyde
131 Rottenrow
Glasgow G4 0NG
Telephone 041–552 4400 ext 3021

Availability
See DOC Report No 3

Language
Fortran

Computer
Univac 1108

902

Program name
Natural Lighting (Version 1·1)

Abstract
This program computes the daylight factor in a rectangular room at user-specified points, or at points on a user-specified grid. It is based on the CIE Standard Overcast Sky approach, incorporating an exact analytical solution of the daylight factor integral. The split-flux method is used for the calculation of the reflected component

References
DOC Evaluation Report No 3

Source
ABACUS Services, Department of Architecture and Building Science
University of Strathclyde
131 Rottenrow, Glasgow G4 0NG
Telephone 041–552 4400 ext 3021

Availability

Language
Univac Fortran V

Computer
Univac 1108 (Under EXEC–8)

903

Program name
GLIM

Abstract
This program is used to evaluate natural or artificial lighting conditions within buildings. It can be used at the outline design stage to select basic options (eg window sizes), at the detail design stage (eg to assist in the design of lighting installations) or as a research tool to prepare accurate design data

References

Source
ARC Limited
4 Jesus Lane
Cambridge CB5 8BA
UK
Telephone 0223 65015

Availability
Purchase

Language
Fortran

Computer
IBM 360, 370
Prime 300

904

Program name
DAYLIGHTING

Abstract
This program calculates natural lighting levels within buildings in accordance with Building Research Establishment methods. Daylight factors and their components are quickly calculated, taking account of window dimensions, external obstructions and surface reflectance

References

Source
ARC Limited
4 Jesus Lane
Cambridge CB5 8BA
UK
Telephone 0223 65015

Availability
Purchase

Language
Fortran

Computer
Prime 300

905

Program name
Daylight coefficients

Abstract
This program allows the calculation of levels of natural lighting in buildings. Surface reflectance is taken into consideration. Windows need not be horizontal

References
Krochmann, J, Uber die berechnung der beleuchtung von innen raumen mit tageslicht. Technik am Bau, October 1971

Source
CE-data
Lundtoftevej 1G
2800 Lyngby
Denmark

Availability
Bureau service

Language

Computer

Program name
SUNPEN

Abstract
This program details the penetration of direct sunlight into a room through windows by presenting the outlines of the sunlit areas of walls and floors. It uses a storage screen and examines one room at a time. Rooms must be rectangular, but the location, position, elevation and time of year and time of day are at the discretion of the user. In addition to the screen, output includes a three-dimensional plot by the copier

References

Source
Department of Architectural Science
The University of Sydney
Sydney
New South Wales 2006
Australia

Availability
Sale, bureau service

Language
Fortran IV

Computer
CDC Cyber 72

907

Program name
DOC Daylight

Abstract
An interactive program which allows a designer to make an appraisal of natural lighting levels in a building. This information may be for specified points or throughout the building presented in the form of contours. It may be used at an early stage of design to evaluate different patterns of fenestration or relationships between buildings and to check levels of natural lighting against standards of thermal performance

References
Incorporates CAD Centre GINO-F and CONTOUR packages

Source
Design Office Consortium
6 Green Street
Cambridge CB2 3JU
UK
Telephone 0223 68387

Availability
Bureau service, hire

Language
ASA Fortran IV

Computer

908

Program name
FLOODLIT

Abstract
This program calculates the horizontal plane illumination at each point on a grid of an area to be floodlit

References

Source
Directorate of Mechanical and Electrical Engineering Services
Property Services Agency
Lunar House, 40 Wellesley Road
Croydon CR9 2EL, UK
Telephone 01–686 3499

Availability

Language
Fortran

Computer
Honeywell MK III

909

Program name
MAINDAY

Abstract
This conversational program computes the daylight factors in a rectangular room at user-specified points or on a user-specified grid. The program is based on the CIE Standard Overcast Sky. The Hopkinson analytical solution of the daylight factor integral is used for the calculation of the sky component, and the BRE split-flux method is used for the calculation of reflected components

References
DOC

Source
Professional Computing Branch,
Directorate of Architectural Services
Property Services Agency
Room 1614, Lunar House
Croydon, Surrey
Telephone 01–686 3499 ext 3393

Availability
See DOC Report No 3

Language
Fortran

Computer
Honeywell

910

Program name
PSA DAYLIGHT

Abstract
This program computes the daylight factors in a rectangular room at user-specified points or on a user-specified grid. It is based on the CIE Standard Overcast Sky. The Hopkinson analytical solution of the daylight-factor integral is used for the calculation of the sky component, and the BRE split-flux method for the calculation of reflected components

References
DOC Evaluation Report No 3

Source
Professional Computing Branch,
Directorate of Architectural Services
Room 1614, Lunar House
Croydon, Surrey
Telephone 01–686 3499

Availability

Language
Fortran IV

Computer
Honeywell Mk III

911

Program name
LIGHTS

Abstract
This program calculates the number of fittings and the glare indices of installations, using fluorescent fittings from the DoE's term contract. It also calculates a comparative present-day value for each fitting and lamp arrangement

References
PSA program library

Source
Directorate of Mechanical and Electrical Engineering Services
Property Services Agency
Lunar House, 40 Wellesley Road
Croydon CR9 2EL, UK
Telephone 01–686 3499

Availability
TSL Bureau

Language
TELCOMP

Computer

912

Program name
GLARE/GLARM

Abstract
These programs calculate the final glare indexes at a working plane of 4ft (1·2m) for all orientation modes, given the characteristics of the room and the light fittings. They work with Imperial or metric units. Tungsten, mercury or fluorescent light fittings may be specified, with BZ classifications from one to ten. For tungsten or mercury fittings the output lists two orientation modes. Four orientation modes are given for fluorescent fittings

References

Source
Faber Computer Operations Limited
Upper Marlborough Road
St Albans
Herts UK
Telephone St Albans 61222

Availability
Bureau service

Language

Computer
IBM 1130, System 7

913

Program name
LUMEN

Abstract
This program calculates the level of illumination at a working plane, 3·5ft high. Any one of four fluorescent, fifteen tungsten or five mercury fittings may be specified. There is an option to use twin tube fluorescent fittings, with a choice of eight tube sizes and four colours. Given the number and type of light fittings, the dimension of the rooms and the reflection characteristics, the program is capable of analysing any number of rooms in one run

References

Source
Faber Computer Operations Limited
Upper Marlborough Road
St Albans
Herts UK
Telephone St Albans 61222

Availability
Bureau service

Language

Computer
IBM 1130, System 7

914

Program name
DAFA

Abstract
The program calculates the daylight factor levels over a working plane. The daylight factor is the ratio of daylight illumination on the internal surface to the illumination on an external horizontal plane from an unobstructed hemisphere of sky. Given the room and window dimensions, internal surface reflection factors and glass properties, the daylight factor is calculated and printed up, followed by a diagram of contours of equal daylight factor on the data plotter

References

Source
Faber Computer Operations Limited
Upper Marlborough Road
St Albans
Herts UK
Telephone St Albans 61222

Availability
Bureau service

Language

Computer
IBM 1130, System 7

915

Program name
FLUD

Abstract
This program calculates the level of illumination on any plane from any number or type of floodlight or spotlight. Given the size of the illuminated surface, the position and focus points of light sources, the level of illumination is calculated on a rectangular grid across the plane. Intermediate printed output is given to show the distribution of illumination across the surface, before proceeding to draw a contour map on the data plotter

References

Source
Faber Computer Operations Limited
Upper Marlborough Road
St Albans
Herts UK
Telephone St Albans 61222

Availability
Bureau service

Language

Computer
IBM 1130, System 7

916

Program name
DAY 1/2

Abstract
This program computes the daylight factors in a rectangular room, at points on a user-specified grid. It is based on the CIE Standard Overcast Sky approach. The user inputs geometry of room, position of windows, reflectivity of surfaces, overhang and external obstruction details and number of calculation points along the X and Y axes of the room. The height of the measurement plane is taken as the average window-sill height

References
DOC

Source
Heating and Ventilating Computed Sizing
7 St Nicholas Street
Bristol
Telephone 0272 29983

Availability
See DOC Report No 3

Language
Basic

Computer
Wang 2212

917

Program name
HVCS DAYLIGHT

Abstract
This program computes the daylight factors in a rectangular room, at points on a user-specified grid. It is based on the CIE Standard Overcast Sky approach and uses the BRE split-flux method. The program outputs daylight factors as a matrix. It also gives minimum, maximum and average daylight factor values

References
DOC Evaluation Report No 3

Source
Heating and Ventilating Computed Sizing
18 The Ridgeway
Radlett, Hertfordshire
Telephone 09276 7805

Availability

Language
Wang Basic

Computer
Wang 2212

918

Program name
LIGHT

Abstract
This program produces the layout of lighting fixtures required to maintain a specified level of illumination in a room of given dimensions and operating environment. The effect of modified conditions can be examined to determine their effect on the illumination level

References
Mark III software library
User manual 5203·02

Source
Honeywell Information Systems Limited
114 to 118 Southampton Row
London WC1B 5AB
UK
Telephone 01–242 5725

Availability
Bureau service

Language
Basic

Computer
Honeywell 6000 series

919

Program name
SPORT, POoo7

Abstract
This program calculates the lighting intensity originating from a haphazard lighting system, on a rectangular area. It is particularly useful for sports installations. Intensity can be calculated at points on a horizontal plane, and through two vertical sections to a certain height above the horizontal. SPORT calculates cylindrical lighting intensity (lighting intensity on a vertical half-cylinder): POoo7 calculates lighting intensity on plan.

References
Danish Building Research Institute
Abstract 48 14 01

Source
Lysteknisk Laboratorium
ATV, Bygning 325
Lundtoftevej 100
2800 Lyngby
Denmark

Availability
Purchase

Language

Computer
Hewlett-Packard 2100A

920

Program name
VIVAB

Abstract
This program calculates transmittance and reflectance of light for windows with up to five layers of obscure or clear glazing. The Gauss-Seidel iterative technique is used for calculation of transmitted, reflected and absorbed rays in individual layers of glazing. Heat gains in the glazing and inside the building can also be calculated

References
Danish Building Research Institute
Abstract 48 14 013

Source
Lysteknisk Laboratorium
ATV, Bygning 325
Lundtoftevej 100
2800 Lyngby
Denmark

Availability
Purchase

Language

Computer
Hewlett-Packard 2100A

921

Program name
HJ001

Abstract
This program calculates the intensity of light from indoor lighting systems. The room is presumed to be box-formed, and the lighting system is considered as a row of points on any one of the six surfaces. Surfaces of walls, floor and ceiling may have different reflectance values. Light intensity is calculated, at any point, as a sum of direct and reflected light

References
Danish Building Research Institute
Abstract 48 14 014

Source
Lysteknisk Laboratorium
ATV, Bygning 325
Lundtoftevej 100
2800 Lyngby
Denmark

Availability
Purchase

Language

Computer
Hewlett-Packard
2100A

922

Program name
SP1

Abstract
This program calculates the altitude of the sun and azimuth for any location at a specified time. Time of sunrise is also calculated

References

Source
PCTS
Box 5841
Coralville
Iowa 52241
USA

Availability
Purchase

Language

Computer
Hewlett-Packard
9815, 9825, 9831
Texas Instruments
SR52

923

Program name
ANL1

Abstract
This interactive program calculates the provision of daylight in a room. Outputs include daylight at points on a grid representing the room. Results at intermediate stages in the calculation, isolating the contribution of various heat gains and losses to the final results may also be obtained. As part of the service an environmental engineer runs the program with the client until a design is arrived at which will give satisfactory thermal performance

References

Source
Pilkington Brothers Limited
Prescot Road
St Helens Merseyside
WA10 3TT UK
Telephone 0744 28882

Availablility
Bureau service, hire

Language
Fortran

Computer

924

Program name
ANNEX

Abstract
This program computes the daylight factors in a rectangular room, at points on a 5x5 or 10x10 grid. It uses the Seshadri method in connection with the CIE Standard Overcast Sky for calculating the sky component. The internally-reflected component calculation is based on the Pilkington method. The program is part of a suite of environmental programs

References
DOC Evaluation Report No 3

Source
Environmental Advisory Service,
Pilkington Brothers Limited
Prescot Road
St Helens, Merseyside WA10 3TT
UK
Telephone 0744 28882

Availability

Language
Fortran IV, Basic

Computer
Honeywell Mk III

925

Program name
Illumination level

Abstract
This program is for the design of lighting installations in rooms The illumination levels of the direct and indirect (average and at points) are calculated
Extensions provide for dispersion of light, variable height of fittings

References

Source
Technies Rekencentrum Polybit bv
Postbus 305, Archipelstraat 96
Nijmegen
Netherlands
Telephone Nijmegen 228382

Availability
Bureau service, remote batch, purchase

Language
Fortran

Computer
CDC 6600

Program name
Ac network reduction

Abstract
This program describes a system of reduced size but electrically equivalent to a larger system, information on which has been input

References
Program made available by ICL

Source
Computel Limited
Eastern Road
Bracknell, Berkshire
UK
Telephone Bracknell 23031

Availability

Language

Computer

927

Program name
GEO 17

Abstract
A program for the generation of resistivity curves

References
GEOCOMP

Source
Computel Limited
Eastern Road
Bracknell, Berkshire
UK
Telephone Bracknell 23031

Availability

Language

Computer

928

Program name
Ac low-load 1 and 2

Abstract
This program computes line and transformer currents, busbar voltages and power outputs of generators. Information on the generation and configuration of the network is required from the user

References
Program made available by ICL

Source
Computel Limited
Eastern Road
Bracknell, Berkshire
UK
Telephone Bracknell 23031

Availability

Language

Computer

929

Program name
Ac single line to ground short-circuits

Abstract
A program for the analysis of the effect of single line to ground short-circuits on an ac electrical power system

References
Program made available by ICL

Source
Computel Limited
Eastern Road
Bracknell, Berkshire
UK
Telephone Bracknell 23031

Availability

Language

Computer

930

Program name
Dc network analysis

Abstract
A program for the analysis of dc load-flow and short-circuit on electrical power systems for batch processing in conversational mode of operation

References
Program made available by ICL

Source
Computel Limited
Eastern Road
Bracknell, Berkshire
UK
Telephone Bracknell 23031

Availability

Language

Computer

931

Program name
Three-phase ac short-circuits

Abstract
A program for the analysis of the performance of an ac power system on the occurrence of three-phase short-circuits

References
Program made available by ICL

Source
Computel Limited
Eastern Road
Bracknell, Berkshire
UK
Telephone Bracknell 23031

Availability

Language

Computer

932

Program name
Transient stability

Abstract
A program for the analysis of the effect of a succession of disturbances to a power system on the stability of the rotating machine attached to it

References
Program made available by ICL

Source
Computel Limited
Eastern Road
Bracknell, Berkshire
UK
Telephone Bracknell 23031

Availability

Language

Computer

933

Program name
ARRAY

Abstract
This program calculates antenna patterns for linear arrays of radiating elements

References
Mark III software library
User manual 5204·03

Source
Honeywell Information Systems Limited
114 to 118 Southampton Row
London WC1B 5AB
UK
Telephone 01–242 5725

Availability
Bureau service

Language
Basic

Computer
Honeywell 6000 series

934

Program name
ACNETS

Abstract
This program analyses the frequency response of a linear electrical network by providing a frequency sweep and a voltage-sensitivity analysis. It has the facility for substituting the characteristics of new components while running

References
Mark III software library
User manual 5204·11

Source
Honeywell Information Systems Limited
114 to 118 Southampton Row
London WC1B 5AB
UK
Telephone 01–242 5725

Availability
Bureau service

Language
Basic

Computer
Honeywell 6000 series

935

Program name
DCNETS

Abstract
This program analyses the response of a linear network to constant excitation. It provides information concerning voltages, currents, power dissipation, voltage sensitivity and a production-simulation analysis. It has the facility for substituting new component characteristics while running. A program is also available which automatically checks the input data file (DCCJKS)

References
Mark III software library
User manual 5204·11

Source
Honeywell Information Systems Limited
114 to 118 Southampton Row
London WC1B 5AB
UK
Telephone 01–242 5725

Availability
Bureau service

Language
Basic

Computer
Honeywell 6000 series

Program name
LAACS

Abstract
This program aids linear analyses of central electrical systems. It provides a Bode plot, a stability analysis and a Laplace transform inversion

References
Mark III software library
User manual 5204·04

Source
Honeywell Information Systems Limited
114 to 118 Southampton Row
London WC1B 5AB
UK
Telephone 01–242 5725

Availability
Bureau service

Language
Basic

Computer
Honeywell 6000 series

937

Program name
CIFLOS

Abstract
This program performs load-flow studies of electrical power systems of up to 100 bus-bars and 400 lines. It uses an iterative method of analysis

References
Mark III software library
User manual 5204·08

Source
Honeywell Information Systems Limited
114 to 118 Southampton Row
London WC1B 5AB
UK
Telephone 01–242 5725

Availability
Bureau service

Language
Basic

Computer
Honeywell 6000 series

938

Program name
CIRCUS–2

Abstract
This background program is used for circuit analysis. It presents a two-level structure to aid modelling. A foreground program is also available giving a command-driven interface (CIRCAID)

References
Mark III software library
User manual 5204·11

Source
Honeywell Information Systems Limited
114 to 118 Southampton Row
London WC1B 5AB
UK
Telephone 01–242 5725

Availability
Bureau service

Language
Basic

Computer
Honeywell 6000 series

939

Program name
ECAPS

Abstract
This program performs complete ac/dc and transient analyses of electronic circuits. It allows new component values to be substituted and gives tolerances for the 'bread-board' evaluation of circuit performance

References
Mark III software library
User manual 5204·06

Source
Honeywell Information Systems Limited
114 to 118 Southampton Row
London WC1B 5AB
UK
Telephone 01–242 5725

Availability
Bureau service

Language
Basic

Computer
Honeywell 6000 series

940

Program name
FLT3PS

Abstract
This program studies short-circuit faults in three-phase electrical power systems of up to 100 bus-bars and 400 lines

References
Mark III software library
User manual 5204·30

Source
Honeywell Information Systems Limited
114 to 118 Southampton Row
London WC1B 5AB
UK
Telephone 01–242 5725

Availability
Bureau service

Language
Fortran

Computer
Honeywell 6000 series

941

Program name
NLNETS

Abstract
This program analyses non-linear dc circuits

References
Mark III software library
User manual 5204·01

Source
Honeywell Information Systems Limited
114 to 118 Southampton Row
London WC1B 5AB
UK
Telephone 01–242 5725

Availability
Bureau service

Language
Basic

Computer
Honeywell 6000 series

942

Program name
CP1

Abstract
This electrical program is concerned with accurate root locus, including the effects of pure time delay. It is used for producing diagrams

References
IEE program library

Source
Institution of Electrical Engineers
Savoy Place
London WC2
UK
Telephone 01–240 1871 Telex 261176

Availability

Language

Computer

943

Program name
CP21

Abstract
This program can be used for the general analysis of electrical control systems, using an operational array technique

References
IEE program library

Source
Institution of Electrical Engineers
Savoy Place
London WC2
UK
Telephone 01–240 1871 Telex 261176

Availability

Language

Computer

944

Program name
CP23

Abstract
A program which calculates the transient response of lumped linear systems from their frequency response

References
IEE program library

Source
Institution of Electrical Engineers
Savoy Place
London WC2
UK
Telephone 01–240 1871 Telex 261176

Availability

Language

Computer

945

Program name
CP29

Abstract
This program enables the dynamic simulation of electrical control systems to be made, using a symbolic-array technique

References
IEE program library

Source
Institution of Electrical Engineers
Savoy Place
London WC2
UK
Telephone 01–240 1871 Telex 261176

Availability

Language

Computer

Program name
CP4

Abstract
A program which enables an assessment of security in electrical distribution systems to be made

References
IEE program library

Source
Institution of Electrical Engineers
Savoy Place
London WC2
UK
Telephone 01–240 1871 Telex 261176

Availability

Language

Computer

947

Program name
LAMSAC Application code 32125121140A

Abstract
This program produces schedules for the maintenance of electrical batteries, for emergency lighting and the like. The slow peripheral unit used is a line printer. The program was first used in 1977

References
LAMSAC

Source
Architect's Department, Bradford City Council
City Hall
Bradford, West Yorkshire BD1 1HY
Telephone Bradford 29577

Availability

Language
Cobol

Computer
ICL 1904A; 10K core
3 magnetic tape units; 1 disc drive

948

Program name
Plant-load and power-factor correction

Abstract
This program provides a plant-loading schedule for each voltage level in the systems calculated by program SIZE; kVAr correction to any required power factor is also printed out on a unit basis

References
See also SIZE

Source
Electrical Research Assocation Ltd
Cleeve Road, Leatherhead
Surrey KT22 7SA
UK
Telephone Leatherhead 74151 Telex 264045

Availability
From owner

Language

Computer

949

Program name
SIZE

Abstract
This program selects and sizes electrical cables for a given voltage drop, thermal and short-circuit rating. Input includes load, route and environment. Output gives a cable schedule and route information on each section

References
Plant-load and power-factor correction

Source
Electrical Research Association Ltd
Cleeve Road, Leatherhead
Surrey KT22 5SA
UK
Telephone Leatherhead 74151 Telex 264045

Availability
From owner

Language

Computer

950

Program name
Line parameters

Abstract
This program calculates the electro-magnetic and electro-static constants for a given geometric pattern of lines. It can process up to ninety conductors in the set and includes facilities for eliminating bundled conductors and earth wires, and correcting earth-return effects. The results can be expressed as pi-equivalents (per mile, kilometre or nominated line length) for use in Load flow, Short circuit and Transient stability programs

References
Power systems analysis library

Source
Electrical Research Association Ltd
Cleeve Road, Leatherhead
Surrey KT22 7SA
UK
Telephone Leatherhead 74151 Telex 264045

Availability
Purchase, hire

Language
Fortran

Computer
Available for most machines

951

Program name
Cable routing and knitting

Abstract
This program is used primarily for routing cables, but can be used for other applications, such as piping, if required. Each route is noded. From this matrix of nodes, the program selects the shortest or preferred route and selects a position for the cable (or pipe) such that the number of crossovers is reduced. Output is a route schedule and a location list

References

Source
Electrical Research Association Ltd
Cleeve Road, Leatherhead
Surrey KT22 7SA
UK
Telephone Leatherhead 74151 Telex 264045

Availability
From owner

Language
Cobol

Computer

952

Program name
CAPICS

Abstracts
This suite of programs is designed to aid the design, installation and cost control of industrial cabling systems in large complexes such as steel mills, power stations and petrochemical installations. It is available in three parts; design, planning and cost control

References

Source
Electrical Research Association Ltd
Cleeve Road, Leatherhead
Surrey KT22 7SA
UK
Telephone Leatherhead 74151 Telex 264045

Availability
From owner

Language

Computer

953

Program name
Planning and progressing

Abstract
This program aids the installation of cable systems by progressing work done and to be done, and planning the disposition of equipment, cables and labour on site

References

Source
Electrical Research Association Ltd
Cleeve Road, Leatherhead
Surrey KT22 7SA
UK
Telephone Leatherhead 74151 Telex 264045

Availability
From owner

Language
Cobol

Computer

954

Program name
Short circuit

Abstract
This program allows the effects of both balanced and unbalanced faults to be studied. Network representation, over a full sequence, is used and the effect of motor infeeds to a fault can be included

References
Power systems analysis library

Source
Electrical Research Association Ltd
Cleeve Road, Leatherhead
Surrey KT22 7SA
UK
Telephone Leatherhead 74151 Telex 264045

Availability
Purchase, hire

Language
Fortran

Computer
Available for most machines

955

Program name
Load flow

Abstract
This Newton-Ralphson program has provisions for automatic transformer top-changing, applying reactive power and power limits to PV and PQ bars respectively, representing three-winding and quadrature-tap transformers and controlling area interchanges. Basic data and results are stored on file for later use (with data modifications) by this program or by Short circuit and Transient stability programs

References
Power systems analysis library

Source
Electrical Research Association Ltd
Cleeve Road, Leatherhead
Surrey KT22 7SA
UK
Telephone Leatherhead 74151 Telex 264045

Availability
Purchase, hire

Language
Fortran

Computer
Available for most machines

Program name
Power systems analysis library

Abstract
This library includes programs for determining load flow, investigating short circuits and transient stability, calculating line parameters and harmonics, and sub-routines for storing and retrieving sparse matrix elements in a common buffer array

References

Source
Electrical Research Association Ltd
Cleeve Road, Leatherhead
Surrey KT22 7SA
UK
Telephone Leatherhead 74151 Telex 264045

Availability
Purchase, hire

Language
Fortran

Computer
Available for most machines

957

Program name
Harmonics

Abstract
This program calculates the harmonic voltages at the busbars and the current flows in the branches of a power system when harmonic currents, generated by thyristor-controlled loads, are injected into the network at specified busbars. It will also calculate the equivalent harmonic impedance to ground as at any busbar

References
Power systems analysis library

Source
Electrical Research Association Ltd
Cleeve Road, Leatherhead
Surrey KT22 7SA
UK
Telephone Leatherhead 74151 Telex 264045

Availability
Purchase, hire

Language
Fortran

Computer
Available for most machines

958

Program name
Transient stability

Abstract
This program, by using network representation, over a full sequence, allows a complete study to be made of unbalanced voltages, currents and impedances, as a function of time, when balanced or unbalanced faults, developing faults and attempted or successful switch reclosures are applied to the system. Generator representation ranges from voltage-behind-transient reactance to a full salient sub-transient model

References
Power systems analysis library

Source
Electrical Research Association Ltd
Cleeve Road, Leatherhead
Surrey KT22 7SA
UK
Telephone Leatherhead 74151 Telex 264045

Availability
Purchase, hire

Language
Fortran

Computer
Available for most machines

959

Program name
ESP (Environmental System Performance)

Abstract
This package allows a rigorous appraisal at the 'building performance/ energy consumption/plant strategy of operation' interface. It provides information on the thermal, lighting and acoustic performance of any enclosure. Graphic output gives variation, over any specified time, of temperatures, energy loadings, natural lighting levels, shadow patterns, daylight factor contours and wall temperature variations

References
ABACUS Occasional Paper No 48

Source
ABACUS studies
University of Strathclyde
131 Rottenrow, Glasgow G4 ONG
UK
Telephone 041–522 4400 ext 3021

Availability
Purchase, hire, interactive bureau service

Language
Fortran IV

Computer
Univac 1108
Tektronix graphics terminal

960

Program name
SERNET

Abstract
This program appraises the interdepartmental service requirements of a whole hospital complex. Input comprises three files: scheme file, providing a description of the buildings' geometry; pipe file, giving various pipe sizes, costs and other characteristics; and network file, showing the co-ordinates of a pipe network throughout the building. The program may be run with the first two only

References
PHASE, ACTNET. ABACUS Occasional Paper No 36 (PHASE)

Source
ABACUS studies
University of Strathclyde
131 Rottenrow, Glasgow G4 ONG
UK
Telephone 041–552 4400 ext 3021

Availability
Purchase, hire, interactive bureau service

Language
Fortran IV

Computer
Univac 1108
Tektronix graphics terminal

961

Program name
MFOURTEEN

Abstract
This program calculates hot and cold water demand in buildings. Each outlet is weighted according to expected demand. The program also gives sizes for components of the supply piping and the hot water system

References

Source
Giffels Associates Incorporated
Marquette Building
243 W Congress
Detroit, Michigan 48226
USA
Telephone 313 961 2084

Availability
Purchase negotiable

Language
Fortran V

Computer
Univac 1108

Transport and communications

Lifts
Internal communications
External communications

962

Program name
LIFTS

Abstract
This program is used to demonstrate the operation of a lift system. Input data includes: number and height of storeys; number of occupants per floor; number, size and speed of lifts; and duration of demonstration. It produces total and average times for passenger waiting and journeys, lift-parking time and average passenger waiting time per floor

References

Source
ABACUS studies
University of Strathclyde
131 Rottenrow, Glasgow G4 ONG
UK
Telephone 041–552 4400 ext 3021

Availability
Purchase, hire, interactive bureau service

Language
Fortran

Computer
Univac 1108
Tektronix graphics terminal

963

Program name
HILIFT

Abstract
This program selects the lift speeds appropriate to the height of a building and calculates the number of lifts required for a building of more than five floors

References
PSA program library

Source
Directorate of Mechanical and Electrical Engineering Services
Property Services Agency
Lunar House, 40 Wellesley Road
Croydon CR9 2EL, UK
Telephone 01–686 3499

Availability

Language
Fortran

Computer
Honeywell MK III

964

Program name
LIFTS

Abstract
This program selects the best lift system by relating performance for peak loading conditions to installed cost

References

Source
Dewco Programming and Computer Services
20 Park Street
Bristol BS1 5JA
UK
Telephone 0272 23352

Availability
Bureau service, remote batch, purchase

Language
Fortran

Computer
Honeywell 6000

965

Program name
LISI

Abstract
This program will calculate, by simulation, the traffic-handling capability of a lift system. By feeding in fairly detailed data as specified by the client, a lift model is created which will accept and store calls from any floor, and cope with the selected conditions of use. Passenger arrivals and arrival and destination floors are randomly generated by the program from average rates supplied by the client

References

Source
Faber Computer Operations Limited
Upper Marlborough Road
St Albans
Herts UK
Telephone St Albans 61222

Availability
Bureau service

Language

Computer
IBM 1130, System 7

966

Program name
LIFT 2

Abstract
This program analyses proposed lift installations in commercial office buildings for the morning incoming peak. The program assumes that passengers enter at the ground floor and alight at the top floor, and that the lift returns empty to the ground floor. Input data consists of details of acceptable lift arrangements from the point of view of space and cost, and the upper and lower performance limits

References

Source
Ove Arup and Partners
13 Fitzroy Street
London W1
UK
Telephone 01–636 1531

Availability
Bureau service

Language
Fortran

Computer
DEC 10

967

Program name
LIFT 3 (T)

Abstract
This program produces performance details of lift installations under two-way traffic conditions. Six fixed lift capacities and seven fixed acceleration/speed combinations can be considered, and installations may have from one to ten lifts of the same type. The program requires details of the building, its population, and the range of acceptable types of lift and their performance

References

Source
Ove Arup and Partners
13 Fitzroy Street
London W1
UK
Telephone 01–636 1531

Availability
Bureau service

Language
Fortran

Computer
DEC 10

968

Program name
Elevators

Abstract
This program determines the most economical system of vertical transport in buildings. Lift installations are compared. That which requires minimum investment and costs in use, and gives maximum capacity is selected. Waiting periods are calculated with various control systems and traffic programs

References

Source
Technies Rekencentrum Polybit bv
Postbus 305, Archipelstraat 96
Nijmegen
Netherlands
Telephone Nijmegen 228382

Availability
Bureau service, remote batch, purchase

Language
Fortran

Computer
CDC 6600

969

Program name
ACTNET

Abstract
This program appraises the performance of a whole hospital complex. Input consists of a description of the geometry of the buildings and the circulation system, ie stairs, lifts and corridors. Graphic output displays the buildings' geometry with departmental entrances located. Tabular output gives the shortest route, in terms of time taken, for any set of critical journeys between pre-specified departments

References
PHASE, SERNET. ABACUS Occasional Paper No 35 (PHASE)

Source
ABACUS studies
University of Strathclyde
131 Rottenrow, Glasgow G4 ONG
UK
Telephone 041–552 4400 ext 3012

Availability
Purchase, hire, interactive bureau service

Language
Fortran IV

Computer
Univac 1108
Tektronix graphics terminal

970

Program name
LOCAL

Abstract
This program can be used to solve location/allocation problems. It can be used for such problems as locating a set of required service centres, so that demand points are served most effectively, eg by reducing travel distance or time to a minimum

References

Source
ABACUS studies
University of Strathclyde
131 Rottenrow, Glasgow G4 ONG
UK
Telephone 041–552 4400 ext 3021

Availability
Purchase, hire, interactive bureau service

Language
Fortran

Computer
Univac 1108
Tektronix graphics terminal

971

Program name
AIR-Q

Abstract
This program appraises a proposed design involving the movement of objects. It is time-based, and indicates areas where congestion and queues may arise. A description of the object system (which may be graphical) to be simulated is input as a network. The network includes average time for utilisation for each activity and the links between the activities represent the possible direction of movement through the network

References

Source
ABACUS studies
University of Strathclyde
131 Rottenrow, Glasgow G4 ONG
UK
Telephone 041–552 4400 ext 3021

Availability
Purchase, hire, interactive bureau service

Language
Fortran IV

Computer
Univac 1108
Tektronix graphics terminal

972

Program name
MIBS

Abstract
This program is for the simulation of movement in buildings. By altering the characteristics of channels of movement, it is possible to assess alternative designs or management strategies. The system was originally developed for use in the design of airports but can cope with many problems of pedestrian and traffic movement and mechanical handling

References

Source
ARC Limited
4 Jesus Lane
Cambridge CB5 8BA
UK
Telephone 0223 65015

Availability
Purchase

Language
Fortran

Computer
Prime 300

973

Program name
Pneumatic tube systems

Abstract
This program selects the best postal pneumatic-tube system by simulation. Various tube systems are compared and the installation which would service the internal mail at minimum cost is selected

References

Source
Technies Rekencentrum Polybit bv
Postbus 305, Archipelstraat 96
Nijmegen
Netherlands
Telephone Nijmegen 228382

Availability
Bureau service, remote batch, purchase

Language
Fortran

Computer
CDC 6600

974

Program name
Traffic assignment with capacity restraint

Abstract
A program for the assignment of an original-destination table of traffic-flow to individual sections of a road network. Allowance is made for restraint of capacity

References
Program made available by ICL

Source
Computel Limited
Eastern Road
Bracknell, Berkshire
UK
Telephone Bracknell 23031

Availability

Language

Computer

975

Program name
SIGSET

Abstract
A program for the setting of traffic signals

References

Source
Computel Limited
Eastern Road
Bracknell, Berkshire
UK
Telephone Bracknell 23031

Availability

Language

Computer

976

Program name
Furness traffic prediction

Abstract
This program estimates future traffic patterns from existing conditions, using the Furness method

References
Program made available by ICL

Source
Computel Limited
Eastern Road
Bracknell, Berkshire
UK
Telephone Bracknell 23031

Availability

Language

Computer

Program name
ENVPLAN

Abstract
A suite of linked programs in varying levels of sophistication, designed for transport modelling which is interactive with land-use planning. Sub-routines are available for analysis of rural, urban and city transport

References
Developed by Scott Wilson Kilpatrick and Partners

Source
Scicon Computer Services Limited
Brick Close, Kiln Farm
Milton Keynes MK11 3EJ
UK
Telephone 0908 565656 Telex 826171

Availability
Bureau service

Language

Computer
Univac 1108

Mathematics and statistics

978

Program name
BES093

Abstract
A set of three fast sub-routines for evaluating the Bessel functions J0, J1 and J2 of an arbitrary argument. These sub-routines, based on a polynomial and trigonometrical approximation, are accurate to the seventh place

References

Source
Centre de Recherches Routieres
Boulevard de la Woluwe 42
B–1200 Brussels
Belgium
Telephone 771 20 80

Availability
Contact owner

Language
Fortran

Computer
GE235

979

Program name
EXP093

Abstract
An iterative program for least-square fitting of a series of exponentials, with an optional linear term to an experimental increasing curve with downward curvature, or to a decay curve. Exponents are in a geometrical progression. The program operates by the collocation method

References

Source
Centre de Recherches Routieres
Boulevard de la Woluwe 42
B–1200 Brussels
Belgium
Telephone 771 20 80

Availability
Contact owner

Language
Basic

Computer
GE235

980

Program name
REG093

Abstract
A general least-square regression program for two variables. It handles unlimited series of data. Regression coefficients are calculated (with standard deviation) between two user-defined functions of the input data, correlation coefficients and confidence intervals. A row of ten choices of function can be handled for the same data in a single run

References

Source
Centre de Recherches Routieres
Boulevard de la Woluwe 42
B–1200 Brussels
Belgium
Telephone 771 20 80

Availability
Contact owner

Language
Basic

Computer
GE235

981

Program name
STEIN

Abstract
A program for the general solution of Steinbrenner elasticity equations for a rigid layer, at depth, overlaid by a material with increasing or constant modulus with depth

References
GEOCOMP

Source
Computel Limited
Eastern Road
Bracknell, Berkshire
UK
Telephone Bracknell 23031

Availability

Language

Computer

982

Program name
POLY

Abstract
This program will create a polynomial curve fitted to a set of points by the method of least square. Given the total number of points, their co-ordinates and the degree of polynomial to be fitted, a statement of the accuracy of the curve fit is generated, together with the coefficients and the arithmetic mean of the y values. A 'conversational' version of the program is available to enable the study of successively higher degrees of fit

References

Source
Faber Computer Operations Limited
Upper Marlborough Road
St Albans
Herts UK
Telephone St Albans 61222

Availability
Bureau service

Language

Computer
IBM 1130, System 7

Program name
SOLN 2

Abstract
This program calculates the solution to a set of simultaneous equations. The method of solving the equation is by elimination, using the largest pivotal divisor. Both the input data and the solution values are printed, together with the original matrix and the original vector of constants

References

Source
Ove Arup and Partners
13 Fitzroy Street
London W1
UK
Telephone 01–636 1531

Availability
Bureau service

Language
Fortran

Computer
DEC 10

984

Program name
GENSTATS

Abstract
This is an interactive program for general statistical analysis. It can calculate basic statistics, such as mean and standard deviations, compute correlations, regressions and T-tests, and perform data transformations, all under the user's control. It also has a general file– handling section

References

Source
Atkins Computing Services Limited
Woodcote Grove, Ashley Road
Epsom, Surrey
UK
Telephone Epsom 40421

Availability
Bureau service, time-sharing. Available in Netherlands

Language
Fortran

Computer
Honeywell Sigma 9

985

Program name
Survey analysis

Abstract
A general-purpose program for processing sample surveys of statistics. Typical applications are market research and traffic surveys

References
Program made available by ICL

Source
Computel Limited
Eastern Road
Bracknell, Berkshire
UK
Telephone Bracknell 23031

Availability

Language

Computer

986

Program name
SERIES

Abstract
A series of statistical programs

References
GEOCOMP

Source
Computel Limited
Eastern Road
Bracknell, Berkshire
UK
Telephone Bracknell 23031

Availability

Language

Computer

987

Program name
TABX and XT suite

Abstract
This suite of programs is used for cross tabulating and analysing statistically data and stock files. Data can also be derived from origin/destination and similar fact-gathering surveys. Data fields may be combined, named, weighted and operated on in various other ways. Tabulations may be filtered, and percentages and averages arrived at on various bases. Twelve column headings and 100 row headings are permitted in any table

References

Source
Document Reading Services Limited
16 Burners Lane, Kiln Farm
Milton Keynes MK11 3AK
UK
Telephone Milton Keynes 567114 Telex 825185

Availability
Bureau service

Language
Fortran

Computer
PDP 15–30

988

Program name
DEVI

Abstract
This program calculates the standard deviation and arithmetic mean of a set of results. It is designed specifically to meet the requirements of 'Statistical Calculation and Quality Control' laid down in BS CP116:1965 (Appendix B) for the assessing of concrete cube strength tests, and calculates standard deviation according to the formula specified in that document

References

Source
Faber Computer Operations Limited
Upper Marlborough Road
St Albans
Herts UK
Telephone St Albans 61222

Availability
Bureau service

Language

Computer
IBM 1130, System 7

989

Program name
QUANAL

Abstract
A program for analysing data obtained from questionnaire and similar surveys. Boolean and numerical data is summed and output in the form of simple totals and totals for any specified combination of answers. The data can be interrogated interactively and printed out in the form of totals, percentages, histograms or graphs. Comments made by respondents can be coded and sorted into significant groups using SORT

References
Surveys on employment of architects and advertising by architects published in The Architects' Journal

Source
Hutton + Rostron
Netley House
Gomshall, Nr Guildford
Surrey. Telephone Shere 3221

Availability
Bureau or sale

Language
PAL

990

Program name
Linear regression scatter

Abstract
A program for producing a complete scatter diagram with regression line and 98 per cent lower confidence line (straight)

References

Source
TRADA
Chiltern House, Hughenden Valley
High Wycombe, Buckinghamshire
UK
Telephone Naphill 3091

Availability

Language

Computer

991

Program name
BUCKS

Abstract
This program scans data for anomalies outside user-defined parameters

References

Source
University of Arizona
College of Architecture
Tempe
Arizona
USA

Availability

Language

Computer
DEC 10

992

Program name
DYSIM

Abstract
This program dynamically simulates systems which can be modelled as functional interconnections. It provides function generators, models of transfer functions, discontinuities of non-linear blocks, methods for handling algebraic loops, and Wye, vacuous and arbitrary blocks

References
Mark III software library
User manual 5204·05

Source
Honeywell Information Systems Limited
114 to 118 Southampton Row
London WC1B 5AB
UK
Telephone 01–242 5725

Availability
Bureau service

Language
Basic

Computer
Honeywell 6000 series

993

Program name
XEBEPF

Abstract
This program performs a finite-element analysis of plane or axisymmetric potential flow, such as heat flow or seepage of water through soil. Results are presented graphically

References

Source
Markworth Design Consultants Limited
Coppers, Pyrford Heath
Surrey GU22 8SR
UK
Telephone Byfleet 41088, 41013

Availability
Bureau service

Language
Fortran

Computer
ICL 1904A

Program descriptions

Heat Gains

Identification

This is a suite of three programs which calculates heat gains through envelope elements of buildings

Purpose

The three programs are as follows

1 HG2 calculates heat gains through external glazing in shade

2 HG3 calculates heat gains through flat roofs

3 HG4 calculates heat gains through external walls

An additional program (HG5) calculates sol-air temperatures throughout a design day, and can be used as part of the data base for program HG4. A bridging program (HG6) prepares the data from HG5 for use with HG4

Language

Basic

Equipment required

No equipment is required by the user. Building Service Designs offer a complete consultancy service. The programs are written for Honeywell Sigma 7 or Sigma 9 computers

Data base

All data is prepared for input by Building Service Designs. Data required for each of the programs is as follows

HG 2 External design air temperature (°F)
Radiation incident on glazing
(The above should be provided for each hour of the design day)
Shading coefficient (dimensionless)
Thermal transmittance (U value, $Btu/hr/ft^2/degF$)
Internal design air temperature (°F)
Window area (ft^2)

The program is based on the following relationship to give the heat gain through glass (H)

$$H = A[D \times S + U(T1 - T2)]$$

Where A is window area, D is diffuse radiation incident on the glazing, S is the shading coefficient, U is the thermal transmittance, T1 and T2 are external and internal design air temperatures

More information on this equation can be found in the ASHRAE guide

HG 3 Sol-air temperatures (°F) at each of twenty-four hours
Internal design air temperatures (°F)
Decrement factor
Time-lag (hr)
Thermal transmittance (U value, $Btu/hr/ft^2/degF$)

The program is based on the equation to give the total equivalent temperature differential (TETD)

$$TETD = T1 - T2 + L(T3 - T1)$$

Where T1 is the daily mean outdoor sol-air temperature, T2 is the internal design air temperature, T3 is the outdoor sol-air temperature, D hours before the time at which TETD is being calculated. L is the decrement factor

The heat gain through the roof is given by

$$\text{Heat gain (per } ft^2) = U \times TETD$$

HG 4 Sol-air temperatures for a building, covering a wall in shade and each elevation
(The above should be provided for each hour of the design day)
Internal design air temperature (°F)
Decrement factor
Time-lag (hr)
Thermal transmittance of wall structure (U value, $Btu/hr/ft^2/degF$)

The program relies on the following equation to give the total equivalent temperature differential (TETD)

$$TETD + T1 - T2 + L(T3 - T1)$$

Where T1 is the daily mean outdoor sol-air temperature, T2 is the internal design air temperature, T3 is the outdoor sol-air temperature, D hours before the time at which TETD is being calculated. L is the decrement factor

The heat gain through the roof is given by

$$\text{Heat gain (per } ft^2) = U \times TETD$$

Output

Output from the program is as follows

HG 2 Heat gains (Btu/h) per square foot of glazing or per window will be printed out for each of the twenty-four hours of the design day. If the heat gain per square foot of window is required, the window area should be given as 1 in data input

HG 3 Heat gains (Btu/h) through the roof will be printed-out for each of the twenty-four hours of the design day

HG 4 Heat gains (Btu/h) through walls in shade, for each of the elevations for which sol-air temperature data was supplied, will be printed out for each of the twenty-four hours of the design day

Technical support

Building Service Designs undertake to prepare the input data, run the programs and supply copies of the print-out for clients. This also applies to their other programs (see abstracts 655, 729, 730 and 731) which deal with air-conditioning design, design air temperatures and sizing of water pipes for given flow rates

Cost

Approximately £10 per run. For program BS1 (see abstract 731) the cost would be approximately £50 for a building with 100 rooms, provided that the client completes the data sheets for input

Availability

Further information is available from:

Building Service Designs, 322 Carshalton Road, Carshalton, Surrey SM5 3QB (Telephone 01–661 1416)

Identification

OXSYS is a general-purpose, computer-aided system, for the design of buildings constructed from co-ordinated components laid out on an orthogonal grid. The program was originally developed for use with the Oxford Method of construction, although the generally applicable sections of the program have been isolated from that related solely to Oxford Method. The division of the system is as follows:

1 Basic Operating System

This contains general routines essential to the system. They allow large quantities of data to be handled effectively, give a high level of interaction, provide for the creation and manipulation of graphic displays and facilitate the development of major integrated systems. This section does not necessarily deal with building problems

2 Building Design System

This is the major part of the whole program. While it is specifically for building design tasks, it is not dependent on Oxford Method

3 Detail Design System

This section of the program is solely for location and selection of components and the creation of detailed designs, using Oxford Method. An analogous sector can be created to deal with other methods of building

Purpose

The use of OXSYS, particularly when combined with a co-ordinated method of building, allows the concentration of resources on planning at the outline design stage. The system provides, automatically, the documentation for the communication of design decisions, carries out routine detail design tasks and allows a range of alternative plans to be examined

Information from a design team is used to create a fully-detailed three-dimensional mathematical model of a building. This model can be evaluated in various ways, and comparisons between alternative designs can be made in terms of both cost and performance. The model is used to generate interim documentation on the progress of the design. When the model is in its final form, it is used to produce automatically any drawings and schedules required for tendering and, eventually, for construction

Language

Fortran

Equipment required

Prime 300 computer (96k), Tektronix storage tube, digitising tablet, teletype or other keyboard. Versions for other equipment are also available

Data base

A design brief is used as a starting point. This can be quite basic, for example, a breakdown of the building into zones with a simple description of size, and the services and environment required in each zone. The Sketch Manipulation System allows development of the form of the building, the allocation of spaces within it and the breakdown of these into smaller units if necessary. The Zone Data System allows refinement of the specification of the functional zones. Equipment lists and data concerning each room are assembled. These processes may be carried out simultaneously or one after the other. The model of the building defined by these two processes is continuously evaluated. Usually, a range of solutions to design problems is developed in parallel, the best to be taken over into the second stage of operation

In the second stage, room layouts and zone data remain relatively static, though changes are still possible. Components from which the building is to be constructed are selected and incorporated in the design. A component may be a prefabricated unit, or a standard detail, constructed in-situ. The components to be used are selected from a pre-defined data base (Codex). This contains data concerning all components to be used, with dimensions, physical characteristics and a graphic representation

Output description

Since the system is interactive, the current design can be inspected and modified at all stages of the design process. At the end of this process, a complete model of the building is created. This can be automatically converted into perspectives, working drawings, schedules and quantities

The model of the building can also be subjected to various evaluation procedures, such as cost estimation or heat balance, without the creation of a separate data base. This can be particularly effective early in the design process when many options are still open

Semi-automatic design and detailing systems are tailored to a particular method of construction. They provide a fast and efficient method of developing a design. These techniques can be applied where the procedure for design is rationalised. Structural and mechanical engineering are in this category, because of their reliance on established techniques of calculation, and so is the design of buildings using a building system, that is, using pre-defined components with rules for their combination. The designer's freedom of choice is not limited, but the consequences of all decisions can be checked and developed at each stage

Technical support

Detailed manual for users. System documentation. Training

Cost

Dependent on scope of system required

Availability

Further information is available from:

E M Hoskins
Applied Research of Cambridge Limited
4 Jesus Lane
Cambridge CB5 8BA

Telephone 0223 65015
Telex 81153 ARCAMS

Building Fire Safety Model

Identification

The Building Fire Safety Model is a mathematical simulation of the development of fires, with emphasis on factors affecting the safety of the occupants of a building. In order to evaluate the safety of a structure, the interactions of all building components are considered, rather than the reaction of each component in a specific situation

Purpose

The program provides an estimate of hazards resulting from spread of fire. Spatial and temporal factors are considered, together with the consequent implications for safety. For example, the relative importance of locations becoming impassable is explored. These factors may be considered for alternative designs

Language

Fortran IV

Equipment required

IBM 370/125

Data base

Fire development is described in terms of a number of transitional states or 'realms'. Each of these is defined by one or more of the following factors: rate of heat release, air temperature near the ceiling of the room and height of flame. Extension of the fire is considered at least as important as the fire development within the room in which it originates

Statistical distribution is used to model the likelihood of the transition of the fire from one state to another. The nature of this transition is considered to be indicated by the length of time in which the fire has undergone no development. Changes in statistical distribution are made to take account of design, finishes and furnishings

Once a particular realm is reached, the means of reaching that realm are no longer considered. Furthermore, fire development does not necessarily involve sequential progression to higher realms, since transitions from one state to another can be regressive, or the transition can be so fast, for example, in case of explosion, that it is impossible to isolate this transition

Simulation of the products of combustion is by linear rate equations. The intensity of combustion will vary also with location and with pressure diffential. As a result, three hazard levels are used to describe the products of combustion. Specific amounts of these at each hazard level will vary with the dimensions of the room considered and ventilation, as well as the types of material burning

The required input data is prepared from full-scale tests and smoke propagation models

The determination of the number of escape routes is approached as a problem on a network, which describes how rooms are connected and possible exits

Output description

Output is in the form of graphs, which express the likelihood of escape routes from particular locations remaining open in the event of fire. The expected characteristics of the development of fire is also output in the form of graphs

Availability

Further information is available from:
National Fire Protection Association
Boston
Massachusetts
USA

Identification

POSTAL is a program for sorting and printing names and addresses for labels and envelopes

Purpose

The program enables an organisation to maintain an up-to-date list of names and addresses for circulating magazines and catalogues, specialised direct mailing, public relations exercises, market research and routine correspondence. It has considerable advantages over the traditional methods of card index or stencil plates. The former involves laborious retyping and both methods are limited by their manual or mechanical methods of sorting. There is a limit to the size of list they can conveniently manage and the number of sub-lists possible, and revision is tedious and fallible. The use of the computer for preparation, filing, sorting, printing-out and revision of a mailing list has considerable advantages and it is possible to link the name and address file with other data-processing activities

Language

PAL8

Equipment required

The program is available as a complete service and no equipment is required by the user. Processing is carried out on a PDP 8/E computer

Data base

The names and addresses are taken from existing mailing lists and directories and coded by hand with a serial number for identification and a multi-character code, classifying the company eg by region, type of organisation, sphere of activities, source of information, date of entry and so on. The coded list is key-punched on paper tape in Selectric, ISO or other suitable code. In the office of Hutton + Rostron the data is prepared using a visual display unit connected to a small computer which monitors the coding, line-lengths and common errors: any type of paper-tape punch can be used, however. The program can handle input and output in capitals or lower-case letters. The paper tapes are used to create magnetic-tape files

A maximum of 26 test fields may be used in any entry, for example:

Name of recipient
Appointment held by recipient
Name of company or organisation
Address
Post Office area code for address

In addition, up to 1259 boolean codes may be used to identify specific characteristics of the entry and these may be combined with the logical operators AND, OR and NOT for selection of entries

For revision, five types of amendment can be made to the data held on the master file:

1 Addition of new entries
2 Change of code
3 Change of text
4 Deletion
5 Insertion

These revisions can be made to any errors detected by the program when the file is created and to maintain it in use. At intervals, all names and addresses of a particular type and year are checked

Output description

The whole file can be output or selected names and addresses retrieved by specifying serial number or appropriate combinations of code characters. Each character can be used to search for or eliminate a characteristic eg architects only, non-architects only, architects and engineers only. The serial number must be used for retrieving a specific address or for making revisions

Output can be in four forms:

1 Customer print: a dated, compact print-out on fan-fold paper for checking by the customer
2 Labels: the addresses printed by the computer on self-adhesive labels ready for mailing
3 Paper tape: a tape in Selectric or ISO 8 channel code to operate an automatic typewriter for addressing individual envelopes
4 Magnetic tape: sub-files of the master file created and re-numbered for special purposes eg market surveys

3 and 4 can be re-formed and/or codes added by program for transfer to other computer operations eg typesetting, invoicing, personal correspondence or alphabetical sorting

Technical support

Hutton + Rostron offer a comprehensive service to users. The full list of names and addresses can be supplied by the client; or he can supply a basic list to be augmented by Hutton + Rostron; or Hutton + Rostron will undertake the complete compilation of the list

Cost

Offered as a service, the cost depends on quantity of information and output required

Availability

Further information is available from:

Hutton + Rostron, Netley House, Gomshall, Surrey GU5 9QA (Telephone Shere 3221, Telex 859167)

```
*
O       00315
F       Maxlove Continuous Limited
A       60 Neasden Lane
T       London NW10
P       01-450 4545
NX      X
RS      X
SU      X

*
O       00316
N       John"McConnell
F       Pentagram Design Partnership Limited
A       61 North Wharf Road
T       London
K       W2 1LA
P       01-402 5511
CL      X
GH      X

*
O       00317
N       Mr"McKerrow
A       38 Station Road
T       Thames Ditton, Surrey
P       Home: 01-398 3426 Office: 01-540 4405
GH      X
NX      X
PE      X
```

1 Input data. Typed on an automatic typewriter from lists provided by client: both punched tape and hard copy are produced by this machine

```
DATE  03/03/79  * * *  C U S T O M E R    P R I N T  * * *        PAGE  0145


00315        Maxlove Continuous Limited
             60 Neasden Lane
             London NW10
             Tel: 01-450 4545                                     NX     RS     SU
00316        John McConnell
             Pentagram Design Partnership Limited
             61 North Wharf Road
             London W2 1LA
             Tel: 01-402 5511                                     CL     GH
00317        Mr McKerrow
             38 Station Road
             Thames Ditton, Surrey
             Tel: Home: 01-398 3426 Office: 01-540 4405           GH     NX     PE
00318        R H McKie
             Managing Director
             RIBA Publications Limited
             Finsbury Mission
             Moreland Street
             London EC1V 8VB
             Tel: 01-251 0791                                     CL     GH     MR
```

2 Customer print. Lineprinter output of main address file: used by client to check that information stored on file is correct

Maxlove Continuous Limited
60 Neasden Lane
London NW10

John McConnell
Pentagram Design Partnership
Limited
61 North Wharf Road
London W2 1LA

R H McKie
Managing Director
RIBA Publications Limited
Finsbury Mission
Moreland Street
London EC1V 8VB

Ian McLaren
PA Design Unit
3 Avon Estate
Avonmore Road
London W14

Microfilm Association of GB
109 Kingsway
London WC2

K Miles and Associates (Pty)
Ltd
First Floor, Randpark Centre
Blackheath
Johannesburg, Transvaal PO Box
35255
South Africa

Modern Electrics
12a St James's Road
Surbiton, Surrey

Professor David Moizer
Carlton University
Ottawa
Canada

National Computer Service
Quay House
Manchester

National Research Development
Corporation
Kingsgate House
66 Victoria Street
London SW1E 6SL

3 Labels. Self-adhesive labels for mailing

Identification

TEXTEDIT is a suite of programs for storing technical information for output in various forms eg printed publications, microfilm, photo-copy data-sheets. It includes facilities for updating

Purpose

The programs are designed to convert text punched on to paper tape into a magnetic-tape file, where it can be progressively sorted and output as required. Updating can be effected by substituting new sections of text for existing ones, either in whole paragraphs or in individual words or phrases. It is also possible to replace a specified character string with a revision wherever it occurs throughout the text

The magnetic-tape file is a data bank from which the information can be output, in whole or part, for printing or photocopying. The object is to give a company an up-to-date central library of information on which to draw when preparing technical manuals, sales literature, data sheets on call for customers' guidance and kits for representatives to use in presenting the firm's activities. It saves time, gives a greater degree of accuracy and prevents duplication of effort by different departments

Language

PAL8

Equipment required

The programs are available as a complete service and no equipment is required by the user. Processing is carried out on a PDP8e which includes console typewriter, lineprinter, magnetic tape handler, tape reader and tape punch

Data base

The input is in the form of texts key-punched in any code on 8–channel paper tape. The texts are usually prepared in the style and form of the main comprehensive technical publication the company produces. The five programs are as follows:

1. Initial file: this is required once only, to give the file an identification code
2. Input and decode: this reads the data, assembles it in records and stores it on the input file
3. Create and edit file: this creates the file and keeps it up-to-date by means of a series of commands ie 'add', 'insert', 'delete', 'replace text'; 'replace (character) string'; 'replace (character) string throughout text'
4. Re-number file: this would be used after a period of time when the number of amendments might make re-numbering of chapters and paragraphs desirable

Output description

Output is obtained in two forms, as paper tape in chosen code or as lineprinter output. It can be full text or first lines only, the latter being useful for checking in lineprinter form. Line lengths must be specified in mm. Programs are available for retrieving selected chapters or selected paragraphs in serial-number order, or for retrieving any chapters or paragraphs by subject matter, for example, to a 12–facet code based on the CIB Master lists for structuring documents relating to buildings, building elements, components, materials and services

Technical support

Hutton + Rostron offer a comprehensive technical editorial service to users. Data preparation is undertaken by Hutton + Rostron from technical literature, articles and notes supplied by the user

Cost

Offered as a service, the cost depends on the amount of information initially filed and the edits and output required

Availability

Further information is available from:

Hutton + Rostron, Netley House, Gomshall, Surrey GU5 9QA (Telephone Shere 3221, Telex 859167)

```
1190 ------------ &L Technical support

1200 ------------ &J Hutton + Rostron will operate the program on a
                     bureau basis to produce a series of related
                     outputs calculated from the options listed above.
                     Consultancy is also available for preparing input
                     and interpreting output
```

1 Lineprinter output. Text is held on magnetic file and can be output for checking and correction

Hutton + Rostron

text revision
edited A Dietrich sheet no 1
punched job no 62·3
date 2.3.79

==	cmd	ch	para	text	instructions
*					
==	STR.	C10	P1200	: above . . . . ments "above"	
==	END.				
(H)(H)					Feed

2 Text revision form. Corrections are marked on the lineprinter output and transferred to the revision form using standard instructions. This data is punched to prepare an edit tape

```
1190 ------------ &L Technical support

1200 ------------ &J Hutton + Rostron will operate the program on a
                     bureau basis to produce a series of related
                     outputs calculated from the options listed above.
                     Consultancy is also available for preparing input
                     and interpreting output
```

3 Lineprinter output. After editing, the file is output to check that alterations have been correctly made. Realignment is carried out automatically on text following a correction, in order to accommodate deletions or insertions

0422 **Technical support**
0423
0424 Hutton + Rostron will operate the program on a
0425 bureau basis to produce a series of related
0426 outputs calculated from the options listed above.
0427 Consultancy is also available for preparing input
0428 and interpreting output

4 Typeset copy. Tape output from the magnetic file is used to operate a photo-typesetting machine. Output from the typesetting machine can take the form of film or paper galleys with each line of type numbered to facilitate proof-reading and layout work

Professional accounting, invoicing and book-keeping system

Identification
ACCSYS is an accounting, invoicing and book-keeping system for professional offices

Purpose
The programs convert unsorted data taken from staff time sheets into statements of charges and expenses for all jobs in progress. Individual job statements, summaries and related management information are produced. For jobs which are charged on the basis of hourly rates, with or without retainers, the job statements may be sent to the client with the invoice, providing him with a detailed record of all work done and sums expended on his behalf. For jobs charged on a lump-sum or scale-fee basis, the job summaries, when compared with the fees due, enable the profitability of jobs to be assessed and provide data for future job pricing. The related management information can be used to assess the efficiency of the office as a whole and of individual staff categories. Because this information is regularly produced, it can pinpoint trends in office turnover and profitability. Ancillary programs provide periodical summaries if required; printed invoices; and ledgers analysed under any choice of cost heads, using punched tape generated in the process of typing cheques and credit transfers. The user does not require any special skill to employ the program. A maximum of 11 months' input and output data is stored on magnetic tape

Language
Digital PAL8

Equipment required
The programs are available as a complete service and no equipment is required by the user. Processing is carried out on a PDP 8e computer, which includes console typewriter, lineprinter, one magnetic tape handler, two disc drives, tape reader and tape punch

Data base
Input is in two parts: basic data on the range of jobs handled by the office, and current data extracted from completed time sheets. On the basic data is listed, for every job, the hourly rates for each grade of staff (up to seven grades can be accommodated). Jobs are given a 'chargeable', or 'non-chargeable' category for summation purposes, enabling every office task including, for example, filing and coffee-making, to be costed. Also included are the name of the firm using the service, expense categories, the percentage to be added or subtracted from expenses before output and the charge per mile for car journeys. All this information is held on the customer's individual magnetic tape, and the information is read into the computer at the start of a program run. Current data are recorded on staff time sheets. The information consists of a number for identifying the time sheet, the appropriate staff grade, short descriptions of tasks carried out (not for input), dates when work was done, job numbers, time spent and, where applicable, distance travelled by car and expenditure on fares and sundries. A modified time sheet is used for equipment such as printing machines and paper-tape punches

Output description
Output is in three parts:

1 Job statements and account summaries for every job included on the time sheets. Data lines are arranged in order of date and time-sheet number; the time spent and rate are recorded and the charge computed. All expenses, adjusted by predetermined percentages, are recorded and a running balance kept. Totals analyse the time, rate and charge for each grade of staff. Expense categories are totalled and any retainers added. Chargeable jobs are identified by an asterisk after the job number. Account summaries list unpaid previous accounts, the total outstanding amount, the total amount invoiced to date and the proportion of budget expended

2 A summary of job statements, which includes a short analysis for each job, together with the proportion of total fees it represents

3 Consolidated fee statements are provided for chargeable jobs only, non-chargeable jobs only and all jobs. A comparison of chargeable fees (income) and unchargeable fees (overheads) enables an estimate to be made of the efficiency not only of the office as a whole but also of each grade of staff

The output data are self-explanatory

Technical support
Hutton + Rostron Data Processing Limited offer a comprehensive service for users. Data preparation is undertaken by Hutton + Rostron from time sheets completed by the user

Cost
The cost of the service is 85p per job statement output. This comprises supplying time sheets, use of program, computer time and supply of output as single or four-part lineprinter paper or punched paper tape. Data punching is undertaken by Hutton + Rostron at agreed rates, depending on the likely volume of work and turn-round required. The number of jobs processed and the charge is printed on the output after the consolidated fee statements. As typical examples of cost, the charge to an office with 12 staff for processing 30 jobs is about £56 and to an office of 22 staff for processing 130 jobs about £185 per run. The time required from receipt of time sheets to despatch of output is 4 to 5 days

Availability
Further information is available from: Hutton + Rostron Data Processing Limited, Netley House, Gomshall, Surrey GU5 9QA (Telephone Shere 3221, Telex 859167)

References
Building program description 3: Professional accounting, invoicing and cost control system. *Building*, 17 October 1969

Hutton + Rostron time and expenses

			—1
month	Feb 1979	folio	928
name	John Barker	rate	3

description	date	job no	hours	—2 miles	—3 fares	—5 sundry
Layouts, proofreading and edits	1	51.50	7			
2 proofs (reading + editing)	2	51.30	6.5			
Layouts	2	51.50	1			
Meeting with VAG re proofs	3	17.62	1			
Layouts	3	17.62	5			
Phone calls to EB + JS re proofs	3	0.9	0.5			
Edits and visit to PWB	6	51.30	5	34		15.35
Coding and checking	6	17.62	2			
2 proofs (reading and editing)	6	17.62	2.5			

1 Time sheet. Numerical information from the sheet is used to prepare a paper tape on a visual display unit. The tape is used as input for the computer and the format of the data is checked during input

HUTTON + ROSTRON
JOB SUMMARY FOR MARCH 1979 PAGE 1

JOB	TIME CHARGE	EXPENSES	RETAINER	JOB TOTAL	% OF FEES	VAT	GROSS FEES
0.20	198.24	30.50	0	228.74	2	0	228.74
0.30	66.08	0	0	66.08	1	0	66.08
0.31	33.04	0	0	33.04	0	0	33.04
0.40	429.52	1.50	0	431.02	4	0	431.02
0.50	363.44	0	0	363.44	3	0	363.44
0.60	66.08	0	0	66.08	1	0	66.08
0.61	231.28	0	0	231.28	2	0	231.28
0.70	99.12	1.70	0	100.82	1	0	100.82
0.71	660.80	0	0	660.80	6	0	660.80
0.90	297.36	60.30	0	357.66	3	0	357.66
1.00	396.48	0	0	396.48	3	0	396.48
17.62*	418.83	113.76	0	532.59	5*	42.60	575.19
18.20*	256.92	11.50	0	268.42	2*	21.47	289.89
18.30*	429.52	4.90	0	434.42	4*	34.75	469.17
18.40*	165.20	8.80	0	174.00	2*	13.92	187.92
29.70*	198.24	32.40	203.90	434.54	4*	34.76	469.30
30.60*	495.60	0	0	495.60	4*	39.64	535.24
92.11*	5079.02	738.24	456.78	6274.04	54*	501.92	6775.96

a

HUTTON + ROSTRON
CONSOLIDATED FEE STATEMENT FOR MARCH 1979 (ALL FEES)

CATEGORY	HOURS	AMOUNT	% OF TOTAL FEES
PARTNER	240.5	4071.34	35
ASSISTANT RATE A	218.5	2518.59	22
ASSISTANT RATE B	245	1759.36	15
ASSISTANT RATE C	194.5	1002.30	9
ASSISTANT RATE D	176	533.18	5
TOTAL TIME CHARGE	1074.5	9884.77	86
EXPENSES		1003.60	9
RETAINERS/LUMP SUMS		660.68	6
TOTAL FEES		11549.05	100
VAT		689.06	
GROSS FEES		12238.11	

	CHARGEABLE	UNCH'ABLE	TOTAL	VAT	GROSS
TOTAL BROUGHT FORWARD	2792.51	0.00	2792.51	223.37	3015.88
TOTAL CURRENT MONTH	8613.61	2935.44	11549.05	689.06	12238.11
TOTAL OUTSTANDING	11406.12	2935.44	14341.56	912.43	15253.99

NUMBER OF STATEMENTS OUTPUT = 19
NUMBER OF JOBS ON FILE = 19

PROCESSING CHARGE = £ 16.15 (£0.85 PER STATEMENT)
PLUS 8% VAT = £ 1.29
TOTAL CHARGE = £ 17.44

VAT INVOICE TO FOLLOW

b

HUTTON + ROSTRON ACCOUNT FOR THE MONTH OF MARCH 1979
JOB NUMBER 17.62*

DATE	FOLIO	HOURS	RATE	CHARGE	EXPENSES TRAVEL	PRINTS/DATA PREP	SUNDRY	BALANCE
1	916	0.5	22.00	11.00				11.00
3	916	1	22.00	22.00				33.00
6	916	1.5	22.00	33.00	39.36			105.36
7	916	2	22.00	44.00				149.36
7	941	2	3.74	7.48		2.00		158.84
8	916	2	22.00	44.00				202.84
8	941						1.95	204.79
8	941	1.5	3.74	5.61		1.50		211.90
22	927	0.5	9.60	4.80				216.70
23	927	1	9.60	9.60	8.32			234.62
24	927	6	9.60	57.60				292.22
30	918	6	22.00	132.00				424.22
31	918	2	22.00	44.00			59.63	527.85
31	943	1	3.74	3.74		1.00		532.59
TOTALS								
PARTNER		15	22.00	330.00				
ASSISTANT B		7.5	9.60	72.00				
ASSISTANT D		4.5	3.74	16.83				
				418.83	47.68	4.50	61.58	532.59
						VALUE ADDED TAX AT 8.00%		42.60
								575.19

c

HUTTON + ROSTRON
JOB NUMBER 17.62 ACCOUNT SUMMARY AT MARCH 1979

	RET/LUMP	CHARGE	TRAVEL	PRINTS/DATA PREP	SUNDRY	VAT	BALANCE
BROUGHT FORWARD							
DECEMBER 1978	0	43.20	0	0.15	0	3.46	46.81
JANUARY 1979	0	22.94	7.68	80.30	0	8.87	119.79
MARCH 1979	0	418.83	47.68	4.50	61.58	42.60	575.19
TOTAL OUTSTANDING	0	484.97	55.36	84.95	61.58	54.93	741.79
TOTAL RECEIVED TO DATE	357.82	307.29	59.77	480.00	1348.07	204.20	2757.15

BUDGET FIGURE: 5000.00 TOTAL COSTS TO DATE: 3239.81 PROPORTION EXPENDED: 64%

d

2 Examples of output
a Summary of time booked on all jobs in any one month
b Consolidated fee statement for one month
c Summary of time spent on individual job in one month
d Summary of time spent on individual job to date

Indexes

The following indexes are to the abstracts of programs on pages 40 to 257 and not to the book as a whole. The references are to the abstract numbers, not page numbers

Index to terms

661 analysis flexibility multiple-branch closed-loop
649 analysis flow grid piping systems
647 analysis flow pipework systems
518 analysis forces off-shore structure
509 analysis frame plated shell structures finite element
483 analysis frame shell linear static dynamic
431 analysis framed structures stiffness linear elastic
481 analysis frames grids non-prismatic members
490 analysis frames static dynamic
454 analysis frames trusses plane grids prismatic
492 analysis frameworks two– three-dimensional
864 analysis fuel consumption council property
460 analysis general frame
278 analysis grillage mesh bridge deck
568 analysis ground beam number of elements
343 analysis group pile cap moments axial shears forces
318 analysis group pile cap moments forces
341 analysis group piles rows verticial raked
342 analysis groups piles settlement moments axial loads
993 analysis heat flow water seepage finite-element
726 analysis heating cooling requirements building air
031 analysis housing investment local authority
436 analysis in-plane loadings finite elements triangular
060 analysis integrated systems energy disposal services
164 analysis invoicing VAT sales ledger
204 analysis job/staff time architect's department
493 analysis land-based offshore structures
652 analysis large-scale pipe networks valves pumps
482 analysis lateral forces indeterminate structures
056 analysis layout tables report writing research
050 analysis library engineering control
966 analysis lift installations office morning peak
426 analysis linear elastic structures shock loads
934 analysis linear electrical network frequency sweep
497 analysis linearly-elastic statically-loaded framed
317 analysis load-displacement freestanding pile groups
937 analysis load-flow electrical power systems
414 analysis loading plane grids grillage
246 analysis mapping system manipulation
533 analysis mechanical design dynamic testing
155 analysis method-building quotations
044 analysis modelling companies financial
776 analysis moist air properties cooling loads
305 analysis multi-span continuous beams elastic
287 analysis multi-span continuous beams load factors
302 analysis multiple-span continuous beams cantilevers
527 analysis natural frequencies models responses
528 analysis Newton-Ralphson stability effects
941 analysis non-linear dc circuits
507 analysis non-linear space frame
156 analysis of debtors credit control sales transaction
519 analysis off-shore structures forces pile foundations
516 analysis off-shore structures model design
520 analysis off-shore structures wave loads design
487 analysis orthogonal frame structures static loads
534 analysis performance mechanical machinery structural
412 analysis pin-jointed plane-frame
660 analysis pipe systems expansion wind loading joints
674 analysis pipework velocity head loss closed systems
446 analysis plane axisymmetric linear elastic
441 analysis plane axisymmetric linear static
434 analysis plane frame elastic supports loads
413 analysis plane frames axial shear forces bending
445 analysis plane frames displacements reactions
423 analysis plane frames grids rigidly-jointed
444 analysis plane frames loads linear elastic plastic
432 analysis plane frames non-linear
415 analysis plane frames stiffness method elastic
475 analysis plane frames trusses grids space frames
435 analysis plane grillages elastic loads grid
496 analysis plane space structures plate shell elements
410 analysis plane structural frames
427 analysis plane structures rod beam membrane
433 analysis plastic collapse linear plane-frame
015 analysis plot critical path data network
418 analysis portal frame elastic deflection
019 analysis precedence networks scheduling resources
615 analysis pressure distribution column bases
289 analysis prestressing forces continuous beam variable
267 analysis problems survey traverses
125 analysis property economic
428 analysis rectilinear plane frames Hardy-Cross
604 analysis reinforced concrete circular tank walls
617 analysis reinforced concrete columns design
489 analysis reinforced concrete design problems
640 analysis reinforced concrete sections linear elastic
132 analysis reports management information
935 analysis response linear network excitation
536 analysis rigid format solutions
476 analysis rigid space frames elastic supports
631 analysis ring frames coplanar loading gables arches
751 analysis room pressures air movement fire
932 analysis rotating machine transient stability
860 analysis running costs energy consumption building
160 analysis sales accounting records statements control
196 analysis schedules payroll summary financial control
352 analysis seepage piezometric head velocity
457 analysis shear bending moments deflections rotations
601 analysis shear stress walls elastic stiffness frame
605 analysis shear walls elastic stiffness method frame
321 analysis sheet-pile retaining wall single tie
817 analysis simulation air-conditioning dimensions
112 analysis sizes room layouts optimum dimensions
494 analysis skeletal finite-element structures
505 analysis skeletal plane frames
596 analysis slab reinforcement bridge decking
594 analysis slabs deflections forces moments shears
338 analysis slope stability Bishop Morgenstern and Price
469 analysis soil building linear elastic dynamic
361 analysis soil stability
883 analysis solar heating cooling
480 analysis space-frame linear
464 analysis space frames eigenvalue vibration
477 analysis space plane frame
549 analysis space trusses two-dimensional structures
344 analysis stability earth slopes Bishop circular arc
355 analysis stability earth slopes Bishop circular arc
315 analysis stability earth slopes safety circular-arc slip
984 analysis statistics regressions T-tests general
381 analysis storm sewer design
498 analysis straight elements frames continuous beams
451 analysis stress heat conduction
438 analysis stress plane frames grids
486 analysis stress tension space frames
531 analysis stress tension thin lapped constructions
618 analysis stresses reinforced concrete member
471 analysis structural frames multi-storey deformation
530 analysis structure houses loads
458 analysis structures digital models finite-element
425 analysis structures static dynamic loads finite element
985 analysis surveys statistics
285 analysis suspension bridges cable structures
175 analysis system cash book
878 analysis systems building solar energy
029 analysis tasks sequence
578 analysis thin-walled girders non-prismatic
472 analysis three-dimensional finite-element
450 analysis three-dimensional frames loading
678 analysis three-dimensional pipework stress
146 analysis timber records
023 analysis time resources construction project
003 analysis time resources costs
463 analysis trussed frame beams rods English elastic
474 analysis two– three-dimensional frame
506 analysis two– three-dimensional space frames linear
938 analysis two-level structure circuit
203 analysis work record architects
332 anchor plate calculation dimensions sheet piling
328 anchor plate calculation distance sheet piling
322 anchor retaining walls sheet-pile sub-system
340 anchor sheet-pile retaining walls design
347 anchor strength sheet piling calculation drive-depths
310 angled retaining walls strength
257 angular measurements traverse co-ordinates of stations
271 angular relationships arcs spirals parabolas
865 annual consumption energy calculation cost heating
852 annual cost energy building calculation
861 annual electricity consumption air-conditioning
853 annual heating cooling building calculation energy
991 anomalies data
933 antenna patterns linear arrays radiating elements
211 application English language design analysis
184 application financial control system purchases
099 appraisal buildings scheme/detail design models
100 appraisal models hospital design graphic
907 appraisal natural lighting levels building
098 appraisal performance schools buildings
108 appraisal road schemes discounting methods
978 arbitrary argument evaluation Bessel functions
470 arbitrary load static dynamic analysis constructions
631 arches analysis ring frames coplanar loading gables
203 architects analysis work record

083 architects calculation bills of quantities CLASP
071 architects calculation bills of quantity
072 architects calculation bills of quantity
074 architects calculation bills of quantity
075 architects calculation bills of quantity
189 architects calculation fee control
183 architects civil engineers job-costing staff time fees
202 architects commitments account
204 architects department analysis job/staff time
093 architects drawings bill of quantities abstracts
218 architectural design graphical manipulation housing
254 architectural drawings graphics engineering
227 architectural engineering library routines plotting
271 arcs spirals parabolas co-ordinates linear angular
206 area comparison sketch designs drawing bar-charts
266 area cross-section rod readings
251 area data desired-line mapping traffic flows
955 area interchanges transformer top-changing control
353 areas calculation earthwork volumes construction site
393 areas moments of inertia radii of gyration figures
028 arrow network critical-path resource allocation
016 arrow network critical path resource levelling
017 arrow network critical path resource levelling
722 ASHRAE calculations heating cooling loads rooms
366 assessment road development noise predictions visual
946 assessment security electrical distribution systems
201 assets financial control depreciation profits losses
103 assignment problems functions spaces solution
755 atmospheric pressure calculation psychrometric
473 automatic design steel structures static analysis
337 axial forces pile cap displacement rotation moments
550 axial forces pin-jointed truss support reactions
614 axial loading bi-axial bending column analysis
610 axial loading bi-axial bending elastic design members
342 axial loads analysis groups piles settlement moments
343 axial shear forces analysis group pile cap moments
413 axial shear forces bending moments elastic analysis
307 axial shear forces bending twisting moments piles
212 axis layout drawings fully-dimensioned
611 axis moment shear column baseplate tension
442 axisymmetric elastic plastic analysis deformations
446 axisymmetric linear elastic analysis plane
441 axisymmetric linear static analysis plane
236 axonometric three-dimensional presentation
922 azimuth sunrise calculation altitude sun
331 back-filled cantilevered retaining walls
327 back-filled stability bearing capacity retaining walls
176 balance-sheet trading summaries nominal-ledger
954 balanced unbalanced faults network representation
206 bar-charts area comparison sketch designs drawing
009 bar-charts diagrams precedence-diagram networks
563 bar-charts schedules concrete beams columns
622 bar-checking weight bar-fixing concrete detailing
622 bar-fixing concrete detailing bar-checking weight
229 bar pie charting graph histogram
597 bar schedules flat slabs design reinforced concrete
592 bar schedules steel quantities flat-slab reinforcement
131 bar summation bending schedules lengths weights
387 barrels box culvert size number
546 bars joints wooden structures rigidity method tensions
139 bars reinforcement weights straight bent
637 bars shear reinforcement design structural concrete
611 baseplate tension compression axis moment shear
052 bases structured data schedules
231 batch graphics display library building
562 beam elastic foundation general analysis
421 beam elements plane grid vertical loading
580 beam loads imposed moments calculations
427 beam membrane analysis plane structures rod
420 beam moment connection analysis bolted column
582 beam reactions shear bending moments fixed-end
581 beam reactions shear forces bending moments
437 beam string column lifts sub-system frames
447 beam-type stiffness displacement dynamic analysis
499 beam-type structures analysis elastic statically-loaded
293 beams analysis design continuous
636 beams calculations speeds rotating shafts frequencies
591 beams columns calculations reinforced concrete
643 beams columns details end-plate connections steel
563 beams columns drawings bar charts schedules
308 beams columns foundations reports sub-systems
564 beams columns plane frames space frames sizing
644 beams columns reinforced concrete building floors
635 beams concrete structural engineering columns
588 beams continuous sub-frames analysis design
440 beams coplanar prismatic variable modified frame
586 beams cross-sectional properties stress distribution
542 beams panels columns tension loads ceilings
633 beams piles columns sections random-access master
556 beams portals load-span charts timber
463 beams rods English elastic analysis trussed frame
577 beams self-documenting calculation beta angle
637 beams slabs columns bars shear reinforcement design
573 beams stiffness method forces moments deformations
587 beams timber laminated ply-web stressed-skin span
330 bearing capacity block strip foundations calculation
331 bearing capacity cantilevered retaining walls stability
327 bearing capacity retaining walls back-filled stability
598 bearing capacity unreinforced concrete rafts
521 bearing structures element method tensions
324 behaviour piles rows three dimensions analysis
323 behaviour piles rows two dimensions
537 behaviour viscoelastic structure assemblies prediction
558 bending deflection steel beams
401 bending moments analysis cylindrical tanks silos
581 bending moments beam reactions shear forces
300 bending moments continuous beams girders unit
422 bending moments deflected forms portal frame
457 bending moments deflections rotations space frame
413 bending moments elastic analysis plane frames axial
582 bending moments fixed-end moments beam reactions
416 bending moments restraint portal frame foundation
288 bending moments shear force deflections continuous
642 bending moments shear force sub-frames partial
303 bending moments shear forces analysis design
304 bending moments shear forces multi-span continuous
319 bending moments shear forces vertical pile lateral
561 bending moments shear reactions span moving load
326 bending moments shear stress retaining walls
559 bending moments slope deflection single-span beam
138 bending reinforcement bars cutting
131 bending schedules lengths weights bar summation
620 bending shear deflection design reinforced-concrete
583 bending torsion cellular structures box girders lift
307 bending twisting moments piles vertical raked axial
139 bent bars reinforcement weights straight
978 Bessel functions arbitrary argument evaluation
577 beta angle beams self-documenting calculation
614 bi-axial bending column analysis axial loading
610 bi-axial bending elastic design members steel axial
068 bill of quantities civil-engineering phrase library
170 billing accounts receivable
093 bills of quantities abstracts calculation dimensions
077 bills of quantities activity costing planning calculation
071 bills of quantities architects calculation
072 bills of quantities architects calculation
074 bills of quantities architects calculation
075 bills of quantities architects calculation
096 bills of quantities cables glands labour installation
084 bills of quantities calculation
085 bills of quantities calculation
086 bills of quantities calculation
087 bills of quantities calculation
088 bills of quantities calculation
089 bills of quantities calculation
083 bills of quantities CLASP architects calculation
079 bills of quantities CLASP calculation
080 bills of quantities CLASP calculation
081 bills of quantities CLASP calculation
082 bills of quantities CLASP calculation
073 bills of quantities county architects calculation
166 bills of quantities LPM rates system internal valuation
063 bills of quantities network analysis valuations
095 bills of quantities order requisitions amendments
092 bills of quantities prices cost data
065 bills of quantities reports Fletcher Moore taking-off
078 bills of quantities SCOLA calculation
069 bills of quantities tenders contract library foreign
344 Bishop circular arc traces analysis stability earth
355 Bishop circular arc traces analysis stability earth
338 Bishop Morgenstern and Price analysis slope stability
350 Bishop Morgenstern and Price slope stability
799 blinds solar radiation transmission characteristics
330 block strip foundations calculation bearing capacity
224 body repetition definition perspective drawing
420 bolted column beam moment connection analysis
193 bonuses process payrolls overtime pay
159 bought ledger purchases invoices credits financial
157 bought ledger remittance advice accounts
263 Bowditch closing error traverse survey
382 box culvert reinforced concrete cross section
387 box culvert size number barrels

385 box culvert unit length reinforced concrete
557 box-girder deflection elasticity Vlasov tensions
583 box-girders lift cores bending torsion cellular
280 box-girders suspension curved erection conditions
626 BRE method design concrete mixes
137 breakdown parts lists schedules materials
024 brewery hospital warehouse design planning
404 bridge buildings library engineering design roads
281 bridge continuous beams cross-section analysis
280 bridge continuous beams slabs box girders
278 bridge deck analysis grillage mesh
596 bridge decking analysis slab reinforcement
277 bridge decking member pre-stressing force analysis
595 bridge decking summing editing reformulation
279 bridge design influence lines positions vehicles
400 bridge design offshore structures buildings
220 bridge highway hidden lines specific locations
282 bridge-slab slab-and-beam analysis finite elements
130 briefing information buildings collection retrieval
760 BRS admittance calculation solar cooling load glazing
657 Btu hour minimum sizes pipe calculations
188 budget monitor variance expense
185 budgeting controlling costs building sites plans
043 budgeting tables data planning
752 building air change conduction heat losses
816 building air change conduction heat losses
726 building air quantities analysis heating cooling
862 building analysis energy consumption
868 building analysis energy consumption
860 building analysis running costs energy consumption
907 building appraisal natural lighting levels
597 building bar schedules flat slabs reinforced concrete
231 building batch graphics display library
738 building calculation air-conditioning loads heating
852 building calculation annual cost energy
790 building calculation cooling load
113 building calculation economics alternative proposals
853 building calculation energy annual heating cooling
866 building calculation energy usage sub-systems
767 building calculation heat losses gains
768 building calculation heat requirements
813 building calculation heating cooling loads
777 building calculation heating cooling loads room
805 building calculation solar heat gains
724 building Carrier calculation hourly cooling load
215 building complexes layouts activities urban regional
744 building component gains temperature cooling loads
221 building construction room size orientation daylight
150 building contracts NEDO formula fluctuations
149 building contracts NEDO series 2 indices price
121 building contracts production work schedules
118 building cost owning operating
750 building demands estimate energy consumption
102 building design outline proposal evaluation
225 building dimensions isometric perspective drawings
822 building energy system estimate requirements zone
770 building envelope calculation thermal energy
644 building floors beams columns reinforced concrete
406 building frames design details reinforced concrete
233 building geometry graphic tablet interactive
807 building heat transmission cooling load solar gain
787 building heating air-conditioning requirements
775 building heating cooling loads room
814 building heating cooling requirements analysis
963 building height selection lift speeds
753 building hour air-conditioning load calculation
871 building hourly calculation thermal electrical loads
192 building industry job-costing payroll
057 building inspections
469 building linear elastic dynamic analysis soil
719 building loads calculation air surface temperatures
783 building loads calculation temperatures heating
893 building measurement environmental performance
806 building model heat transfer calculation cooling load
214 building prismatic allocations activities spaces
126 building project analysis economic feasibility
127 building project residential housing economic
128 building project shopping-centre economic feasibility
109 building projects cash flows economic analyses
187 building projects forecast monthly expenditure
207 building proposal stage diagram layout
718 building radiator selection calculation heat losses
185 building sites plans schedules budgeting controlling
878 building solar energy analysis systems
110 building technical financial commercial feasibility
735 building temperature zones cross-section
720 building temperatures heating cooling requirements
736 building thermal-response heating cooling load
754 building three-dimensional model calculation air
402 building velocities wind pressure profile
859 building year zones calculation energy
721 building zones heating cooling requirements
798 buildings air-conditioning calculation thermal
865 buildings annual consumption energy calculation cost
098 buildings appraisal performance schools
400 buildings bridges design offshore structures
876 buildings calculation energy consumption
785 buildings calculation heat loss
784 buildings calculation summertime temperatures
769 buildings Carrier estimate cooling loads rooms
210 buildings co-ordinated components orthogonal grid
130 buildings collection retrieval modification re-use
875 buildings consumption cost estimate energy
904 buildings daylight factors calculation natural lighting
815 buildings design mechanical systems heating cooling
403 buildings detail reinforced concrete
723 buildings evaluation cooling heating loads
903 buildings evaluation lighting conditions
887 buildings ground display shadows
846 buildings hourly calculation indoor temperatures
739 buildings indoor temperatures cooling loads
749 buildings indoor temperatures heating cooling loads
404 buildings library engineering design roads bridges
968 buildings lift comparison vertical transport
727 buildings loads temperatures simulation thermal
867 buildings model energy usage
972 buildings pedestrian traffic mechanical handling
961 buildings piping water demand
792 buildings radiant convective heat losses rooms
743 buildings radiant panels radiators heat loss rooms
869 buildings room calculation heat losses
099 buildings scheme/detail design models appraisal
801 buildings temperatures energy consumption thermal
839 by-pass Carrier sizing steam coils
526 cable networks static analysis non-linear
409 cable strengths plane frame grid tensions reactions
285 cable structures non-linear elastic analysis suspension
953 cable systems progressing planning
143 cables calculation drum lengths
095 cables glands bill of quantities order requisitions
096 cables glands labour installation bills of quantities
951 cables nodes schedule location list knitting routing
745 calculation absorption transmission thermal radiation
761 calculation air-conditioning designs cooling load
738 calculation air-conditioning loads heating cooling
757 calculation air environmental temperature
754 calculation air movement building three-dimensional
845 calculation air radiation temperatures room
719 calculation air surface temperatures building loads
922 calculation altitude sun azimuth sunrise
852 calculation annual cost energy building
330 calculation bearing capacity block strip foundations
577 calculation beta angle beams self-documenting
084 calculation bills of quantities
085 calculation bills of quantities
086 calculation bills of quantities
087 calculation bills of quantities
089 calculation bills of quantities
077 calculation bills of quantities activity costing planning
079 calculation bills of quantities CLASP
080 calculation bills of quantities CLASP
081 calculation bills of quantities CLASP
082 calculation bills of quantities CLASP
083 calculation bills of quantities CLASP architects
088 calculation bills of quantity
071 calculation bills of quantity architects
072 calculation bills of quantity architects
074 calculation bills of quantity architects
075 calculation bills of quantity architects
073 calculation bills of quantity county architects
078 calculation bills of quantity SCOLA
657 calculation Btu hour minimum sizes pipe
753 calculation building hour air-conditioning load
892 calculation capacity capabilities industrial exhaust
264 calculation co-ordinates geometry
950 calculation constants geometric pattern lines
090 calculation contract remeasurement quantity
790 calculation cooling load building
806 calculation cooling load building model heat transfer
740 calculation cooling loads summer heating winter
865 calculation cost heating cooling buildings annual
863 calculation costs insulation savings heat requirements

281 continuous beam cross-section analysis bridges
304 continuous beam deflection rotation bending moment
305 continuous beam elastic discontinuous foundation
299 continuous beam flexibility influence-coefficient
424 continuous beam frame analysis
300 continuous beam girders unit loads reactions shears
291 continuous beam load conditions support reactions
287 continuous beam load factors analysis multi-span
294 continuous beam load stress moments
295 continuous beam load-train stress
292 continuous beam loads analysis design
296 continuous beam loads stress tension
298 continuous beam moments shears support reactions
306 continuous beam multispan support moments
279 continuous beam plane frames bridge design
411 continuous beam prismatic members two-dimensional
286 continuous beam prismatic section analysis
560 continuous beam rectangular T-shaped stress tension
584 continuous beam reinforced concrete analysis design
290 continuous beam simply supported multi-span
280 continuous beam slabs box girders suspension curved
585 continuous beam ultimate limit state deflections
289 continuous beam variable cross-section analysis
459 continuous finite elements sub-system truss frame
293 continuous reinforced-concrete beams analysis
593 continuous slabs one-way spanning prismatic section
588 continuous sub-frames analysis design reinforced
252 contour maps functions surfaces variables
265 contour maps quantitative description surfaces
255 contour proximal map conformant
376 contoured alignment highway plans three-dimensional
245 contouring interpolation integration system variables
069 contract library foreign languages bills of quantities
121 contract production work schedules building
179 contract record movement money
090 contract remeasurement quantity surveyors
167 contracting organisation cash-flow patterns
050 control analysis library engineering
160 control analysis sales accounting records statements
955 control area interchanges transformer top-changing
005 control critical paths financial statement planning
237 control data analysis diagram costing statistics
033 control empty property
172 control financial report general ledger sub-accounts
171 control information system financial
161 control order-point inventory analysis
011 control planning progress
026 control projects planning
239 control system graphics terminal
004 control time-analysis resource allocation planning
185 controlling costs building sites plans schedules
136 controlling managing stock recording
779 convection radiation heat-transfer analysis conduction
792 convective heat losses rooms buildings radiant
883 cooling analysis solar heating
738 cooling building calculation air-conditioning loads
853 cooling building calculation energy annual heating
783 cooling building loads calculation temperatures
865 cooling buildings annual consumption energy
815 cooling buildings design mechanical systems heating
742 cooling calculation heat gains air
837 cooling coils Carrier sizing direct-expansion
836 cooling coils match condensing units
857 cooling cost fuels calculation energy heating
788 cooling heat pump heating
117 cooling heating equipment financial analysis
741 cooling heating loads air-conditioning system
723 cooling heating loads buildings evaluation
806 cooling load building model heat transfer calculation
736 cooling load building thermal-response heating
725 cooling load factors solar radiation thermal
808 cooling loads air-conditioning inner temperatures
790 cooling loads building calculation
813 cooling loads building calculation heating
744 cooling loads building component gains temperature
739 cooling loads buildings indoor temperatures
749 cooling loads buildings indoor temperatures heating
761 cooling loads calculations air-conditioning designs
829 cooling loads design analysis air-conditioning heating
765 cooling loads gain zone infiltration mechanical
774 cooling loads hour rooms calculation heat gains
782 cooling loads indoor air surface temperatures heating
776 cooling loads psychrometric analysis moist air
777 cooling loads room building calculation heating
775 cooling loads room building heating
737 cooling loads room calculation heating
772 cooling loads room Carrier calculation heating
722 cooling loads rooms ASHRAE calculations heating
769 cooling loads rooms buildings Carrier estimate
773 cooling loads rooms hour calculation heat gains
807 cooling loads solar gain building heat transmission
762 cooling loads structural conduction gains
740 cooling loads summer heating winter calculation
804 cooling loads zone calculation heating
843 cooling model environmental control heating
848 cooling performance coils selection heating
814 cooling requirements analysis environment building
726 cooling requirements building air quantities analysis
721 cooling requirements building zones heating
720 cooling requirements zones building temperatures
691 cooling systems internal resistance two-pipe heating
692 cooling systems internal resistance two-pipe heating
631 coplanar loading gables arches analysis ring frames
440 coplanar prismatic variable modified frame
685 copper piping systems calculations stresses linear
261 corner points section properties co-ordinates
948 correction plant-loading schedule power-factor
173 cost accounting time labour consultants
012 cost activities program network duration
123 cost air-distribution systems monthly energy
116 cost alternative housing layouts
003 cost analyses time resources
185 cost building sites plans schedules budgeting
855 cost calculation energy consumption heating
821 cost centrifugal absorption refrigeration systems
541 cost composite deck shear connectors design analysis
952 cost control industrial cabling design planning
007 cost control network analysis resource allocation
030 cost control resource-allocation project management
174 cost control time expenses sheets invoicing
006 cost critical path analysis complex projects time
092 cost data bills of quantities prices
129 cost drawings schedule estimates
875 cost estimate energy buildings consumption
857 cost fuels calculation energy heating cooling
865 cost heating cooling buildings annual consumption
863 cost insulation savings heat requirements calculation
190 cost item job number
181 cost nominal ledger headings
122 cost operation initial investment system energy
118 cost owning operating building
461 cost reduction joint difference
066 cost reports description measurement interim
013 cost resource-allocation schedules projects
858 cost savings comparison energy requirements
964 cost selection lift system loading
002 cost simulation project management time resource
648 cost sizing components pipe networks recirculated
778 cost TRU–70 heat pipe evaluation
180 costing construction industry payroll job
077 costing planning calculation bills of quantities activity
191 costing research expenditure system
882 costing sizing solar-energy systems
237 costing statistics planning control data analysis
864 council property analysis fuel consumption
073 county architects calculation bills of quantity
076 county architects quantity surveying services
881 cover solar collectors heat loss
147 creation access random data-base system
148 creation interrogation updating schedules
067 creation interrogation updating schedules item type
156 credit control sales transaction statement
159 credits financial bought ledger purchases invoices
006 critical path analysis complex projects time resource
015 critical path data network analysis plot
005 critical path financial statement planning control
021 critical path network planning construction
025 critical path network reports project management
027 critical path networks analysis
028 critical path resource allocation arrow networks
017 critical path resource levelling arrow network
016 critical path resource levelling arrow networks
018 critical path time resource analyses
283 critical wind speed flutter suspension bridge
281 cross-section analysis bridges continuous beams
382 cross-section box culvert reinforced concrete
735 cross-section building temperature zones
407 cross-section calculation tensions deformations
367 cross-section earthworks quantities highway design
624 cross-section irregular shapes calculations properties
266 cross-section rod readings area
630 cross-section structural elements tension elasticity

700 ducted air system design high-velocity
701 ductwork constant-friction constant-velocity
702 ductwork constant-friction constant-velocity
703 ductwork equal-friction static-regain
709 ductwork friction dynamic loss regain air velocity
716 ductwork lining calculations sound attenuation
708 ductwork static-regain constant-friction sizing
012 duration cost activities program network
890 dust collection exhaust-air systems model design
891 dust collection systems sizes components design
490 dynamic analyses frames static
447 dynamic analysis beam-type stiffness displacement
483 dynamic analysis frame shell linear static
469 dynamic analysis soil building linear elastic
470 dynamic analysis constructions arbitrary load static
527 dynamic loads analysis natural frequencies models
425 dynamic loads finite element analysis structures static
709 dynamic loss regain air velocity ductwork friction
284 dynamic relaxation three-span suspension bridges
535 dynamic structural problems solution static
059 dynamic sub-routines sparse matrix elements
397 dynamic systems analogue computer simulation
533 dynamic testing analysis mechanical design
169 early payment discounts accounts payable liabilities
316 earth-retaining structures stability ground penetration
344 earth slopes Bishop circular arc traces analysis
355 earth slopes Bishop circular arc traces analysis
315 earth slopes safety circular-arc slip plane analysis
359 earth volume edge characteristics mathematical
354 earthworks comparison cut-and-fill site plans volumes
378 earthworks design highway alignments sections plans
377 earthworks pavement quantities profile levels road
367 earthworks quantities highway design initial alignment
379 earthworks structures system alignments highways
353 earthworks volumes construction site areas
609 eccentric loads column simply supported calculations
109 economic analyses building projects cash flows
125 economic analysis property
126 economic feasibility building project analysis
127 economic feasibility building project residential
128 economic feasibility building project shopping-centre
113 economics alternative proposals building calculation
314 economy dimensions pile soil strata
359 edge characteristics mathematical model earth
250 edit frame analysis display graphic check
062 edit master specification project
061 editing data base lists compilation
595 editing reformulation stresses deflections bridge
048 editing text specification
055 editing validation data
104 educational policies curriculum spatial implications
888 efficiency glazing shading comparison
464 eigenvalue vibration analysis space frames
299 elastic analysis continuous beams flexibility
468 elastic analysis design general space framework linear
431 elastic analysis framed structures stiffness linear
446 elastic analysis plane axisymmetric linear
413 elastic analysis plane frames axial shear forces
415 elastic analysis plane frames stiffness method
285 elastic analysis suspension bridges cable structures
463 elastic analysis trussed frame beams rods English
453 elastic calculation deformation tension linear
418 elastic deflection analysis portal frame
610 elastic design members steel axial loading bi-axial
390 elastic design reinforced culverts
305 elastic discontinuous foundation analysis multi-span
469 elastic dynamic analysis soil building linear
562 elastic foundation general analysis beam
368 elastic layered structure stress
435 elastic loads grid analysis plane grillages
417 elastic multi-bay portal frames plastic design
442 elastic plastic analysis deformations plane
444 elastic plastic analysis plane frames loads linear
504 elastic skeletal frames straight members linear
499 elastic statically-loaded beam-type structures analysis
503 elastic statically-loaded frame truss structures analysis
488 elastic statically-loaded structures linear analysis
601 elastic stiffness frame analysis shear stress walls
605 elastic stiffness method frame analysis shear walls
392 elastic stiffness reinforcement analysis culverts
476 elastic supports analysis rigid space frames
434 elastic supports loads analysis plane frame
333 elasticity calculation pile foundations static load
334 elasticity calculation pile foundations static load
981 elasticity equations rigid layer solution Steinbrenner
630 elasticity theory constants cross-sections structural
557 elasticity Vlasov tensions movements reactions
947 electrical batteries schedules maintenance
949 electrical cables schedule route information selection
943 electrical control systems operational array analysis
945 electrical control systems symbolic-array simulation
946 electrical distribution systems assessment security
871 electrical loads building hourly calculation thermal
858 electrical mechanical cost savings comparison energy
934 electrical network frequency sweep analysis linear
937 electrical power systems analysis load-flow
942 electrical root locus pure time delay diagrams
861 electricity consumption air-conditioning estimate
874 electricity-generating plant energy balance design
939 electronic circuits ac/dc transient analyses
594 element analysis slabs deflections forces moments
521 element method tensions movement bearing
240 elevations isometric drawings perspective plotter
983 elimination solution simultaneous equations
695 emissions mass flows pipe sizes pressure loss
032 employment files local authorities land-use
033 empty property control
959 enclosure thermal lighting acoustic performance
643 end-plate connections steel frames beams columns
567 ends stress slenderness ratio safety margin mid-span
872 energy air-handling system mechanical plant
853 energy annual heating cooling building calculation
874 energy balance design electricity-generating plant
852 energy building calculation annual cost
859 energy building year zones calculation
875 energy buildings consumption cost estimate
865 energy calculation cost heating cooling buildings
862 energy consumption building analysis
868 energy consumption building analysis
860 energy consumption building analysis running costs
750 energy consumption building demands estimate
876 energy consumption buildings calculation
802 energy consumption comparison fenestration glazing
855 energy consumption heating ventilating costs
870 energy consumption residential buildings calculation
873 energy consumption simulation air-distribution system
801 energy consumption thermal performance buildings
123 energy costs air-distribution systems monthly
122 energy costs operation initial investment system
060 energy disposal services analysis integrated systems
857 energy heating cooling cost fuels calculation
858 energy requirements electrical mechanical cost
830 energy requirements equipment selection
756 energy requirements Post Office buildings
850 energy requirements viability analysis
818 energy simulation air-conditioning dimensions
879 energy solar radiation roof angles calculation
746 energy surfaces room calculation interchange
822 energy system estimate requirements zone building
867 energy usage buildings model
866 energy usage sub-systems building calculation
254 engineering architectural drawings graphics
050 engineering control analysis library
404 engineering design roads bridges buildings library
227 engineering library routines plotting commercial
091 engineers abstracts quantity surveyors
259 engineers survey calculations design roads sites
463 English elastic analysis trussed frame beams rods
211 English language design analysis application
235 English measurements repetition drawings
613 Engresser working stress columns parabolic-Euler
035 enquiry system property
770 envelope calculation thermal energy building
814 environment building heating cooling requirements
843 environmental control heating cooling model
893 environmental performance building measurement
757 environmental temperature calculation air
703 equal-friction static-regain ductwork
981 equations rigid layer solution Steinbrenner elasticity
789 equations two-dimensional heat flow solution
383 equations water-distribution network
462 equilibrium problems displacement finite-element
849 equipment coils fans air-handling units selection
117 equipment financial analysis combinations cooling
119 equipment investment analysis cash flow capital
049 equipment preventative maintenance
825 equipment selection air-conditioning
830 equipment selection consumption energy
277 equivalent loading bridge decking member
280 erection conditions bridge continuous beams slabs
684 erection drawing-office aid piping components
861 estimate annual electricity consumption

769 estimate cooling loads rooms buildings Carrier
129 estimate costs drawings schedule
875 estimate energy buildings consumption cost
750 estimate energy consumption building demands
847 estimate heat losses transmission radiator choice
877 estimate performance solar-energy model
070 estimate quantities materials pipework projects
822 estimate requirements zone building energy system
811 estimate temperature thermal comfort room
978 evaluation Bessel functions arbitrary argument
102 evaluation building design outline proposal
831 evaluation constant-volume systems variable-volume
723 evaluation cooling heating loads buildings
778 evaluation costs TRU–70 heat pipe
659 evaluation forces moments stresses piping system
903 evaluation lighting conditions buildings
362 excavation prismatic cut-out calculation cut-and-fill
935 excitation analysis response linear network
890 exhaust-air systems model design dust-collection
892 exhaust duct calculation capacity capabilities
660 expansion wind loading joints analysis pipe systems
191 expenditure system costing research
188 expense budget monitor variance
979 exponentials curve collocation least-square
759 external facade solar intensities orientation slope
728 external glazing shade calculation heat gains
645 external loads pipework systems temperature pressure
733 external walls sol-air temperatures heat gains
094 extract specification clauses select
704 extraction duct systems sizing ventilating
684 fabrication erection drawing-office aid piping
889 facades obstructional shading calculation
781 facades roofs windows calculation solar radiation
226 facilities routines graphics
725 factors solar radiation thermal conduction cooling
849 fans air-handling units selection equipment coils
835 fans pressure ducted air-conditioning horsepower
529 fatigue life intersections tubular steel structure
954 faults network representation balanced unbalanced
958 faults transient stability unbalanced voltages currents
126 feasibility building project analysis economic
127 feasibility building project residential housing
128 feasibility building project shopping-centre economic
110 feasibility building technical financial commercial
111 feasibility development defined site
189 fee control architects calculation
183 fees architects civil engineers job-costing staff time
419 feet fixity loading frame data-geometry haunching
802 fenestration glazing energy consumption comparison
270 field stations co-ordinates setting out
393 figures areas moments of inertia radii of gyration
987 files cross tabulation analysis data stock
037 files index property
032 files local authorities land-use employment
034 files manipulation property
117 financial analysis combinations cooling heating
044 financial analysis modelling companies
159 financial bought ledger purchases invoices credits
110 financial commercial feasibility building technical
196 financial control analysis schedules payroll summary
201 financial control depreciation profits losses assets
171 financial control information system
184 financial control system purchases application
172 financial report general ledger sub-accounts control
005 financial statement planning control critical paths
182 finished goods work-in-progress stock control
458 finite-element analyses structures digital models
509 finite-element analysis frame plated shell structures
993 finite-element analysis heat flow water seepage
594 finite-element analysis slabs deflections forces
425 finite-element analysis structures static dynamic loads
472 finite-element analysis three-dimensional
506 finite-element analysis two– three-dimensional space
282 finite-element concrete bridge-slab slab-and-beam
619 finite-element graphic displays stress analysis
462 finite-element linear equilibrium problems
502 finite-element linear non-linear design analysis
501 finite-element models graphics
465 finite-element orthotropic stress analysis
312 finite-element simple retaining walls
632 finite-element stress analysis
494 finite-element structures analyses skeletal
436 finite-element triangular mesh analysis in-plane
751 fire analysis room pressures air movement
688 fire-protection pipe sizes hydraulic calculations
913 fittings calculation fluorescent tungsten mercury
912 fittings calculation glare indices tungsten mercury
665 fittings design two-pipe systems hot-water
911 fittings glare indices fluorescent calculation
223 fixed-area plans modular spaces
582 fixed-end moments beam reactions shear bending
141 fixed-length stock seamless tubing metal bars timber
512 fixed-offshore platforms safety margin joint punching
394 flanges design analysis
599 flat ribbed slabs analysis design
597 flat-slab reinforced concrete building bar schedules
592 flat-slab reinforcement details bar schedules steel
065 Fletcher Moore taking-off data abstracts
299 flexibility influence-coefficient elastic analysis
698 flexibility multiple branch closed-loop pipe systems
661 flexibility multiple-branch closed-loop pipework
517 flexural data off-shore structures geometrical
915 floodlight spotlight calculation illumination level
908 floodlighting horizontal plane illumination
644 floor beams columns reinforced concrete building
543 floor reinforced concrete slabs universal beams
682 flow balance pipe network calculations
024 flow-diagrams brewery hospital warehouse design
649 flow grid piping systems analysis
683 flow head loss water-distribution system calculations
650 flow pipe size pressure heat design pipework
647 flow pipework systems analysis
687 flow pressure meshed pipe networks
658 flow pressures gas water networks calculations
667 flow rate pipe diameter pipe-flow head loss
677 flow rate pressure drop relationship pipe size
655 flow rate velocity sizes steel pipes
150 fluctuations building contracts NEDO formula
669 fluid flow friction loss velocity pipe sizing chart
668 fluid flow pipework sizes pressure temperature
663 fluid flow sizing one-pipe systems pressures
664 fluid flow sizing two-pipe systems pressures
911 fluorescent calculation fittings glare indices
912 fluorescent fittings calculation glare indices tungsten
913 fluorescent tungsten mercury fittings calculation
283 flutter suspension bridge calculation critical wind
318 forces analysis group pile cap moments
343 forces analysis group pile cap moments axial shears
336 forces deformations sheet-piling wall calculations
603 forces distortion walls multi-storey buildings
552 forces double sloping trusses
573 forces moments deformations beams stiffness method
594 forces moments shears finite element analysis slabs
659 forces moments stresses piping system evaluation
518 forces off-shore structure analysis
519 forces pile foundations analysis off-shore structures
514 forces submerged structure sea-wave calculation
553 forces truss single top chord vertical posts
513 forces velocities calculation structures sea waves
187 forecast monthly expenditure building projects
069 foreign languages bills of quantities tenders contract
242 forms regular irregular
305 foundation analysis multi-span continuous beams
519 foundation analysis off-shore structures forces pile
416 foundation reactions bending moments restraint
311 foundation reinforcement dimensions
308 foundation reports sub-systems beams columns
500 foundation shock vibrational response frame
424 frame analysis continuous beam
250 frame analysis display graphic check edit
460 frame analysis general
489 frame analysis reinforced concrete design problems
605 frame analysis shear walls elastic stiffness method
477 frame analysis space plane
474 frame analysis two– three-dimensional
437 frame beam string column lifts sub-system
463 frame beams rods English elastic analysis trussed
485 frame calculation stresses
498 frame continuous beams analysis straight elements
411 frame continuous beams prismatic members
459 frame continuous finite elements sub-system truss
419 frame data-geometry haunching feet fixity loading
481 frame grids non-prismatic members analysis
478 frame grids plane space
450 frame loading analysis three-dimensional
479 frame orthogonal multi-storey moment distribution
509 frame plated shell structures finite element analysis
467 frame prismatic hollow steel design
483 frame shell linear static dynamic analysis
490 frame static dynamic analyses
449 frame straight prismatic static elastic analysis
455 frame stress tension plane space

500 frame structures foundation shock vibrational
487 frame structures static loads analysis orthogonal
448 frame tensions reactions deflections
503 frame truss structures analysis elastic statically-loaded
454 frame trusses plane grids prismatic analysis
497 framed structures analysis linearly-elastic
495 framed structures small- to medium-sized design
431 framed structures stiffness linear elastic analysis
468 frameworks linear elastic analysis design general
492 frameworks two- three-dimensional analysis
317 freestanding pile groups analysis load-displacement
068 French bill of quantities civil-engineering phrase
636 frequency beams calculations speeds rotating shafts
934 frequency sweep analysis linear electrical network
944 frequency transient response lumped linear systems
408 frequency vibrations reactions deflections structure
709 friction dynamic loss regain air velocity ductwork
669 friction loss velocity pipe sizing chart fluid flow
864 fuel consumption council property analysis
857 fuels calculation energy heating cooling cost
212 fully-dimensioned axis layout drawings
399 fully-saturated media pressures seepage pores
992 functional interconnections simulation model
103 functions spaces solution assignment problems
252 functions surfaces variables contour maps
976 Furness traffic prediction
631 gables arches analysis ring frames coplanar loading
767 gains building calculation heat losses
805 gains building calculation solar heat
762 gains cooling loads structural conduction
764 gains load calculation internal
800 gains losses radiation air-conditioning heat
731 gains losses rooms air-flow rates calculations heat
656 gains underground pipes transfer heat losses
765 gains zone infiltration mechanical ventilation cooling
658 gas water networks calculations flows pressures
562 general analysis beam elastic foundation
984 general analysis statistics regressions T-tests
460 general frame analysis
172 general ledger sub-accounts control financial report
197 general payroll deductions cheques summaries
468 general space framework linear elastic analysis design
927 generation resistivity curves
928 generators ac currents voltages power outputs
339 geohydrological characteristics levels current ground
950 geometric pattern lines calculation constants
517 geometrical topological flexural data off-shore
264 geometry calculations co-ordinates
233 geometry graphic tablet interactive building
300 girders unit loads reactions shears bending moments
095 glands bill of quantities order requisitions
096 glands labour installation bills of quantities cables
911 glare indices fluorescent calculation fittings
912 glare indices tungsten mercury fluorescent fittings
799 glass blinds solar radiation transmission
797 glass calculation solar heat gains
760 glazing BRS admittance calculation solar cooling load
717 glazing calculations internal noise levels window
802 glazing energy consumption comparison fenestration
888 glazing shading comparison efficiency
638 glue-laminated portal arches design
456 glued-wood frames design curved corners
895 Goff and Gratch thermodynamic properties air
320 granular soils analysis designs concrete cantilever
229 graph histogram bar pie charting
209 graph plotter display terminal perspective rectilinear
100 graphic appraisal models hospital design
250 graphic check edit frame analysis display
245 graphic contouring interpolation integration system
243 graphic display shapes visual unit
619 graphic displays stress analysis finite elements
101 graphic modelling housing layout
022 graphic networking system interactive
256 graphic representation net site area
539 graphic structures analysis design
233 graphic tablet interactive building geometry
218 graphical manipulation housing sites architectural
231 graphics display library building batch
254 graphics engineering architectural drawings
226 graphics facilities routines
501 graphics finite element models
239 graphics terminal control system
515 gravity off-shore structures loadings waves current
335 gravity-type retaining walls design
435 grid analysis plane grillages elastic loads
438 grid analysis stress plane frames
414 grid grillage analysis loading plane
219 grid lines zones macros shapes working drawings
481 grid non-prismatic members analysis frames
649 grid piping systems analysis flow
478 grid plane space frames
423 grid rigidly-jointed analysis plane frames
475 grid space frames analysis plane frames trusses
409 grid tensions reactions deflections cable strengths
269 grid transformation co-ordinates survey stations
414 grillage analysis loading plane grids
435 grillage elastic loads grid analysis plane
278 grillage mesh bridge deck analysis
568 ground beam number of elements analysis
887 ground display shadows buildings
316 ground penetration analysis earth-retaining structures
339 ground water sections geohydrological characteristics
343 group pile cap moments axial shears forces analysis
318 group pile cap moments forces analysis
341 group piles rows vertical raked analysis
342 group piles settlement moments axial loads analysis
234 half-tone shading shadows model perspectives
047 handling data-file
145 handling storage timber-yard
428 Hardy-Cross analysis rectilinear plane frames
957 harmonics calculation voltages current flows
956 harmonics load flow short circuits stability parameters
419 haunching feet fixity loading frame data-geometry
674 head loss closed systems analysis pipework velocity
667 head loss flow rate pipe diameter pipe-flow
673 head loss velocity open systems piping
683 head loss water-distribution system calculations flow
352 head velocity analysis seepage piezometric
181 headings cost nominal ledger
451 heat conduction analysis stress
894 heat conduction superposition response factors
650 heat design pipework flow pipe size pressure
789 heat flow solution equation two-dimensional
812 heat flow walls roofs ceilings calculation
993 heat flow water seepage finite-element analysis
771 heat gains air-conditioned building weather
742 heat gains air cooling calculation
805 heat gains building calculation solar
774 heat gains cooling loads hour rooms calculation
773 heat gains cooling loads rooms hour calculation
728 heat gains external glazing shade calculation
733 heat gains external walls sol-air temperatures
797 heat gains glass calculation solar
732 heat gains horizontal roofs sol-air temperatures
793 heat gains information tables radiation temperature
800 heat gains losses radiation air-conditioning
731 heat gains losses rooms air-flow rates calculations
748 heat gains solar radiation calculation
752 heat losses building air change conduction
816 heat losses building air change conduction
718 heat losses building radiator selection calculation
785 heat losses buildings calculation
869 heat losses buildings room calculation
786 heat losses calculation
881 heat losses cover solar collectors
767 heat losses gains building calculation
656 heat losses gains underground pipes transfer
734 heat losses room design hot-water heating system
792 heat losses rooms buildings radiant convective
743 heat losses rooms buildings radiant panels radiators
697 heat losses temperatures two-pipe systems
847 heat losses transmission radiator choice estimate
675 heat losses underground pipes calculations
707 heat losses uninsulated insulated air space
788 heat pump heating cooling
768 heat requirements building calculation
863 heat requirements calculation costs insulation savings
832 heat requirements closed-circuit heating chill-water
880 heat solar collector calculation
779 heat transfer analysis conduction convection radiation
806 heat transfer calculation cooling load building model
780 heat transfer multilayer wall calculation
807 heat transmission cooling load solar gain building
787 heating air-conditioning requirements building
832 heating chill-water network heat requirement
883 heating cooling analysis solar
738 heating cooling building calculation air-conditioning
853 heating cooling building calculation energy annual
783 heating cooling building loads calculation
865 heating cooling buildings annual consumption energy
815 heating cooling buildings design mechanical systems
857 heating cooling cost fuels calculation energy

053 labelling printing records publications indexes
040 labels mailing addresses selection output letters
173 labour consultants cost accounting time
096 labour installation bills of quantities cables glands
587 laminated ply-web stressed-skin span tables beams
036 land-agents property management
493 land-based offshore structures analysis
032 land-use employment files local authorities
977 land-use planning transport modelling
067 language creation interrogation updating schedules
165 large companies ledger accounting
652 large-scale pipe networks valves pumps analysis
482 lateral forces indeterminate structures analyses
319 lateral bending moment shear forces vertical pile
215 layout activities urban regional institutional building
207 layout building proposal stage diagram
116 layout costs alternative housing
101 layout graphic modelling housing
918 layout lighting fixtures illumination level room
217 layout lines co-ordinate system curves drawing
216 layout planning simple language spaces
222 layout rooms circulation plans
056 layout tables report writing research analysis
510 LEAP frame structure calculation wave forces
982 least-square curve fit polynominal curve
979 least-square exponentials curve collocation
980 least-square regression two variables
165 ledger accounting large companies
162 ledger accounting purchase
163 ledger accounting sales
164 ledger analysis invoicing VAT sales
131 length weight bar summation bending schedules
634 length weight quantities reinforcement structural
040 letters labels mailing addresses selection output
339 levels current ground water sections geohydrological
144 levels timber products re-order quantities
717 levels window room glazing calculations internal
169 liabilities early payment discounts accounts payable
231 library building batch graphics display
058 library circulation periodicals
050 library engineering control analysis
404 library engineering design roads bridges buildings
069 library foreign languages bills of quantities tenders
020 library multiple calendars precedence network
227 library routines plotting commercial architectural
064 library system quantity surveyors description items
238 library three-dimensional model shapes
968 lift comparison vertical transport buildings
583 lift cores bending torsion cellular structures box
966 lift installations office morning peak analysis
962 lift parking passenger waiting time operation
965 lift simulation traffic-handling capability
963 lift speeds building height selection
964 lift system loading cost selection
967 lift two-way traffic performance
921 light indoor room intensity
920 light windows calculation transmittance reflectance
959 lighting acoustic performance enclosure thermal
905 lighting calculation natural
903 lighting conditions buildings evaluation
918 lighting fixtures illumination level room layout
925 lighting installations rooms design
919 lighting intensity rectangular area sports installations
114 limits married quarters housing cost yardstick
373 line vertical alignment highway optimisation
936 linear analysis central electrical systems
504 linear analysis elastic skeletal frames
488 linear analysis elastic statically-loaded structures
480 linear analysis space-frame
271 linear angular relationships arcs spirals parabolas
933 linear arrays radiating elements antenna patterns
468 linear elastic analysis design general space framework
431 linear elastic analysis framed structures stiffness
446 linear elastic analysis plane axisymmetric
453 linear elastic calculation deformation tension
469 linear elastic dynamic analysis soil building
444 linear elastic plastic analysis plane frames loads
625 linear elastic stability method calculations tensions
497 linear elastic statically-loaded framed structures
426 linear elastic structures shock loads analysis
640 linear elastic theory analysis reinforced concrete
934 linear electrical network frequency sweep analysis
462 linear equilibrium problems displacement
506 linear finite element analysis two– three-dimensional
935 linear network excitation analysis response
502 linear non-linear design analysis finite elements
433 linear plane-frame analysis plastic collapse
046 linear programming product form inverse method
441 linear static analysis plane axisymmetric
483 linear static dynamic analysis frame shell
685 linear steel copper piping systems calculations
950 lines calculation constants geometric pattern
217 lines co-ordinate system curves drawing layout
220 lines specific locations perspective bridge highway
219 lines zones macros shapes working drawings grid
716 lining calculations sound attenuation ductwork
884 liquid air design solar-heating
061 lists compilation editing data base
806 load building model heat transfer calculation cooling
736 load building thermal-response heating cooling
753 load calculation building hour air-conditioning
764 load calculation internal gains
540 load calculations rectangular plate concrete
291 load conditions support reactions moment shear force
317 load displacement freestanding pile groups analysis
287 load factors analysis multi-span continuous beams
544 load factors deflections weight sizes portal frames
725 load factors solar radiation thermal conduction
937 load-flow electrical power systems analysis
930 load-flow short-circuit analysis dc
956 load-flow short circuits stability parameters harmonics
556 load-span charts timber beams portals
555 load-span tables roof truss
294 load stress moments continuous beam
395 load tables storage tanks depth calculation
295 load train stress continuous beam
450 loading analysis three-dimensional frames
964 loading cost selection lift system
419 loading frame data-geometry haunching feet fixity
523 loading integral structural design
414 loading plane grids grillage analysis
515 loading waves current wind gravity off-shore
741 loads air-conditioning system cooling heating
292 loads analysis design continuous beams
434 loads analysis plane frame elastic supports
530 loads analysis structure houses
813 loads building calculation heating cooling
871 loads building hourly calculation thermal electrical
723 loads buildings evaluation cooling heating
719 loads calculation air surface temperatures building
783 loads calculation temperatures heating cooling
542 loads ceilings beams panels columns tension
829 loads design analysis air-conditioning heating cooling
435 loads grid analysis plane grillages elastic
580 loads imposed moments calculations deflections
782 loads indoor air surface temperatures heating cooling
297 loads influence lines shears moments support
444 loads linear elastic plastic analysis plane frames
776 loads psychrometric analysis moist air properties
777 loads room building calculation heating cooling
775 loads room building heating cooling
737 loads room calculation heating cooling
772 loads room Carrier calculation heating cooling
722 loads rooms ASHRAE calculations heating cooling
491 loads statically-determinate pin-jointed
296 loads stress tension continuous beams
686 loads stresses pipework system
727 loads temperatures simulation thermal behaviour
804 loads zone calculation heating cooling
031 local authority analysis housing investment
032 local authority land-use employment files
970 location allocation problems solution
951 location list knitting routing cables nodes schedule
268 longitudinal cross-sectional data horizontal
374 longitudinal horizontal alignments design highways
201 losses assets financial control depreciation profits
752 losses building air change conduction heat
816 losses building air change conduction heat
767 losses gains building calculation heat
656 losses gains underground pipes transfer heat
800 losses radiation air-conditioning heat gains
731 losses rooms air-flow rates calculations heat gains
710 low-pressure air ducts sizing low-velocity
711 low-velocity design air-ducts high-velocity
166 LPM rates system internal valuation bill of quantities
944 lumped linear systems frequency transient response
219 macros shapes working drawings grid lines zones
040 mailing addresses selection output letters labels
947 maintenance electrical batteries schedules
124 management accounting plant depot hire company
132 management information analysis reports
036 management land agents property

168 management reporting job-costing accounting
136 managing stock recording controlling
389 manholes pipe diameters design sewer surface
246 manipulation analysis mapping system
218 manipulation housing sites architectural design
248 manipulation mapping point-referenced data
249 manipulation mapping polygonal areas
275 manipulation printing multi-way tables survey data
034 manipulation property file
255 map conformant contour proximal
365 map noise contours road
248 mapping point-referenced data manipulation
249 mapping polygonal areas manipulation
246 mapping system manipulation analysis
251 mapping traffic flows area data desired-line
114 married quarters housing cost yardstick limits
690 mass current pressure networks water supply pipes
695 mass flows pipe sizes pressure loss emissions
198 mass memory payroll processing
633 master file design steel beams piles columns sections
062 master specification project edit
836 match condensing units cooling coils
137 materials breakdown parts lists schedules
070 materials pipework projects estimates quantities
359 mathematical model earth volume edge
345 mathematical representation surface underground
443 maximum tension stress plane rectangular
988 mean concrete cube strength deviation
120 measured quantities interim valuations
893 measurement environmental performance building
066 measurement interim certificate cost reports
235 measurement repetition drawings English
272 measurement site survey printed listing stations
858 mechanical cost savings comparison energy
533 mechanical design dynamic testing analysis
972 mechanical handling simulation movement buildings
534 mechanical machinery structural analysis performance
872 mechanical plant energy air-handling system
815 mechanical systems heating cooling buildings design
765 mechanical ventilation cooling load gain zone
618 members analysis stresses reinforced concrete
610 members steel axial loading bi-axial bending elastic
427 membrane analysis plane structures rod beam
913 mercury fittings calculation fluorescent tungsten
912 mercury fluorescent fittings calculation glare indices
842 meshed pipe networks district heating calculations
687 meshed pipe networks flow pressure
141 metal bars timber cutting plan fixed-length stock
155 method-building quotations analysis
108 methods appraisal road schemes discounting
567 mid-span ends stress slenderness ratio safety margin
313 Mindlin's Solution moments pile group
679 minimum pipe thickness temperature pressure
657 minimum sizes pipe calculations Btu hour
099 model appraisal buildings scheme/detail design
754 model calculation air movement building
516 model design analysis off-shore structures
890 model design dust-collection exhaust-air systems
867 model energy usage buildings
843 model environmental control heating cooling
877 model estimate performance solar-energy
992 model functional interconnections simulation
806 model heat transfer calculation cooling load building
100 model hospital design graphic appraisal
234 model perspectives half-tone shading shadows
527 model responses dynamic loads analysis natural
885 model simulation solar-energy systems
844 model total energy plant
044 modelling companies financial analysis
101 modelling housing layout graphic
105 modelling project evaluation system planners
130 modification re-use briefing information buildings
440 modified frame continuous beams coplanar prismatic
223 modular spaces fixed area plans
776 moist air properties cooling loads psychrometric
574 moment amplification modifiers sections columns
420 moment connection analysis bolted column beam
629 moment diagram spiral staircase step loading
479 moment distribution frame orthogonal multi-storey
611 moment shear column baseplate tension compression
291 moment shear force analysis design continuous
342 moments axial loads analysis groups piles settlement
343 moments axial shears forces analysis group pile cap
294 moments continuous beam load stress
457 moments deflections rotations space frame analysis
573 moments deformations beams stiffness method forces
318 moments forces analysis group pile cap
393 moments of inertia radii of gyration figures areas
313 moments pile group Mindlin's Solution
623 moments reinforcement stresses sections direct loads
602 moments shear forces stresses wind forces walls
337 moments shears axial forces pile cap displacement
594 moments shears finite element analysis slabs
298 moments shears support reactions multi-span
575 moments soil pressure settlement values influence
659 moments stresses piping system evaluation forces
297 moments support reactions loads influence lines
179 money contract record movement
042 monitor service networks
123 monthly energy costs air-distribution systems
187 monthly expenditure building projects forecast
065 Moore taking-off data abstracts bills of quantities
338 Morgenstern and Price analysis slope stability
364 Morgenstern and Price non-circular slip stability slope
350 Morgenstern and Price slope stability Bishop
325 Morgenstern and Price stability slope
966 morning peak analysis lift installations office
521 movement bearing structures element method
972 movement buildings pedestrian traffic mechanical
179 movement money contract record
547 movement tension stressed-cable construction static
548 movement tension stressed-cable construction static
971 movement time-based congestion queues object
557 movements reactions box-girder deflection elasticity
561 moving load bending moments shear reactions span
154 MTCE expenditure commitment system repairs
417 multi-bay portal frames plastic design elastic
290 multi-span analysis continuous beams
304 multi-span continuous beam deflection rotation
305 multi-span continuous beams elastic discontinuous
287 multi-span continuous beams load factors analysis
298 multi-span continuous beams moments shears
214 multi-storey building prismatic allocations activities
603 multi-storey buildings calculation forces distortion
471 multi-storey deformation analysis structural frames
479 multi-storey moment distribution frame orthogonal
275 multi-way tables survey data construction
780 multilayer wall calculation heat transfer
698 multiple-branch closed-loop pipe systems
661 multiple-branch closed-loop pipework analysis
020 multiple calendars precedence network resource
302 multiple-span continuous beams cantilevers analysis
306 multispan support moments continuous beam
527 natural frequencies models responses dynamic loads
628 natural frequency chimney Holzer
904 natural lighting buildings daylight factors calculation
905 natural lighting calculation
907 natural lighting levels building appraisal
150 NEDO formula fluctuations building contracts
149 NEDO series 2 indices price adjustments building
256 net site area graphic representation
015 network analysis plot critical path data
007 network analysis resource allocation scheduling cost
063 network analysis valuations bill of quantities
934 network frequency sweep analysis linear electrical
832 network heat requirement closed-circuit heating
926 network reduction ac
954 network representation balanced unbalanced faults
388 network results storm sewer design TRRL hydrograph
960 network service requirements hospital scheme pipe
022 networking system interactive graphic
027 networks analysis critical-path
658 networks calculations flows pressures gas water
842 networks district heating calculations meshed pipe
690 networks water supply pipes mass current pressure
383 Newton-Ralphson equations water-distribution
528 Newton-Ralphson stability effects analysis
951 nodes schedule location list knitting routing cables
365 noise contours road map
717 noise levels internal window room glazing
366 noise predictions visual shading effects assessment
158 nominal accounting purchase
176 nominal-ledger balance-sheet trading summaries
181 nominal-ledger headings cost
358 non-circular slip calculation safety factor sliding
364 non-circular slip stability slope Morgenstern and Price
432 non-linear analysis plane frames
526 non-linear cable networks static analysis
941 non-linear dc circuits analysis
502 non-linear design analysis finite elements linear
285 non-linear elastic analysis suspension bridges cable
507 non-linear space frame analysis

578 non-prismatic analysis thin-walled girders
579 non-prismatic beam stiffness carry-over factors
481 non-prismatic members analysis frames grids
391 non-prismatic waterways water-surface profiles
387 number barrels box culvert size
568 number of elements analysis ground beam
386 number pipes circular culvert size
971 object system design movement time-based
889 obstructional shading calculation facade
518 off-shore structure analysis forces
493 off-shore structures analysis land-based
400 off-shore structures buildings bridges design
519 off-shore structures forces pile foundations analysis
517 off-shore structures geometrical topological flexural
515 off-shore structures loadings waves current wind
516 off-shore structures model design analysis
511 off-shore structures steel concrete
520 off-shore structures wave loads design analysis
966 office morning peak analysis lift installations
827 one-pipe central heating comparison
676 one-pipe systems hot-water radiators sizing
663 one-pipe systems pressures fluid flows sizing
593 one-way spanning prismatic section continuous slabs
705 open-ended air-duct networks pressure losses sizing
671 open-ended combined pipe networks pressure
673 open systems piping head loss velocity
118 operating building cost owning
122 operation initial investment system energy costs
962 operation lift parking passenger waiting time
943 operational array analysis electrical control systems
373 optimisation calculation line vertical alignment
370 optimisation roads vertical alignment
112 optimum dimensions analyses sizes room layouts
696 optimum relationship isolation thickness pipes
161 order-point inventory analysis control
095 order requisitions amendments cables glands
221 orientation daylight evaluation building construction
759 orientation slope external facade solar intensities
487 orthogonal frame structures static loads analysis
411 orthogonal frames continuous beams prismatic
210 orthogonal grid design buildings
479 orthogonal multi-storey moment distribution frame
429 orthogonal plastic design two-dimensional frames
430 orthogonal plastic design two-dimensional frames
465 orthotropic stress analysis finite elements
102 outline proposal evaluation building design
040 output letters labels mailing addresses selection
247 overlay square-grid polygonal areas
193 overtime pay bonuses process payrolls
118 owning operating building cost
635 pad-footings pile-caps beams concrete
309 pad-foundations design reinforced-concrete
542 panels columns tension loads ceilings beams
271 parabolas co-ordinates linear angular relationships
613 parabolic-Euler secant Engresser working stress
551 parallel-chorded Warren truss zig-zag shear members
956 parameters harmonics load flow short circuits stability
642 partial safety factors printed plotted bending moment
137 parts lists schedules materials breakdown
962 passenger waiting time operation lift parking
369 pavement deformation rut depth road
377 pavement quantities profile levels road earthworks
193 pay bonuses process payrolls overtime
194 pay deductions payroll company weekly information
200 pay-slip salary allowances tax
192 payroll building industry job-costing
194 payroll company weekly information pay deductions
199 payroll documents records tax insurance
180 payroll job costing construction industry
198 payroll processing mass memory
196 payroll summary financial control analysis schedules
195 payroll year-end tax returns
193 payrolls overtime pay bonuses process
972 pedestrian traffic mechanical handling simulation
326 penetration bending moments shear stress
906 penetration sunlight room windows
848 performance coils selection heating cooling
959 performance enclosure thermal lighting acoustic
969 performance hospital departmental entrances route
967 performance lift two-way traffic
534 performance mechanical machinery structural analysis
098 performance schools buildings appraisal
877 performance solar-energy model estimate
763 periodic solar cooling load calculation
058 periodicals libraries circulation
236 perspective axonometric three-dimensional
220 perspective bridge highway hidden lines specific
228 perspective designs digital models hidden lines
224 perspective drawing body repetition definition
225 perspective drawings building dimensions isometric
240 perspective plotter plans elevations isometric
209 perspective rectilinear graph plotter display terminal
232 perspective three-dimensions isometric
230 perspective three-dimensions shaded areas
234 perspectives half-tone shading shadows model
253 photogrammetry plotted contour maps surveying
213 photomontage wire-line perspective structure
068 phrase library French bill of quantities
229 pie charting graph histogram bar
352 piezometric head velocity analysis seepage
337 pile cap displacement rotation moments shears axial
343 pile cap moments axial shears forces analysis group
318 pile cap moments forces analysis group
635 pile caps beams concrete structural engineering
519 pile foundations analysis off-shore structures forces
348 pile foundations calculation strength stability
333 pile foundations static load elasticity calculation
334 pile foundations static load elasticity calculation
313 pile group Mindlin's Solution moments
314 pile soil strata economy dimensions
633 piles columns sections random-access master file
324 piles rows three dimensions analysis behaviour
323 piles rows two dimensions behaviour
341 piles rows vertical raked analysis group
342 piles settlement moments axial loads analysis groups
307 piles vertical raked axial shear forces bending twisting
545 pin-ended members static linear analysis
412 pin-jointed plane-frame analysis
491 pin-jointed triangulated frame loads
550 pin-jointed truss support reactions axial forces
657 pipe calculations Btu hour minimum sizes
667 pipe diameter pipe-flow head loss flow rate
389 pipe diameters design sewer surface profiles
667 pipe flow head loss flow rate pipe diameter
666 pipe friction turbulent flow calculations
682 pipe network calculations flow balance
960 pipe network service requirements hospital scheme
842 pipe networks district heating calculations meshed
687 pipe networks flow pressure meshed
671 pipe networks pressure balance closed open-ended
648 pipe networks recirculated flow cost sizing
662 pipe networks steady incompressible flow sizing
652 pipe networks valves pumps analysis large-scale
677 pipe size flow rate pressure drop relationship
650 pipe size pressure heat design pipework flow
688 pipe sizes hydraulic calculations design sprinkler
695 pipe sizes pressure loss emissions mass flows
669 pipe sizing chart fluid flow friction loss velocity
660 pipe systems expansion wind loading joints analysis
698 pipe systems flexibility multiple branch closed-loop
679 pipe thickness temperature pressure calculations
675 pipes calculations heat losses underground
386 pipes circular culvert size number
655 pipes flow rate velocity sizes steel
690 pipes mass current pressure networks water supply
696 pipes optimum relationship isolation thickness
689 pipes pumped systems pressure-loss pressure-shock
651 pipes stress Whessoe program
656 pipes transfer heat losses gains underground
661 pipework analysis flexibility multiple-branch
693 pipework calculations internal resistance
650 pipework flow pipe size pressure heat design
070 pipework projects estimates quantities materials
668 pipework sizes pressure temperature fluid flow
678 pipework stress analysis three-dimensional
694 pipework supply domestic sizing calculations internal
686 pipework system loads stresses
647 pipework systems analysis flow
645 pipework systems temperature pressure weight
674 pipework velocity head loss closed systems analysis
684 piping components fabrication erection drawing-office
673 piping head loss velocity open systems
659 piping system evaluation forces moments stresses
680 piping system pump head direct-return reverse-return
685 piping systems calculations stresses linear steel
961 piping water demand buildings
442 plane axisymmetric elastic plastic analysis
446 plane axisymmetric linear elastic analysis
441 plane axisymmetric linear static analysis
412 plane frame analysis pin-jointed
433 plane frame analysis plastic collapse linear
477 plane frame analysis space

606 plane frame calculations tensions reactions
434 plane frame elastic supports loads analysis
409 plane frame grid tensions reactions deflections cable
413 plane frames axial shear forces bending moments
279 plane frames bridge design influence lines positions
445 plane frames displacements reactions analysis
438 plane frames grids analysis stress
423 plane frames grids rigidly-jointed analysis
428 plane frames Hardy-Cross analysis rectilinear
444 plane frames loads linear elastic plastic analysis
432 plane frames non-linear analysis
564 plane frames space frames sizing beams columns
415 plane frames stiffness method elastic analysis
508 plane frames stress collapse analysis concrete
475 plane frames trusses grids space frames analysis
421 plane grid vertical loading beam elements
439 plane grids calculation static loads
414 plane grids grillage analysis loading
454 plane grids prismatic analysis frames trusses
435 plane grillages elastic loads grid analysis
443 plane rectangular cross-section maximum tension
478 plane space frames grids
455 plane space frames stress tension
496 plane space structures plate shell elements analysis
410 plane structural frames analysis
427 plane structures rod beam membrane analysis
105 planners modelling project evaluation system
043 planning budgeting tables data
953 planning cable systems progressing
077 planning calculation bills of quantities activity costing
021 planning construction critical path network
005 planning control critical paths financial statement
237 planning control data analysis diagram costing
026 planning control projects
004 planning control time-analysis resource allocation
952 planning cost control industrial cabling design
024 planning flow-diagrams brewery hospital warehouse
011 planning progress control
014 planning routines time resource precedence network
216 planning simple language spaces layout
378 plans earthworks design highway alignments sections
240 plans elevations isometric drawings perspective
222 plans layouts rooms circulation
223 plans modular spaces fixed area
185 plans schedules budgeting controlling costs building
376 plans three-dimensional views contoured alignment
124 plant depot hire company management accounting
948 plant loading schedule power-factor correction
107 plant register capital equipment
442 plastic analysis deformations plane axisymmetric
444 plastic analysis plane frames loads linear elastic
433 plastic collapse linear plane-frame analysis
417 plastic design elastic multi-bay portal frames
466 plastic design traced rectilinear steel frames
429 plastic design two-dimensional frames orthogonal
430 plastic design two-dimensional frames orthogonal
496 plate shell elements analysis plane space structures
509 plated shell structures finite element analysis frame
015 plot critical path data network analysis
642 plotted bending moment shear force sub-frames
253 plotted contour maps surveying photogrammetry
240 plotter plans elevations isometric drawings
241 plotter two-dimensional drawings
276 plotters Post Office line incremental
227 plotting commercial architectural engineering library
258 plotting survey paths calculation
274 plotting system site recording
587 ply-web stressed-skin span tables beams timber
973 pneumatic tube simulation internal mail
598 point loads bearing capacity unreinforced concrete
248 point-referenced data manipulation mapping
249 polygonal areas manipulation mapping
247 polygonal areas overlay square-grid
982 polynominal curve least square curve fit
638 portal arches design glue-laminated
422 portal frame bending moment deflected forms
418 portal frame elastic deflection analysis
416 portal frame foundation reactions bending moments
544 portal frames load factors deflections weight sizes
417 portal frames plastic design elastic multi-bay
556 portals load-span charts timber beams
279 positions vehicles continuous beams plane frames
756 Post Office buildings energy requirements
276 Post Office line incremental plotters
948 power-factor correction plant-loading schedule
928 power outputs generators ac currents voltages
277 pre-stressing force analysis equivalent loading bridge
641 pre-tensioned single spans constant inertia
009 precedence-diagram networks bar-charts diagrams
014 precedence network planning routines time resource
020 precedence network resource levelling library
019 precedence networks scheduling resources time
537 prediction behaviour viscoelastic structure assemblies
841 pressure air flow damp-throttling air-conditioning
671 pressure balance closed open-ended combined pipe
670 pressure balance sizing two-pipe systems temperature
679 pressure calculations minimum pipe thickness
615 pressure distribution column bases analysis
851 pressure drop re-heat coils water flow
677 pressure drop relationship pipe size flow rate
835 pressure ducted air-conditioning horsepower fans
766 pressure gradients calculation surface temperatures
650 pressure heat design pipework flow pipe size
695 pressure loss emissions mass flows pipe sizes
689 pressure loss pressure-shock water pipes pumped
705 pressure losses sizing open-ended air-duct networks
687 pressure meshed pipe networks flow
690 pressure networks water supply pipes mass current
653 pressure-pipe weight thermal effects stress
689 pressure-shock water pipes pumped systems
668 pressure temperature fluid flow pipework sizes
645 pressure weight external loads pipework systems
663 pressures fluid flows sizing one-pipe systems
664 pressures fluid flows sizing two-pipe systems
658 pressures gas water networks calculations flows
326 pressures penetration bending moments shear stress
399 pressures seepage pores fully-saturated media
569 prestressed concrete sections calculations
639 prestressed concrete ultimate bending moment
641 prestressed pre-tensioned single spans constant
289 prestressing forces continuous beam variable
600 prestressing hoops analysis circular tank wall
571 pretensioned single-span beams design
049 preventative maintenance equipment
149 price adjustments building contracts NEDO series 2
092 prices cost data bills of quantities
730 print-out air temperatures HG5
272 printed listing stations measurements site survey
642 printed plotted bending moment shear force
275 printing multi-way tables survey data construction
053 printing records publications indexes labelling
214 prismatic allocations activities spaces multi-storey
454 prismatic analysis frames trusses plane grids
362 prismatic cut-out calculation cut-and-fill volumes
467 prismatic hollow steel design frames
411 prismatic members two-dimensional orthogonal
286 prismatic section analysis continuous beams
593 prismatic section continuous slabs one-way spanning
449 prismatic static elastic analysis frames straight
440 prismatic variable modified frame continuous beams
462 problems displacement finite-element linear
103 problems functions spaces solution assignment
142 problems schedules results work-sampling
970 problems solution location allocation
535 problems solution static dynamic structural
525 problems solution structural engineering
267 problems survey traverses analysis
193 process payrolls overtime pay bonuses
198 processing mass memory payroll
538 processor SDRC SUPERB SUPERB/DYNAMICS
046 product form inverse method linear programming
177 production cheques purchase ledger remittance
121 production work schedules building contracts
402 profile building velocities wind pressure
377 profile levels road earthworks pavement quantities
389 profiles manholes pipe diameters design sewer
201 profits losses assets financial control depreciation
012 program network duration cost activities
011 progress control planning
953 progressing planning cable systems
126 project analysis economic feasibility building
010 project control constraints time resources cash flows
186 project costs quantity surveyor design changes
062 project edit master specification
105 project evaluation system planners modelling
025 project management critical path network reports
030 project management schedules cost-control
002 project management time resource cost simulation
008 project network time schedules
127 project residential housing economic feasibility
128 project shopping-centre economic feasibility building
013 projects cost resource-allocation schedules

070 projects estimates quantities materials pipework
026 projects planning control
261 properties co-ordinates corner points section
776 properties cooling loads psychrometric moist air
624 properties cross-sections irregular shapes
038 property acquisition
125 property economic analysis
035 property enquiry system
034 property file manipulation
037 property files index
153 property insurance register
036 property management land agents
041 property register
152 property valuations insurance
207 proposal stage diagram layout building
208 proposed scheme two-dimensions sketch
923 provision daylight room
255 proximal map conformant contour
776 psychrometric moist air properties cooling loads
755 psychrometric charts altitude atmospheric pressure
051 publications chapters descriptive code text
053 publications indexes labelling printing records
680 pump head direct-return reverse-return piping system
654 pump head water-pipe system sizing components
689 pumped systems pressure-loss pressure-shock water
652 pumps analysis large-scale pipe networks valves
512 punching shear fixed offshore platforms safety margin
162 purchase ledger accounting
177 purchase ledger remittance advices production
158 purchase nominal accounting
184 purchases application financial control system
159 purchases invoices credits financial bought ledger
942 pure time delay diagrams electrical root locus
262 quadrilateral triangulation co-ordinates vertices
265 quantitative description surfaces co-ordinate values
070 quantities materials pipework projects estimates
634 quantities reinforcement structural members length
065 quantities reports Fletcher Moore taking-off data
076 quantity surveying services county architects
186 quantity surveyor design changes distribution project
090 quantity surveyors calculation contract
064 quantity surveyors description items library system
091 quantity surveyors engineers abstracts
135 quantity surveyors information retrieval
989 questionnaire surveys analysis data
971 queues object system design movement time-based
155 quotations analysis method-building
794 R factor types temperature calculation
792 radiant convective heat losses rooms buildings
743 radiant panels radiators heat loss rooms buildings
810 radiant temperature room calculation
933 radiating elements antenna patterns linear arrays
800 radiation air-conditioning heat gains losses
779 radiation heat-transfer analysis conduction convection
793 radiation temperature heat gains information tables
845 radiation temperatures room calculation air
847 radiator choice estimate heat losses transmission
718 radiator selection calculation heat losses building
681 radiators dimensions two-pipe central-heating system
743 radiators heat loss rooms buildings radiant panels
676 radiators sizing one-pipe systems hot-water
393 radii of gyration figures areas moments of inertia
598 rafts distributed loads point loads bearing capacity
341 raked analysis group piles rows vertical
307 raked axial shear forces bending twisting moments
633 random-access master file design steel beams piles
147 random data-base system creation access
166 rates system internal valuation bill of quantities LPM
182 raw material finished goods work-in-progress stock
851 re-heat coils water flow pressure drop
819 re-heat simulation air-conditioning variable volumes
820 re-heating system capacities components simulation
144 re-order quantities levels timber products
140 re-order report activity inventory status
130 re-use briefing information buildings collection
445 reactions analysis plane frames displacements
557 reactions box-girder deflection elasticity Vlasov
409 reactions deflections cable strengths plane frame grid
606 reactions deflections columns plane frame
408 reactions deflections structure frame frequencies
448 reactions deflections three-dimensional frame
582 reactions shear bending moments fixed-end moments
581 reactions shear forces bending moments beam
300 reactions shears bending moments continuous beams
561 reactions span moving load bending moments shear
054 rearrangement records table character values
648 recirculated flow cost sizing components pipe
179 record movement money contract
136 recording controlling managing stock
146 records analysis timber
053 records publications indexes labelling printing
160 records statements control analysis sales accounting
054 records table character values rearrangement
199 records tax insurance payroll documents
919 rectangular area sports installations lighting intensity
443 rectangular cross-section maximum tension stress
115 rectangular detached houses insulation
540 rectangular plate reinforced concrete load
902 rectangular room calculation daylight factor
901 rectangular room calculation daylight factors
909 rectangular room calculation daylight factors
910 rectangular room calculation daylight factors
916 rectangular room daylight factors
917 rectangular room daylight factors
924 rectangular room Seshadri daylight factors
699 rectangular sizing ducts high-velocity systems circular
572 rectangular T L design reinforced concrete beams
560 rectangular T-shaped stress tension continuous
616 rectangular-tied columns design check circular-spiral
209 rectilinear graph plotter display terminal perspective
428 rectilinear plane frames Hardy-Cross analysis
466 rectilinear steel frames plastic design traced
926 reduction ac network
461 reduction joint difference cost
920 reflectance light windows calculation transmittance
595 reformulation stresses deflections bridge decking
821 refrigeration systems comparison costs centrifugal
709 regain air velocity ductwork friction dynamic loss
215 regional institutional building complexes layouts
107 register capital equipment plant
041 register property
153 register property insurance
990 regression line scatter diagram
980 regression two variables least square
984 regressions T-tests general analysis statistics
242 regular irregular forms
831 reheat evaluation constant-volume systems
591 reinforced concrete beams columns calculations
588 reinforced concrete beams continuous sub-frames
572 reinforced concrete beams rectangular T L design
566 reinforced concrete beams sizes spacing analysis
385 reinforced concrete box culvert unit length
597 reinforced concrete building bar schedules flat slabs
644 reinforced concrete building floors beams columns
406 reinforced concrete building frames design details
403 reinforced concrete buildings detail
627 reinforced concrete chimneys shell thickness steel
604 reinforced concrete circular tank walls analysis
607 reinforced concrete columns design
617 reinforced concrete columns design analysis
590 reinforced concrete continuous beams analysis design
382 reinforced concrete cross section box culvert
489 reinforced concrete design problems structural frames
540 reinforced concrete load calculations rectangular
618 reinforced concrete member analysis stresses
309 reinforced concrete pad-foundations design
620 reinforced concrete sections bending shear deflection
640 reinforced concrete sections linear elastic theory
543 reinforced concrete slabs universal beams floor
534 reinforced concrete towers chimneys stresses
390 reinforced culverts elastic design
569 reinforced prestressed concrete sections calculations
639 reinforced prestressed concrete ultimate bending
392 reinforcement analysis culverts elastic stiffness
138 reinforcement bars cutting bending
311 reinforcement dimensions foundations
623 reinforcement stresses sections direct loads moments
634 reinforcement structural members length weight
139 reinforcement weights straight bent bars
570 reinforcing wires concrete girders dimensions
696 relationship isolation thickness pipes optimum
677 relationship pipe size flow rate pressure drop
157 remittance advice accounts bought ledger
177 remittance advices production cheques purchase
154 repairs MTCE expenditure commitment system
224 repetition definition perspective drawing body
235 repetition drawings English measurements
140 report activity inventory status re-order
056 report writing research analysis layout tables
065 reports Fletcher Moore taking-off data abstracts bills
197 reports general payroll deductions cheques
132 reports management information analysis

025 reports project management critical path network
308 reports sub-systems beams columns foundations
056 research analysis layout tables report writing
191 research expenditure system costing
870 residential buildings calculation energy consumption
127 residential housing economic feasibility building
927 resistivity curves generation
028 resource allocation arrow networks critical-path
004 resource allocation planning control time-analysis
030 resource allocation project management schedules
013 resource allocation schedules projects cost
007 resource allocation scheduling cost control network
018 resource analyses critical path time
006 resource cost critical path analysis complex projects
002 resource cost simulation project management time
017 resource levelling arrow network critical path
016 resource levelling arrow networks critical path
020 resource levelling library multiple calendars
014 resource precedence network planning routines time
010 resources cash flows project control constraints time
023 resources construction project analysis time
003 resources costs analyses time
019 resources time analysis precedence networks
894 response factors heat-conduction superposition
935 response linear network excitation analysis
944 response lumped linear systems frequency transient
527 responses dynamic loads analysis natural frequencies
416 restraint portal frame foundation reactions bending
133 results concrete cube crushing test
134 results cube crushing tests concrete storage
142 results work-sampling problems schedules
320 retaining wall granular soils analysis designs concrete
312 retaining wall simple analysis
321 retaining wall single tie analysis sheet-pile
327 retaining walls back-filled stability bearing capacity
589 retaining walls cross-sectional elastic analysis
340 retaining walls design anchor sheet-pile
335 retaining walls design gravity-type
326 retaining walls pressures penetration bending
322 retaining walls sheet-pile sub-system anchor
331 retaining walls stability back-filled bearing capacity
310 retaining walls strength angled
130 retrieval modification re-use briefing information
135 retrieval quantity surveyors information
106 returns hire rates analysis capital
715 reverberation total sound absorption surfaces room
680 reverse-return piping system pump head direct-return
599 ribbed slabs analysis design flat slabs
536 rigid format solutions analysis
981 rigid layer solution Steinbrenner elasticity equations
476 rigid space frames elastic supports analysis
546 rigidity method tensions bars joints wooden structures
423 rigidly-jointed analysis plane frames grids
631 ring frames coplanar loading gables arches analysis
371 road design tabulated form calculation
372 road design vertical alignment calculation
366 road development noise predictions visual shading
377 road earthworks pavement quantities profile levels
365 road map noise contours
974 road network traffic assignment capacity restraint
369 road pavement deformation rut depth
108 road schemes discounting methods appraisal
404 roads bridges buildings library engineering design
259 roads sites engineers survey calculations design
370 roads vertical alignment optimisation
427 rod beam membrane analysis plane structures
266 rod readings area cross-section
463 rods English elastic analysis trussed frame beams
565 rolled-steel joists castellated girders design
879 roof angles calculation energy solar radiation
555 roof truss load-span tables
781 roofs windows calculation solar radiation facades
812 roofs ceilings calculation heat flow walls
823 room air-diffuser selection
777 room building calculation heating cooling loads
775 room building heating cooling loads
845 room calculation air radiation temperatures
869 room calculation heat losses buildings
737 room calculation heating cooling loads
746 room calculation interchange energy surfaces
810 room calculation radiant temperature
772 room Carrier calculation heating cooling loads
734 room design hot-water heating system calculation
811 room estimate temperature thermal comfort
717 room glazing calculations internal noise levels
921 room intensity light indoor
918 room layout lighting fixtures illumination level
112 room layouts optimum dimensions analyses sizes
751 room pressures air movement fire analysis
923 room provision daylight
715 room reverberation total sound absorption surfaces
221 room size orientation daylight evaluation building
906 room windows penetration sunlight
886 rooms air-conditioning calculation temperatures
731 rooms air-flow rates calculations heat gains losses
722 rooms ASHRAE calculations heating cooling loads
769 rooms buildings Carrier estimate cooling loads
792 rooms buildings radiant convective heat losses
743 rooms buildings radiant panels radiators heat loss
774 rooms calculation heat gains cooling loads hour
222 rooms circulation plans layouts
714 rooms complete structures calculations sound levels
925 rooms design lighting installations
773 rooms hour calculation heat gains cooling loads
942 root locus pure time delay diagrams electrical
932 rotating machine transient stability analysis
304 rotation bending moment shear forces multi-span
337 rotation moments shears axial forces pile cap
457 rotations space frame analysis shear bending
949 route information selection sizing electrical cables
969 route performance hospital departmental entrances
226 routines graphics facilities
227 routines plotting commercial architectural engineering
014 routines time resource precedence network planning
951 routing cables nodes schedule location list knitting
324 rows three dimensions analysis behaviour piles
323 rows two dimensions behaviour piles
341 rows vertical raked analysis group piles
860 running costs energy consumption building analysis
369 rut depth road pavement deformation
315 safety circular-arc slip plane analysis stability earth
346 safety factor circular slip calculation slope stability
358 safety factor sliding circular non-circular slip
357 safety factor sliding wedge calculation
512 safety margin joint punching shear fixed offshore
567 safety margin mid-span ends stress slenderness ratio
205 salary allocation system
200 salary allowances tax pay-slip
160 sales accounting records statements control analysis
163 sales ledger accounting
178 sales ledger accounts documents statements
164 sales ledger analysis invoicing VAT
156 sales transaction statement analysis of debtors credit
863 savings heat requirements calculation costs insulation
990 scatter diagram regression line
097 schedule design secondary school accommodation
129 schedule estimates costs drawings
951 schedule location list knitting routing cables nodes
948 schedule power-factor correction plant-loading
949 schedule route information selection sizing electrical
052 schedules bases structured data
185 schedules budgeting controlling costs building sites
563 schedules concrete beams columns drawings bar
030 schedules cost-control resource-allocation project
148 schedules creation interrogation updating
067 schedules item type language creation interrogation
131 schedules lengths weights bar summation bending
947 schedules maintenance electrical batteries
137 schedules materials breakdown parts lists
196 schedules payroll summary financial control analysis
013 schedules projects cost resource-allocation
142 schedules results work-sampling problems
007 scheduling cost control network analysis resource
019 scheduling resources time analysis precedence
960 scheme pipe network service requirements hospital
099 scheme detail design models appraisal buildings
108 schemes discounting methods appraisal road
098 schools buildings appraisal performance
078 SCOLA calculation bills of quantity
538 SDRC SUPERB SUPERB/DYNAMICS processor
514 sea wave calculation forces submerged structure
513 sea waves accelerations forces velocities calculation
141 seamless tubing metal bars timber cutting plan
613 secant Engresser working stress columns
097 secondary school accommodation schedule design
261 section properties co-ordinates corner points
620 sections bending shear deflection design
363 sections calculation volume cut-and-fill straight
574 sections columns slenderness ratios moment
623 sections direct loads moments reinforcement stresses
339 sections geohydrological characteristics levels current
640 sections linear elastic theory analysis reinforced

378 sections plans earthworks design highway alignments
633 sections random-access master file design steel
946 security electrical distribution systems assessment
352 seepage piezometric head velocity analysis
399 seepage pores fully-saturated media pressures
094 select extract specification clauses
577 self-documenting calculation beta angle beams
029 sequence analyses tasks
986 series statistics
042 service networks monitor
960 service requirements hospital scheme pipe network
924 Seshadri daylight factors rectangular room
273 setting out co-ordinates civil engineers surveyors
270 setting out field stations co-ordinates
342 settlement moments axial loads analysis groups piles
575 settlement values influence lines moments soil
381 sewer design analysis storm
389 sewer surface profiles manholes pipe diameters
728 shade calculation heat gains external glazing
230 shaded areas perspective three-dimensions
888 shading comparison efficiency glazing
366 shading effects assessment road development noise
887 shadows buildings ground display
234 shadows model perspectives half-tone shading
238 shapes library three-dimensional model
243 shapes visual unit graphic display
219 shapes working drawings grid lines zones macros
401 shear bending moments analysis cylindrical tanks
457 shear bending moments deflections rotations space
582 shear bending moments fixed-end moments beam
611 shear column baseplate tension compression axis
541 shear connectors design analysis cost composite deck
620 shear deflection design reinforced-concrete sections
291 shear force analysis design continuous beams load
288 shear force deflections continuous beam analysis
642 shear force sub-frames partial safety factors printed
303 shear forces analysis design continuous beams
581 shear forces bending moments beam reactions
413 shear forces bending moments elastic analysis plane
559 shear forces bending moments slope deflection
304 shear forces multi-span continuous beam deflection
602 shear forces stresses wind forces walls calculations
319 shear forces vertical pile lateral moment bending
561 shear reactions span moving load bending moments
637 shear reinforcement design structural concrete beams
326 shear stress retaining walls pressures penetration
601 shear stress walls elastic stiffness frame analysis
605 shear walls elastic stiffness method frame analysis
337 shears axial forces pile cap displacement rotation
300 shears bending moments continuous beams girders
594 shears finite element analysis slabs deflections forces
297 shears moments support reactions loads influence
298 shears support reactions multi-span
321 sheet-pile retaining wall single tie analysis
340 sheet-pile retaining walls design anchor
322 sheet-pile sub-system anchor retaining walls
328 sheet-piling anchor plate calculation distance
332 sheet-piling anchor plates calculation dimensions
347 sheet-piling calculation drive-depths anchor strength
336 sheet-piling wall calculations forces deformations
483 shell linear static dynamic analysis frame
627 shell thickness steel area reinforced concrete
484 shells stress calculation symmetrical
426 shock loads analysis linear elastic structures
128 shopping-centre economic feasibility building project
930 short circuit analysis dc load-flow
940 short circuit faults three-phase
929 short circuits ac single line to ground
956 short circuits stability parameters harmonics load flow
713 shut-off air-volume ductwork VariTrane boxes
401 silos shear bending moments analysis cylindrical
216 simple language spaces layout planning
312 simple retaining walls analysis finite-element
609 simply supported calculations tension eccentric loads
290 simply supported multi-span analysis continuous
817 simulation air-conditioning dimensions analysis
818 simulation air-conditioning dimensions energy
819 simulation air-conditioning variable volumes re-heat
873 simulation air-distribution system energy consumption
945 simulation electrical control systems symbolic-array
973 simulation internal mail pneumatic tube
992 simulation model functional interconnections
972 simulation movement buildings pedestrian traffic
002 simulation project management time resource cost
820 simulation re-heating system capacities components
885 simulation solar-energy systems models
397 simulation solution dynamic systems analogue
727 simulation thermal behaviour buildings loads
824 simulation thermal performance central heating water
965 simulation traffic-handling capability lift
039 simulation urban growth
983 simultaneous equations elimination solution
929 single line to ground short-circuits ac
559 single span beam shear forces bending moments
576 single span beams analysis design
641 single spans constant inertia prestressed
321 single tie analysis sheet-pile retaining wall
553 single top chord vertical posts forces truss
354 site plans volumes earthworks comparison cut-and-fill
274 site recording plotting system
272 site survey printed listing stations measurements
259 sites engineers survey calculations design roads
387 size number barrels box culvert
386 size number pipes circular culvert
891 sizes components design dust collection systems
544 sizes portal frames load factors deflections weight
668 sizes pressure temperature fluid flow pipework
112 sizes room layouts optimum dimensions analyses
897 sizes smoke shafts vents calculation
566 sizes spacing analysis design reinforced concrete
655 sizes steel pipes flow rate velocity
672 sizes two-pipe system heating
564 sizing beams columns plane frames space frames
694 sizing calculations internal resistance pipework supply
706 sizing chart air-duct
838 sizing chilled-water coils Carrier
648 sizing components pipe networks recirculated flow
662 sizing components pipe networks steady
654 sizing components pump head water-pipe system
646 sizing components steam pipe networks
837 sizing direct-expansion cooling coils Carrier
699 sizing ducts high-velocity systems circular rectangular
708 sizing ductwork static-regain constant-friction
949 sizing electrical cables schedule route information
840 sizing hot-water coils Carrier
710 sizing low-velocity low-pressure air ducts
676 sizing one-pipe systems hot-water radiators
663 sizing one-pipe systems pressures fluid flows
705 sizing open-ended air-duct networks pressure losses
882 sizing solar-energy systems costing
839 sizing steam coils by-pass Carrier
664 sizing two-pipe systems pressures fluid flows
670 sizing two-pipe systems temperature pressure balance
704 sizing ventilating extraction duct systems
494 skeletal finite-element structures analyses
505 skeletal plane frames analysis
206 sketch designs drawing bar-charts area comparison
208 sketch proposed scheme two-dimensions
282 slab-and-beam analysis finite elements concrete
596 slab reinforcement bridge decking analysis
280 slabs box girders suspension curved erection
637 slabs columns bars shear reinforcement design
594 slabs deflections forces moments shears finite
567 slenderness ratio safety margin mid-span ends stress
574 slenderness ratios moment amplification modifiers
358 sliding circular non-circular slip calculation safety
357 sliding wedge calculation safety factor
356 slip-circle failure stability slopes
315 slip-plane analysis stability earth slopes safety
559 slope deflection single-span beam shear forces
759 slope external facade solar intensities orientation
364 slope Morgenstern and Price non-circular slip stability
325 slope Morgernstern and Price stability
350 slope stability Bishop Morgenstern and Price
338 slope stability Bishop's Morgenstern and Price
346 slope stability safety factor circular slip calculation
356 slopes slip-circle failure stability
495 small– to medium-sized design framed structures
897 smoke shafts vents calculation sizes
469 soil building linear elastic dynamic analysis
575 soil pressure settlement values influence lines
361 soil stability analysis
314 soil strata economy dimensions pile
733 sol-air temperatures heat gains external walls
732 sol-air temperatures heat gains horizontal roofs
729 sol-air temperatures solar intensities calculation
880 solar collector calculation heat
881 solar collectors heat loss cover
763 solar cooling load calculation periodic
760 solar cooling load glazing BRS admittance calculation
878 solar-energy analysis systems building
877 solar-energy model estimate performance

882 solar-energy systems costing sizing
885 solar-energy systems models simulation
807 solar gain building heat transmission cooling load
805 solar heat gains building calculation
797 solar heat gains glass calculation
883 solar-heating cooling analysis
884 solar-heating liquid air design
729 solar intensities calculation sol-air temperatures
759 solar intensities orientation slope external facade
809 solar radiation calculation
796 solar radiation calculation day length
748 solar radiation calculation heat gains
781 solar radiation facades roofs windows calculation
879 solar radiation roof angles calculation energy
725 solar radiation thermal conduction cooling load
799 solar radiation transmission characteristics glass
103 solution assignment problems functions spaces
397 solution dynamic systems analogue computer
789 solution equation two-dimensional heat flow
970 solution location allocation problems
983 solution simultaneous equations elimination
535 solution static dynamic structural problems
981 solution Steinbrenner elasticity equations rigid layer
525 solution structural engineering problems
715 sound absorption surfaces room reverberation total
716 sound attenuation ductwork lining calculations
714 sound levels rooms complete structures calculations
507 space frame analysis non-linear
457 space frame analysis shear bending moments
480 space frame linear analysis
475 space frames analysis plane frames trusses grids
486 space frames analysis stress tension
464 space frames eigenvalue vibration analysis
476 space frames elastic supports analysis rigid
478 space frames grids plane
506 space frames linear finite element analysis
564 space frames sizing beams columns plane frames
455 space frames stress tension plane
468 space framework linear elastic analysis design general
477 space plane frame analysis
496 space structures plate shell elements analysis plane
549 space trusses two-dimensional structures analysis
216 spaces layout planning simple language
214 spaces multi-storey building prismatic allocations
103 spaces solution assignment problems functions
561 span moving load bending moments shear reactions
587 span tables beams timber laminated ply-web
059 sparse matrix elements dynamic sub-routines
104 spatial implications educational policies curriculum
220 specific locations perspective bridge highway
094 specification clauses select extract
048 specification editing text
795 specified day calculation hourly temperatures
963 speeds building height selection lift
636 speeds rotating shafts frequencies beams calculations
629 spiral staircase step loading moment diagram
271 spirals parabolas co-ordinates linear angular
919 sports installations lighting intensity rectangular area
915 spotlight calculation illumination level floodlight
688 sprinkler fire-protection pipe sizes hydraulic
247 square-grid polygonal areas overlay
331 stability back-filled bearing capacity cantilevered
327 stability bearing capacity retaining walls back-filled
344 stability earth slopes Bishop circular-arc traces
355 stability earth slopes Bishop circular-arc traces
315 stability earth slopes safety circular-arc slip plane
528 stability effects analysis Newton-Ralphson
316 stability ground penetration analysis earth-retaining
956 stability parameters harmonics load flow short circuits
348 stability pile foundations calculation strength
364 stability slope Morgenstern and Price non-circular slip
325 stability slope Morgernstern and Price
356 stability slopes slip-circle failure
349 stability three-dimensional wedges
898 stack effect air movement air-handling
183 staff time fees architects civil engineers job-costing
384 standard step surface profiles water calculation
156 statement analysis of debtors credit control sales
160 statements control analysis sales accounting records
178 statements sales ledger accounts documents
473 static analysis automatic design steel structures
526 static analysis non-linear cable networks
441 static analysis plane axisymmetric linear
490 static dynamic analyses frames
483 static dynamic analysis frame shell linear
470 static dynamic analysis constructions arbitrary load
425 static dynamic loads finite element analysis structures
535 static dynamic structural problems solution
449 static elastic analysis frames straight prismatic
545 static linear analysis three-dimensional truss
333 static load elasticity calculation pile foundations
334 static load elasticity calculation pile foundations
547 static load movement tension stressed-cable
548 static load movement tension stressed-cable
487 static loads analysis orthogonal frame structures
439 static loads plane grids calculation
708 static-regain constant-friction sizing ductwork
701 static-regain ductwork constant-friction
702 static-regain ductwork constant-friction
703 static-regain ductwork equal-friction
491 statically-determinate pin-jointed triangulated frame
499 statically-loaded beam-type structures analysis elastic
503 statically-loaded frame truss structures analysis elastic
497 statically-loaded framed structures analysis
488 statically-loaded structures linear analysis elastic
272 stations measurements site survey printed listing
985 statistics analysis surveys
237 statistics planning control data analysis diagram
984 statistics regressions T-tests general analysis
986 statistics series
662 steady incompressible flow sizing components pipe
839 steam coils by-pass Carrier sizing
646 steam pipe networks sizing components
627 steel area reinforced concrete chimneys shell
610 steel axial loading bi-axial bending elastic design
558 steel beams bending deflection
633 steel beams piles columns sections random-access
608 steel columns design
612 steel compression members design
511 steel concrete offshore structures
685 steel copper piping systems calculations stresses
643 steel frames beams columns details end-plate
466 steel frames plastic design traced rectilinear
655 steel pipes flow rate velocity sizes
592 steel quantities flat-slab reinforcement details bar
396 steel storage tanks design
473 steel structures static analysis automatic design
981 Steinbrenner elasticity equations rigid layer solution
629 step loading moment diagram spiral staircase
579 stiffness carry-over factors non-prismatic beam
447 stiffness displacement dynamic analysis beam-type
431 stiffness linear elastic analysis framed structures
415 stiffness method elastic analysis plane frames
573 stiffness method forces moments deformations beams
182 stock control raw material finished goods
987 stock files cross tabulation analysis data
136 stock recording controlling managing
134 storage results cube crushing tests concrete
395 storage tanks depth calculation load tables
532 storage tanks derricks analysis design drilling rigs
396 storage tanks design steel
145 storage timber-yard handling
381 storm sewer design analysis
388 storm sewer design TRRL hydrograph network results
139 straight bent bars reinforcement weights
498 straight elements frames continuous beams analysis
504 straight members linear analysis elastic skeletal
449 straight prismatic static elastic analysis frames
363 straight trench sections calculation volume
351 strata calculation cut-and-fill volumes
310 strength angled retaining walls
348 strength stability pile foundations calculation
632 stress analysis finite elements
619 stress analysis finite elements graphic displays
465 stress analysis finite elements orthotropic
678 stress analysis three-dimensional pipework
484 stress calculation symmetrical shells
508 stress collapse analysis concrete plane frames
295 stress continuous beam load-train
329 stress deformation cellar walls calculation
586 stress distribution beams cross-sectional properties
368 stress elastic layered structure
451 stress heat conduction analysis
294 stress moments continuous beam load
438 stress plane frames grids analysis
443 stress plane rectangular cross-section maximum
653 stress pressure-pipe weight thermal effects
567 stress slenderness ratio safety margin mid-span ends
621 stress tension calculations
296 stress tension continuous beams loads
560 stress tension continuous beams rectangular
455 stress tension plane space frames

486 stress tension space frames analysis
531 stress tension thin lapped constructions analysis
651 stress Whessoe program pipes
547 stressed-cable construction static load movement
548 stressed-cable construction static load movement
587 stressed-skin span tables beams timber laminated
595 stresses deflections bridge decking summing editing
485 stresses frames calculation
685 stresses linear steel copper piping systems
686 stresses pipework system loads
659 stresses piping system evaluation forces moments
618 stresses reinforced concrete member analysis
534 stresses reinforced concrete towers chimneys
623 stresses sections direct loads moments reinforcement
602 stresses wind forces walls calculations moments
534 structural analysis performance mechanical machinery
637 structural concrete beams slabs columns bars shear
762 structural conduction gains cooling loads
523 structural design loading integral
630 structural elements tension elasticity theory constants
635 structural engineering columns pad-footings pile-caps
525 structural engineering problems solution
410 structural frames analysis plane
489 structural frames analysis reinforced concrete design
471 structural frames multi-storey deformation analysis
634 structural members length weight quantities
535 structural problems solution static dynamic
408 structure frame frequencies vibrations reactions
530 structure houses loads analysis
213 structure photomontage wire-line perspective
052 structured data schedules bases
494 structures analyses skeletal finite-element
539 structures analysis design graphic
499 structures analysis elastic statically-loaded beam-type
503 structures analysis elastic statically-loaded frame truss
493 structures analysis land-based offshore
458 structures digital models finite-element analyses
509 structures finite element analysis frame plated shell
519 structures forces pile foundations analysis off-shore
488 structures linear analysis elastic statically-loaded
496 structures plate shell elements analysis plane space
513 structures sea waves accelerations forces velocities
495 structures small- to medium-sized design framed
473 structures static analysis automatic design steel
425 structures static dynamic loads finite element analysis
379 structures system alignments highways earthworks
172 sub-accounts control financial report general ledger
588 sub-frames analysis design reinforced concrete beams
642 sub-frames partial safety factors printed plotted
059 sub-routines sparse matrix elements dynamic
001 sub-sets clusters tree diagram design problems
322 sub-system anchor retaining walls sheet-pile
437 sub-system frames beam string column lifts
459 sub-system truss frame continuous finite elements
308 sub-systems beams columns foundations reports
866 sub-systems building calculation energy usage
514 submerged structure sea-wave calculation forces
176 summaries nominal-ledger balance-sheet trading
197 summaries reports general payroll deductions
196 summary financial control analysis schedules payroll
131 summation bending schedules lengths weights bar
740 summer heating winter calculation cooling loads
784 summertime temperatures buildings calculation
595 summing editing reformulation stresses deflections
922 sun azimuth sunrise calculation altitude
899 sun position horizon calculation
906 sunlight room windows penetration
922 sunrise calculation altitude sun azimuth
538 SUPERB/DYNAMICS SDRC pre- post-processor
894 superposition response factors heat-conduction
694 supply domestic sizing calculations internal resistance
306 support moments continuous beam multispan
550 support reactions axial forces pin-jointed truss
297 support reactions loads influence lines shears
291 support reactions moment shear force analysis design
298 support reactions multi-span continuous beams
476 supports analysis rigid space frames elastic
389 surface profiles manholes pipe diameters design
384 surface profiles water calculation standard step
719 surface temperatures building loads calculation air
782 surface temperatures heating cooling loads indoor air
766 surface temperatures pressure gradients calculation
345 surface underground features cut-and-fill
265 surfaces co-ordinate values contour maps quantitative
746 surfaces room calculation interchange energy
715 surfaces room reverberation total sound absorption
252 surfaces variables contour maps functions
259 survey calculations design roads sites engineers
275 survey data construction manipulation printing
258 survey paths calculation plotting
269 survey stations grid transformation co-ordinates
267 survey traverses analysis problems
260 surveying networks co-ordinates determination
253 surveying photogrammetry plotted contours maps
135 surveyors information retrieval quantity
273 surveyors setting out co-ordinates civil engineers
989 surveys analysis data questionnaire
985 surveys statistics analysis
283 suspension bridge calculation critical wind speed
285 suspension bridges cable structures non-linear elastic
284 suspension bridges vibration dynamic relaxation
280 suspension curved erection conditions bridge
945 symbolic-array simulation electrical control systems
484 symmetrical shells stress calculation
379 system alignments highways earthworks structures
175 system cash book analysis
191 system costing research expenditure
147 system creation access random data-base
122 system energy costs operation initial investment
171 system financial control information
239 system graphics terminal control
022 system interactive graphic networking
166 system internal valuation bill of quantities LPM rates
246 system manipulation analysis mapping
105 system planners modelling project evaluation
035 system property enquiry
184 system purchases application financial control
205 system salary allocation
274 system site recording plotting
245 system variables graphic contouring interpolation
878 systems building solar energy analysis
665 systems hot-water fittings design two-pipe
890 systems model design dust-collection exhaust-air
885 systems models simulation solar-energy
831 systems variable-volume reheat evaluation
572 T L design reinforced concrete beams rectangular
560 T-shaped stress tension continuous beams
984 T-tests general analysis statistics regressions
054 table character values rearrangement records
043 tables data planning budgeting
554 tables designs timber portal frames
371 tabulated form calculation road design
065 taking-off data abstracts bills of quantities reports
029 tasks sequence analyses
199 tax insurance payroll documents records
200 tax pay-slip salary allowances
195 tax returns payroll year-end
110 technical financial commercial feasibility building
757 temperature calculation air environmental
794 temperature calculation R factor types
744 temperature cooling loads building component gains
791 temperature differences walls calculation
668 temperature fluid flow pipework sizes pressure
793 temperature heat gains information tables radiation
670 temperature pressure balance sizing two-pipe systems
679 temperature pressure calculations minimum pipe
645 temperature pressure weight external loads pipework
811 temperature thermal comfort room estimate
735 temperature zones cross-section building
719 temperatures building loads calculation air surface
784 temperatures buildings calculation summertime
846 temperatures buildings hourly calculation indoor
801 temperatures energy consumption thermal
783 temperatures heating cooling building loads
782 temperatures heating cooling loads indoor air surface
720 temperatures heating cooling requirements zones
845 temperatures room calculation air radiation
886 temperatures rooms air-conditioning calculation
727 temperatures simulation thermal behaviour buildings
795 temperatures specified day calculation hourly
697 temperatures two-pipe systems heat loss
896 temperatures walls vapour pressures calculation
069 tenders contract library foreign languages
621 tension calculations stress
611 tension compression axis moment shear column
296 tension continuous beams loads stress
560 tension continuous beams rectangular T-shaped
452 tension deformation isoperimetric calculation
609 tension eccentric loads column simply supported
630 tension elasticity theory constants cross-sections
453 tension linear elastic calculation deformation
542 tension loads ceilings beams panels columns

Index to computers

Honeywell G430
807

Honeywell GE
827

Honeywell GE635
715

Honeywell GZ65
742

Honeywell H6080
441 442 483 779 841

Honeywell Mk III
113 187 221 743 773 774 896 908 910 924 963

IBM
138 183 277 278 279 280 400 424 433 460 461 472
473 474 509 510 511 527 528 563 595 596 622 882

IBM 1130
015 062 068 139 225 232 233 261 262 263 264 265
291 292 320 321 355 401 402 434 435 436 475 476
512 513 514 529 549 567 568 614 615 627 628 629
646 647 648 649 650 669 670 671 701 705 706 722
751 752 753 754 755 793 821 823 832 852 859 912
913 914 915 965 982 988

IBM 360
017 018 019 032 040 049 055 056 058 062 091 092
093 094 120 121 129 176 177 178 190 216 237 255
281 282 293 322 323 324 325 353 356 358 374 384
403 404 437 477 541 547 548 569 597 600 601 613
650 666 667 672 701 702 722 741 745 746 747 756
828 829 856 860 870 876 883 890 897 898 903

IBM 365
858

IBM 370
011 017 018 019 021 030 032 033 035 037 038 055
056 058 070 072 077 078 082 083 085 087 089 091
092 093 094 120 121 129 134 135 153 190 217 237
255 269 270 271 272 274 281 282 293 303 304 305
322 323 324 325 336 337 356 359 363 374 384 403
404 432 437 469 477 487 488 533 541 546 547 548
569 578 597 599 600 601 625 634 672 713 782 814
815 849 850 854 860 870 875 876 878 893 903

ICL
129 280 400 433 472 473 474 511 527 528

ICL 1100
738

ICL 1900
003 006 020 032 063 064 065 106 107 158 180 181
255 275 281 282 293 322 323 324 325 326 356 357
358 374 384 403 404 405 437 477 541 569 597 600
601 644 672 783

ICL 1902T
151 675 676 677 678 679 769 770 771 861

ICL 1903A
137 159 160 192 193 414

ICL 1903T
034 073 080 154 155 864

ICL 1904
022

ICL 1904A
074 081 084 204 218 250 338 446 947 993

ICL 1904S
034 057 071 080 086 152 186 202 785 786 879

ICL 1905E
806

ICL 1906A
189 205 508

ICL 2900
275

ICL 3/70
275

ICL 4/70
041 088 275

ICL 4120
051 174

ICL 4130
011

NCR Century 200
075

NCR Century 251
036 076

Philips 1400
281 282 293 322 323 324 325 356 374 384 403 404
437 477 541 569 597 600 601 672

Philips P350
805

Prime
129

Prime 300
031 042 130 210 226 244 245 246 247 248 249 281
282 293 322 323 324 325 345 356 365 366 374 384
403 404 437 477 541 569 597 600 601 672 903 904
972

Prime 3000
213 289

Sigma
590

Sigma 3
870

Sigma 7
655 728 729 730 731 732 733

Sigma 9
002 043 044 045 046 105 136 156 157 227 346 367
380 394 410 450 522 533 618 619 651 652 655 723
728 729 730 731 732 733 984

Spectra 70–46
860

System 4
032 255 281 282 293 322 323 324 325 356 374 384
403 404 437 477 541 569 597 600 601 672

System 7
068 139 232 233 261 262 263 264 265 291 292 320
321 355 401 402 434 435 436 475 476 512 513 514
529 549 567 568 614 615 627 628 629 669 670 671
705 706 751 752 753 754 755 832 859 912 913 914
915 965 982 988

Texas Instruments SR52
794 795 796 797 880 881 900 922

Trask 2
739

Univac
129 255 882

Univac 1100
058 237 281 282 293 322 323 325 356 374 384 403
404 437 477 533 541 569 597 600 601 672 789 870

Univac 1106
104 124 199 200 207 224 273 280 400 433 443 444
451 452 453 471 472 473 474 486 511 527 528 727
784 824

Univac 1108
001 016 025 097 098 099 100 101 102 103 118 122
123 206 208 209 220 236 238 254 256 276 280 378
379 388 389 390 400 433 449 471 472 473 474 495
496 497 511 515 516 517 518 519 520 527 528 532
585 644 661 673 674 707 708 716 724 738 756 767
768 803 804 860 871 872 873 891 901 902 959 960
961 962 969 970 971 977

Univac 1130
853

Wang 2200
498 734

Wang 2212
916 917

Index to languages

GRADIS-A
243

GRADIS-F
243

IBM Assembler
055 056

ICL extended Fortran
786

NCR Neat
011 023 051

PAL
051 052 053 054 174 175 989

PL/1
011 037 038 072 077 091 092 093 094 120 121 153
190 274 548 850 854

PL/1 Assembler
035

Plan
006 020 065 073 074 086 137 151 159 160 189 192
193 202 204 414

RPG BAL
205

TELCOMP
911

Index to contributors

A/S Regnecentralen
407 408 409 448 521 557 606

AAA Technology and Specialties
645

AB Bahco Ventilation
719

AB Svenska Flaktfabriken
699 720 721 817 818 819 820 886

ABACUS studies
001 097 098 099 100 101 102 103 104 206 207 208 209 224 256 901 902 959 960 962 969 970 971

ACTS Computing Corporation
700

Albert Kahn Associates
225 646 647 648 649 821 852

American Gas Association
822

APEC Executive Office
062 650 701 702 722 823

ARC Limited
031 042 130 210 226 244 245 246 247 248 249 345 365 366 893 903 904 972

Associated British Consultants (Computers) Limited
644

Association for Computer Aided Design Limited
449

Atkins Computing Services Limited
002 043 044 045 046 105 136 156 157 227 346 367 380 394 410 450 522 618 619 651 652 723 984

Australian Department of Construction
724

Auton Computing Corporation
653

Ayres and Hayakawa
654 725

B & W Engineering
451 452 453

Barber-Colman Company
726

Berkeley Solar Group
877

Berkshire County Council
071

Birmingham City Council
189

Boeing Computer Centres Limited
003 063 106 107 158 180 181

Bolton Metropolitan Borough Council
864

Bradford City Council
081 218 947

Bridgers and Paxton Incorporated
853

British Gas Corporation
727 824

Buckinghamshire County Council
073 154

Building Computer Services Limited
211 212 286 308 411 454 592 593 594

Building Service Designs
655 728 729 730 731 732 733

Cadsden International Management Services
734

Cambridge Computer Services Limited
137 159 160 192 193

Cambridgeshire County Council
089

Camutek
131 287 309 412 413 523 544 558 559 607 608 620

Cardiff City Council
786

Carrier Machinery and Systems
825

CE-data
310 311 347 348 395 396 455 456 524 540 560 609 621 735 905

CEGB Engineering Document Unit
004 005

Cement and Concrete Association
414

Center for Building Technology, IAT
656 736 894 895

Centre-File (Northern) Limited
006 064 065

Centre de Recherches Routieres
368 369 978 979 980

Charles Stark Draper Laboratory
883

Cheshire County Council
854

Civil and Structural Computing (Northern) Limited
415 416 417 418 421 422 610

Clwyd County Council
083

Colorado State University
878

Compu-Serve Network Incorporated
737

Computel Limited
007 047 108 132 161 162 163 164 182 194 195 257 258 288 312 313 349 350 351 370 371 372 373 381 397 398 399 423 457 525 562 657 658 659 660 926 927 928 929 930 931 932 974 975 976 981 985 986

Computer Aided Design Centre
213 228 229 230 231 250 251 289 458

Computer Consortium Services Ltd
138 183 277 278 279 424 460 461 509 510 563 595 596 622

Computer Sciences Sigma Limited
165

Computer Services (South West) Limited
066

Computerskills Limited
184 196 201

Construction Computing Limited
166

Control Data
425 426 564

COSMIC
049 661 662

CRC Engineering Services
167 259 260 290 314 315 316 317 318 319 352 382
383 427 428 462 463 464 623 624

CSIRO, Division of Building Research
008 109 110 214 215 429 430 431 465 466 467 468
545 565 612 738

CSTC
185 663 664 714 816 826 827 855

Cusdin, Burden and Howitt
009 067 147 148 715

Cybernet Time Sharing Limited
010 168

Danmarks Ingeniorakademi
432 469 546 625

Danmarks tekniske, Hojskole
470 547 548

Data Center Services
353 613 666 667

Datasystem AB
739

Daverman Associates Incorporated
668 703 740

Deere & Company
741 828 829 890

Department of the Environment
742

Derbyshire County Council
087

Design Office Consortium
149 150 354 907

Dewco Programming and Computer Services
665 704 744 964

DJ Hardy
748

Document Reading Services Limited
987

Duke Power Company 857

Durham County Council
077

Dyfed County Council
879

Easams Limited
011

East Sussex County Council
074

Edison Electric Institute
858

Ekono
749

Electrical Research Association Ltd
059 095 096 143 948 949 950 951 952 953 954 955
956 957 958

Electricity Council
875

Electronic Calculus Limited
280 400 433 472 473 474 511 527 528

Envirodyne Energy Services
117 750 830 831

Essex County Council
079 203

Faber Computer Operations Limited
068 139 232 233 261 262 263 264 265 291 292 320
321 355 401 402 434 435 436 475 476 512 513 514
529 549 567 568 614 615 627 628 629 669 670 671
705 706 751 752 753 754 755 832 859 912 913 914
915 965 982 988

Friedrich Uhde GmbH
069

GARD
756 860

Genair (Data Processing) Limited
757 758 759 760 761 762 763 764 765 766 899

GENESYS Limited
281 282 293 322 323 324 325 356 374 384 403 404
437 477 541 569 597 600 601 672

Geocomp UK Limited
326 357 358

Geodata A/S
294 295 296 327 328 329 330 331 332 333 334 438
439 478 530 531 542 570 598 630

Geoteknisk Institut
359

Giffels Associates Incorporated
118 673 674 707 708 716 767 768 891 961

Greater London Council
085

Haden Young Limited
675 676 677 678 679 769 770 771 861

Hampshire County Council
072

Hankins and Anderson Incorporated
680 772 833

Heating and Ventilating Computed Sizing
773 774 916 917

Henning, Hansen & Erik Carlsen
681

Hertfordshire County Council
036 076

Hewlett-Packard Limited
140 169 170 171 172 173 188 197 198 297 298 440
479 480 571 572 573 574 575 602 616 631 682 775

Highway Engineering Computer Branch
299 385 617

Honeywell Incorporated
862

Honeywell Information Systems Limited
012 013 050 119 141 142 266 267 300 335 360 361
375 386 387 481 482 550 576 577 632 633 683 834
918 933 934 935 936 937 938 939 940 941 992

Hoskyns Systems Limited
032

Humphreys and Glasgow Limited
014 684

Hutton + Rostron
051 052 053 054 174 175 989

IBM United Kingdom Limited
301 302

ICI Limited
070

Idan Computers Ltd
253 268 362

Inatome and Associates
685 776 777 778 835 836 837 838 839 840 863 892

Industridata AB
441 442 483 484 485 686 687 779 780 841 842

Ingeniorfirma FRI
443 444 486

Institute for Industrial Research and Standards
015

Institution of Electrical Engineers
942 943 944 945 946

Jaserve Limited
040 176 177 178

John FS Pryke and Partners Limited
445

K & H Business Consultants Ltd
016 017 018 019 020

Kent County Council
086

Koolshade Corporation
888

Laboratoriet for Varmeisolering
781 782

Laing Computing Services
021 134 217 269 270 271 272 303 304 305 336 337
363 487 488 578 599 634

Lancashire County Council
022 084

Lanchester Polytechnic
783

Leeds City Council
057

Leeds Polytechnic
048 234

Leicestershire County Council
273 784

Libra Computing Ltd
055 056

Lincolnshire County Council
204

Liverpool Polytechnic, Department of Architecture
235

LOLA (London On-Line Local Authorities) Computer
Bureau
033 037 038

London Transport Executive
186

Lothian Regional Council
041 088

Lysteknisk Laboratorium
919 920 921

Maersk data
489

Markworth Design Consultants Limited
338 446 490 993

McDonnell Douglas Automation Company
787 865

Mechanical Engineering Data Services Inc
788 843 844 866 867

Metricomp Programmes (Pty) Limited
306 491 551 552 553 579 580 581 582

Mid-Glamorgan County Council
785

M&M Protection Consultants
688

Moss Consortium
376

NASA, Construction Engineering Branch
868

NASA, Urban Systems Project
060

National Computing Centre Limited
255

National Research Council
745 746 747 856 897 898

NCR Limited
023

Newcastle-upon-Tyne City Council
152

Nielsen & Rauschenberger
339 689 690 869

North-East London Polytechnic
236

Northamptonshire County Council
202

Northern Ireland Polytechnic
405

Northumberland County Council
082

Norwegian Building Research Institute
058 789 870

Nottinghamshire County Council
034 080

Oldacres Computers Limited
091 092 093 094 120 121 190

Ontwerp-en Adviesbureau
691 692 693 694 709 790

Ove Arup and Partners
179 219 377 492 493 494 583 584 635 695 710 791
792 793 966 967 983

P-E Consulting Group
024

PCTS
794 795 796 797 880 881 900 922

Pilkington Brothers Limited
717 798 799 800 801 845 889 923 924

PPG Industries
802

Property Services Agency
113 114 115 133 187 566 626 743 896 908 909 910 911 963

Redditch Development Corporation
205

Renfrew District Council
075

Repko bv
237

Ross F Meriwether and Associates
122 123 803 804 871 872 873

Rosser & Russell Ltd
805

Rothampstead Experimental Station
275

SBI
603 846

Scicon Computer Services Limited
220 238 254 276 378 379 388 389 390 495 515 516 517 518 519 520 532 977

Scientific and Engineering Division, INFONET
496 497

Scott Wilson Kirkpatrick & Partners
585

Sheffield Polytechnic
221

Sigma Project Services
025

Singer Company
848

Solar Heating and Cooling Information Center
882

Somerset County Council
155

Southbank Polytechnic
806

ST-data A/S
498

Structural Dynamics Research Corporation
447 499 500 501 533 534 535 536 537 538 586 636

System Share Limited
807

Taylor and Beeby
637

Technies Rekencentrum Polybit bv
696 711 712 808 809 810 811 812 847 874 925 968 973

Tektronix UK Limited
239

Telford Development Corporation
090

Time Sharing Limited
026

TRADA
144 145 146 191 554 555 556 587 638 990

Trane Company
713 849 850

UCC (GB) Ltd
124 199 200

UCC, University Computing Company
027 028 340 341 342 343 344 364 391 392 406 502 503 504 539 543 588 589 604 605 639 640 641 642 697 698

UMIST
283 284 285 505 506 507 508 643

University of Arizona
029 039 125 126 127 128 222 223 240 241 242 813 991

University of Edinburgh
116

University of Sydney
111 112 216 471 526 887 906

University of the Witwatersrand
252 459

University of Wisconsin Solar Energy Laboratory
884 885

User Group Software, CTL
243

Viggo Michaelsen A/S
591

W J Crocker and Partners
590

West Sussex County Council
035 078 135 274

Westinghouse Electric Corporation
030 814 815

Wiltshire County Council
153

Wrexham Maelor Borough Council
151

WTA Computer Services
851 876

Index to names of programs

938 CIRCUS–2
742 CLOADS
832 CLOP
657 Closed-circuit pipe sizing
032 CLUSTER
001 CLUSTR
108 COBA
262 COCA
064 Coded quantities
888 COE
259 COGO
264 COGO
271 COGO
522 COGO
375 COGOS
848 Coil selection
753 COLD
617 COLDES
640 COLDES
612 COLUMN
613 COLUMN
541 COMP-CONSTRUCT/1
543 COMP-CONSTRUCT/1
014 Compact II
195 COMPANY ID
168 COMPASS
812 Composite wall
167 COMPUNET
302 CONBEAM
585 CONBEAM 4 and 5
290 CONBEM
299 CONBEM
309 Concrete-pad foundation design
134 Concrete cube test analysis (Imperial units version)
301 CONDEFO
896 CONDNS
836 CONDX
676 CONFLO
548 CONGRAD
180 Construction industry payroll and job costing
173 Consultants' cost accounting
288 Continuous beam analysis
298 Continuous beams
303 Continuous beams 1
294 Continuous beams I
296 Continuous beams II
304 Continuous beams II
365 CONTOUR
773 COOL
790 Cooling load
808 Cooling load
186 COST
181 Cost and nominal ledger
942 CP1
293 CP110–BEAMS/1
588 CP110–BEAMS/1
943 CP21
944 CP23
945 CP29
946 CP4
291 CPCON
029 CPM
012 CPMSYSTEM (Critical path method system)
561 CRANE
621 Cross-section
630 Cross-section
110 CSIROCA
133 CUBES
382 CULV
385 CULV
390 CULV
392 CULV
386 CULVRS
345 Cut and fill
351 Cut and fill
138 CUTSHED
838 CWCOIL
417 D4 package (DTAIL, DSIGN, DFLEC and DPICT)
703 DADDS
914 DAFA
493 DAFT
447 DAGS
500 DAGSMIC
916 DAY 1/2
905 Daylight coefficients
904 DAYLIGHTING
930 Dc network analysis
935 DCNETS
637 DECIDE 30
816 DEPI
055 DES
216 DESIGN
803 Design point requirements
757 Design temperatures
988 DEVI
549 DFL2
418 DFLEC
244 DHIST
112 DIMENSION/DP4
237 DISSPLA (Display Integrated Software System and Plotting Language)
842 District heating (R22003)
907 DOC Daylight
584 DP102
422 DPICT
212 DRAW
591 DS411
308 DSIGN
416 DSIGN
419 DTAIL
701 DUCT
704 DUCT
710 DUCT 1
706 DUCT 3
828 DUCTAN
835 DUCTS
705 DUNE
837 DXCOIL
458 DYNADATA
228 DYNADRAW
469 DYNAMIC
230 DYNASHADE
992 DYSIM
822 E CUBE 75
363 Earth calculations
525 EASANAL
043 EASYPLAN
056 EASYTAB
939 ECAPS
628 ECHO
400 ECLIPSE (Electronic Calculus Library of Integrated Programs and Services)
097 ECOLE 1
099 ECOLE 3
111 ECONFES
122 Economic Comparison of Systems/B
045 EDMS
432 ELAPLA
462 ELAS
575 Elastically bedded beams
968 Elevators
467 ELFRAME
011 EMPRENT
870 ENCORE (Energy consumption of residential buildings)
748 ENDSOP
872 Energy-systems and analysis series
853 Energy analysis
871 Energy requirements estimate
859 ENPRO
977 ENVPLAN
873 Equipment Energy Consumption/B
825 Equipment selection
060 ESOP
959 ESP (Environmental System Performance)
420 EVCON
892 EXHAU
890 EXHAUST
979 EXP093
188 Expense/budget monitor
068 FACEMS
027 FASNET
276 FASTPLOT
529 FATIG

725 FCCAL
884 FCHART
359 FEAST
233 FIBS
171 Financial control and information system
632 FINGEN and FINITE
506 Finite element system
583 FINWL
394 Flange design
660 FLAPS
597 FLAT-SLAB/1
599 Flat slab
908 FLOODLIT
940 FLT3PS
915 FLUD
658 Fluid-distribution network-analysis Mark 3
854 FMS (Cheshire)
030 FOCAS (Forecasted cost and schedule)
187 FORECAST
242 FORMS
149 FORPA
047 FORTRAN data-file handling
311 Foundations
411 FRAME
415 FRAME
428 FRAME
434 FRAME
471 FRAME
477 Frame analysis/2
504 Frame analysis/2
250 Frame analysis graphics
485 Frame calculation (R01025)
449 FRAMEM
372 FREEWAY
595 FRIDAY
592 FSLAB
751 FUME
976 Furness traffic prediction
744 GAINS
496 GASP (General Analysis of Structural Problems)
568 GB1
292 GCPCN
172 General ledger
197 General payroll
252 General Purpose Contouring Program
067 General scheduling program (GSP)
404 GENESYS
984 GENSTATS
398 GEO 12
349 GEO 15
399 GEO 16
927 GEO 17
260 GEONET
227 GINO-F
231 GINO-F
229 GINOGRAF
251 GINOZONE
565 GIRDER
300 GIRDRS
635 GLADYS
912 GLARE/GLARM
760 Glazing cooling load
165 GLII
903 GLIM
456 Glued-wood frames
278 GMESH
044 GPOS
243 GRADIS-F, GRADIS-A
208 GRAMP
421 GRID
435 GRID
269 Grid transformation
339 Ground water
313 GROUP
876 HACE
957 Harmonics
145 HASTY (Handling and storage in timber yards)
722 HCC
843 HCE1RH, HCE2HCO, HCE3MZ, HCE4VV
788 HCE8REC
866 HCENERG
749 HEAT
718 Heat load and radiator selection
787 Heat loads
691 Heating pipe resistance, simple
692 Heating pipe resistance, two-pipe
775 Heating, ventilating and air conditioning
101 HELP (Housing Evaluation Layout Package)
562 HETENYI
728 HG2
732 HG3
733 HG4
729 HG5
730 HG7
220 HIDDEN LINES
374 HIGHWAYS/1
963 HILIFT
031 HIM
921 HJoo1
794 HL1
900 HL2
209 HLE
224 HLEIN
772 HLHG
279 HLOAD
024 HOCUS III
320 HOLD
373 HOPS
379 HOPS
116 Housing-site layout
743 HTLOSS
793 HVAC 1
791 HVAC 2
792 HVAC 4
917 HVCS DAYLIGHT
700 HVDUCT
840 HWCOIL
380 HYANDRY
688 HYDEDP
755 HYGRO
802 HYPER
016 I/J System
017 I/J System
130 IBES
925 Illumination level
066 IMACE
856 Infiltration
297 Influence lines
427 INSTRUCTA
115 INSUL
863 INSUL
523 Integral structural design system
764 Internal gains load
113 INVAPP
140 Inventory control
136 Inventory management
106 Investment appraisal
164 Invoicing
696 Isolation
070 ISOPEDAC
183 JCP
190 Job costing
028 K & H
936 LAACS
638 Laminated arch design
078 LAMSAC Application code 32025422380A
084 LAMSAC Application code 32031122230A
085 LAMSAC Application code 32031400010A
086 LAMSAC Application code 32032122220A
079 LAMSAC Application code 32032842150A
087 LAMSAC Application code 32033432100A
077 LAMSAC Application code 32033432131A
072 LAMSAC Application code 32033432170A
073 LAMSAC Application code 32034112040A
080 LAMSAC Application code 32034122300A
081 LAMSAC Application code 32035121140A
071 LAMSAC Application code 32035122030A
074 LAMSAC Application code 32035122140A
075 LAMSAC Application code 32035257100A
082 LAMSAC Application code 32035442280A
088 LAMSAC Application code 32035537040A
083 LAMSAC Application code 32036436010A
089 LAMSAC Application code 32037442050A
076 LAMSAC Application code 32037835530A

090 LAMSAC Application code 32037835530A
135 LAMSAC Application code 32055422380A
785 LAMSAC Application code 32063126070A
784 LAMSAC Application code 32064952240A
786 LAMSAC Application code 32065126170A
879 LAMSAC Application code 32066126020A
036 LAMSAC Application code 32123252190A
057 LAMSAC Application code 32124121230A
034 LAMSAC Application code 32124122300A
864 LAMSAC Application code 32125111130A
947 LAMSAC Application code 32125121140A
152 LAMSAC Application code 32125121270A
035 LAMSAC Application code 32125422380A
153 LAMSAC Application code 32125432390A
038 LAMSAC Application code 32125460040A
033 LAMSAC Application code 32125460041A
037 LAMSAC Application code 32125460042A
041 LAMSAC Application code 32125527040A
151 LAMSAC Application code 3212810640A
274 LAMSAC Application code 32155422380A
273 LAMSAC Application code 32164952240A
155 LAMSAC Application code 32205112330A
218 LAMSAC Application code 32205121140A
203 LAMSAC Application code 32502842150A
154 LAMSAC Application code 32504112040A
202 LAMSAC Application code 32504122270A
204 LAMSAC Application code 32505102250A
205 LAMSAC Application code 32505102250A
189 LAMSAC Application code 32901141120A
022 Lancashire interactive graphic networking system
272 Land Survey
319 LATPILE
460 LEAP
596 LEAPWA
966 LIFT 2
967 LIFT 3 (T)
962 LIFTS
964 LIFTS
918 LIGHT
911 LIGHTS
950 Line parameters
046 Linear programming system (LP)
990 Linear regression scatter
965 LISI
699 LK003
721 LK012
886 LK015
817 LK022
818 LK042
820 LK043
819 LK044
141 LMCPLS
955 Load flow
395 Load tables for storage tanks
970 LOCAL
752 LOSS
672 LPHW-PIPES/1
697 LPHW-PIPES/1
441 LUCAS (R01041)
442 LUCAS III (R01044)
913 LUMEN
768 M–27
707 M–28
852 MA33
647 MA36
865 MACE (McDonnell Annual Consumption of Energy)
830 MACP–101
750 MACP–201
831 MACP–202
117 MACP–301
909 MAINDAY
132 Management information
425 Marc-CDC
516 MARCS
050 Mark III program library
198 Mass memory payroll processing
443 MATSTR
648 MC27
661 MEC 21
254 MEDALS
867 MEDSI library
716 MEIGHT
671 MESH
806 MET 7
961 MFOURTEEN
972 MIBS
626 MIX
673 MNINE
646 MO28
821 MO32
649 MO54
440 Modified moment distribution
827 MONO
123 Monthly utility costs
376 MOSS
114 MQCOST
708 MSEVEN
368 MTC093
767 MTEN
096 MTO design
095 MTO requisition
674 MTOSIX
118 MTWELVE
891 MTWO
656 MULPIP
431 MULT
287 Multi-span beam analysis
479 Multi-storey moment distribution
799 Multiple glazing program
366 MWAY
536 NASTRAN
901 NATLIT
902 Natural Lighting (Version 1·1)
736 NBSLD
813 NBSLD
868 NECAP
246 NETMAP
015 NETPLOT
683 NETWKS
690 Network optimise
893 New ARC environmental package
941 NLNETS
650 NO1P
176 Nominal iedger
325 NON-CIRCULAR SLIP/1
364 Non-circular slip/1
505 Non-linear plane frame
507 Non-linear space frame program
520 NPLWAVE
265 NST
091 Numeric
889 Obstructional shading
511 Offshore structures
008 ONENET
663 ONEPIPE C/ONEPIPE 4
849 Optimised equipment selection
369 ORN093
240 OTOTROL
247 OVERLAY
210 OXSYS
002 P1
263 PACE
102 PACE 1
652 PANP
465 PARBEL
206 PARTIAL
668 PASS
194 Payroll
196 Payroll package
199 Payroll system
763 Periodic cooling load
234 PERS
007 PERT
026 PERT7
003 PERTPAC
317 PGELV
342 PGROUP
100 PHASE
213 Photomontage
321 PILE
323 PILE–2D/1
341 PILE–2D/1
307 PILE–3D/1
324 PILE–3D/1

519 PILE/AN
348 Pile foundations
337 Pile group
314 PILEBR
318 PILEGRP
333 Piling I
334 Piling II
412 Pin-jointed plane-frame analysis
677 PIPDAT
669 PIPE
680 PIPE
682 Pipe-network balancing
695 PIPE 1
681 Pipe dimensions (central-heating systems)
693 Pipe resistance, Tiggelmann
686 Pipe stress (R01019)
659 Pipe stressing
667 PIPEFLO
666 PIPEFRC
665 PIPES
685 PIPEX
662 PIPLQ
410 PLANE
424 PLANE
436 PLANE
445 Plane-frame analysis
413 Plane-frame elastic analysis
438 Plane frame
439 Plane grids
953 Planning and progressing
124 PLANT
948 Plant-load and power-factor correction
107 Plant and asset accounting
444 PLASTE
509 PLATE
611 PLATE
025 PMS
023 PNA-Time, PNA-Resources (Aggregation)
405 PNC1
973 Pneumatic tube systems
248 POINTMAP
982 POLY
249 POLYMAP
429 POPDES 1, POPDES 3
756 Post office program
956 Power systems analysis library
051 PR
641 PREBEM
009 Precedence diagram analysis (PDA)
019 Precedence System
020 Precedence System
109 PRELAN
277 PRELOAD
018 PREMIS
289 PRESBEAM
571 Prestressd beam analysis and design
061 PROBE (T)
121 Production and work schedules
126 PROJCT
261 PROPX
655 PS1
651 PSA 5
910 PSA DAYLIGHT
512 PSHER
776 PSYCH
895 PSYCHR
654 PUMPHD
430 PUNDES
158 Purchase and nominal accounting
162 Purchase ledger
177 Purchase ledger
157 Purchase ledger system
184 Purchases application
052 QBANK
778 QDOT1, QDOT2
989 QUANAL
362 QUANTA
746 Radiant energy interchange
810 Radiant temperatures
845 RADZON
483 RAMSES (R01054)
684 RAPID
406 RC-Buildings/1
403 RC building /1
618 RCSECT
851 Re-heat coil
125 REAP 4
127 REAP3
855 RECUP
980 REG093
609 Reinforced columns
572 Reinforced concrete beam design
560 Reinforced concrete beams
616 Reinforced concrete column design
620 Reinforced concrete design
508 Reinforced concrete frames
570 Reinforced concrete girders
540 Reinforced concrete plates
634 Reinforcement quantities from bending schedules
461 RENUMBER
894 RESPTK
327 Retaining walls
589 RETWAL
312 RETWALL
326 RETWALL 1
335 RETWLS
150 REVOP 2
275 RGSP (Rothamsted general survey program)
833 RH
631 Ring-frame analysis
555 Roof truss design
222 ROOMS
857 RUNO 1620
530 S-calculation
594 SAFE
499 SAGS
200 Salary system
156 Sales ledger
163 Sales ledger
178 Sales ledger
453 SAP IV
586 SASA
161 SCAN
148 Scheduling program system (SPS)
191 SCORE (System for costing research expenditure)
860 SCOUT
533 SDRC Mechanical Design Library
515 SEALOAD
624 SECPROP
623 SECSTRESS
352 Seepage
053 SELECT
040 Selective mailing
986 SERIES
960 SERNET
211 SESAME
414 SGR2 and SGR3 grillage analysis
883 SHACSAC–1
887 SHAD
605 SHEAR-WALL/1
602 Shear walls
601 SHEARWALL/1
336 Sheet piling
347 Sheet piling
332 Sheet piling 1
322 SHEETPILE/1
340 SHEETPILE/1
484 Shell calculations (R01002, R01023, R01030)
316 SHEPILE
603 SHEWALLS
128 SHOPCE
954 Short circuit
975 SIGSET
144 SIM 25
558 Simply-supported steel-beam design
878 SIMSHAC
105 SIMSTRAT
544 Single-bay portal-frame design
559 Single-span beam analysis
058 SIRK
256 SITE
354 Site excavation
217 Site layout
353 SITEPREP

949 SIZE
282 Slab-bridge/1
593 SLADE
344 Slip-circle/1
356 Slip-cirle/1
315 SLIPCIRC
350 SLIPSYST
358 SLIPSYST
355 SLOPE
004 SMART 2
897 Smoke shafts
005 SNAP
042 SNIP
361 SOILXS
882 Sol Cost
759 Solar intensities
809 Solar radiation
805 Solcool
781 SOLIND
983 SOLN 2
223 SOM
054 SORT
922 SP1
796 SP2
795 SP3
797 SP4
881 SP5
880 SP6
450 SPACE
468 SPACE
476 SPACE
486 SPACE
480 Space-frame analysis
457 Space frame analysis
104 SPACES 1
207 SPACES 2
098 SPACES 3
698 SPAN
556 Span chart plotting
587 Span tables for timber beams
059 Sparse matrix handling sub-routines
048 SPEC
094 Specifications
062 SPECS
221 SPEED
049 Sperry preventative maintenance
343 SPILE
636 SPIN
919 SPORT, POoo7
388 SSDP (Storm sewer design)
377 SSLEW
478 ST10
346 STAB
426 STARDYNE
789 STAST
270 Station setting out
839 STCOIL
762 Steady cooling load
608 Steel-column design
574 Steel beam columns
981 STEIN
629 STEP
492 STIN
494 STIN-F
182 Stock control
396 Storage tanks
381 Storm sewer design and analysis
498 STRAC
518 STRAN
454 STRESS
463 STRESS
475 STRESS
488 STRESS
495 STRESS
497 STRESS
503 STRESS
481 STRESS (Structural engineering systems solver)
305 Strip footing on elastic foundation
487 Structural analysis
455 Structural frames
459 STRUDL
532 STRUDL
489 STRUDL II/1 & 2
564 STRUPAK
642 Sub-frame/1
437 SUBFRAME/1
235 SUE
131 Summation of bending schedules
774 SUMTEMP
877 SUN
899 Sun position
906 SUNPEN
538 SUPER
535 SUPERB
702 SUPERDUCT
501 SUPERTAB
985 Survey analysis
284 Suspension bridge dynamic relaxation program
283 Suspension bridge flutter program
285 Suspension bridge program
255 SYMAP
607 Symmetrically-reinforced-concrete columns
241 SYMVU
824 SYSTEM
987 TABX and XT suite
738 TEMPER
766 Temperature and pressure gradients
783 Temperature history and heat balance
735 Temperature zones
846 TEMPFO4
780 TEMPO (R02001)
239 Terminal control system
268 TERRA
490 THEANER
727 THERM
737 THERMAL
811 Thermal comfort
758 Thermal transmittance factors
578 Thin-walled sections
531 Thin lapped constructions
238 THINGS
573 Three-dimensional beam analysis
931 Three-phase ac short-circuits
554 Timber portal frames
401 TKI
542 Toadstool ceiling
215 TOPAZ
874 Total energy
844 TOTEN
524 Towers and chimneys
670 TPSS 2
850 TRACE (Trane Air Conditioning Economics)
974 Traffic assignment with capacity restraint
146 TRAID (Timber records, analysis)
932 Transient stability
958 Transient stability
847 Transmission and radiator choice
257 Traverse computation
267 TRAVRS
645 TRIFLEX
885 TRNSYS (Transient system simulation)
545 TRUSS
546 TRUSS
550 TRUSS
689 TRYKSTOD
664 TWOPIPE
569 UBM/1
639 UBM/1
185 ULYSSE
643 UMIST structural steelwork system
598 Unreinforced concrete raft flooring
675 UPIPE
039 URBAN
370 VALOR
166 Valuation system
713 VariTrane duct program
869 VARMETAB
687 Velocity calculation (R02004)
720 VENTAC
765 Ventilation cooling load
232 VIEW
537 VISCOSUPERB
464 VISTA
920 VIVAB